The Master List of
Design Projects
of the
Olmsted Firm

1857~1979

Landscape architects, surveyors, engineers and other members of the Palos Verdes planning team, circa 1922. Frederick Law Olmsted Jr. is middle of front row with Stella Obst, his long-time secretary, behind him. Job #5950 – Palos Verdes (Palos Verdes, CA).

Contributors

Julia S. Bachrach

Charles E. Beveridge

Ethan Carr

Lee Farrow Cook

Rolf Diamant

Nancy Pollack-Ellwand

Susan L. Klaus

Francis R. Kowsky

Lucy Lawliss

Arleyn A. Levee

Caroline Loughlin

Lauren Meier

Catherine Nagel

Anthony Reed

Jill Trebbe

The Master List of
Design Projects
of the
Olmsted Firm

1857~1979

Edited by

Lucy Lawliss, Caroline Loughlin, Lauren Meier

National Association for Olmsted Parks
National Park Service — Frederick Law Olmsted National Historic Site

2nd Edition, 2008

Frederick Law Olmsted with Marion Olmsted at Rivercliff Cottage, circa 1895.
Job #170 – George W. Vanderbilt/Biltmore (Asheville, NC).

Background: Detail of Planting List, January 23, 1910. Job #2695 – Volunteer
Park (Seattle, WA).

ISBN 0-615-155439000

Designed by Jamison Design, J. Spittler

Printed in China

Contents

Illustrations

The Sheep Pasture on Schoolmaster Hill, 1904. Job #918 – Franklin Park (Boston, MA).

FOREWORD

National Association for Olmsted Parks

Catherine Nagel

Established in 1980, the National Association for Olmsted Parks is the country's principal organization dedicated to the preservation, revitalization and maintenance of historic parks and landscapes throughout North America, with a focus on the work of Frederick Law Olmsted—the country's first landscape architect—and the firm that continued to operate under the direction of his sons John Charles Olmsted and Frederick Law Olmsted Jr., their partners and their successors.

NAOP formed in response to decades of neglect, decay and development pressures that threatened the continued existence of a distinctly American legacy of urban parks across the country. The legacy began in 1857 with the Greensward Plan for New York City's Central Park by Frederick Law Olmsted and Calvert Vaux. The idea of large public spaces open to the public and not reserved for the wealthy was a new concept in the nineteenth century that remains important in the twenty-first century. These landscapes—including the parks —are still, as they were designed to be, places where a variety of people can come together to work, to play and to be refreshed. Recognizing these parks' irreplaceable qualities and resources and the role they played in creating more livable communities, a group of concerned and passionate individuals came together in 1980 to form NAOP in Buffalo, New York, where Olmsted and Vaux first realized a city-wide system of parks and boulevards.

Since that time, NAOP has taken a leadership role in raising public awareness of the importance of this historic and artistic landscape heritage. As a result, government officials and community leaders as well as professionals and academics throughout the world of landscape design—all of whom exert enormous authority over the fate of parks and

Left: Olmsted's signature elm on the South Lawn at Fairsted. Job #673 – F.L. Olmsted Estate/Fairsted (Brookline, MA).

landscapes—have a better understanding of these irreplaceable resources. NAOP continues to foster scholarship, publish key reference materials, develop and sustain local park rehabilitation projects and provide technical and historical information to ongoing preservation efforts. Today, notable Olmsted parks have been reclaimed or are in the process of rehabilitation; strong community groups in a number of urban areas advocate for and preserve Olmsted parks and landscapes; a body of Olmsted documents and information is readily available to scholars, park advocates and park managers in print and online; and Olmsted's historic home and office in Brookline, Massachusetts, is a national park.

Boston families take part in a ranger-led landscape exploration near The Resting Grounds, Franklin Park. Job #918 – Franklin Park (Boston, MA).

Frederick Law Olmsted
National Historic Site

Lee Farrow Cook and Jill Trebbe

Frederick Law Olmsted National Historic Site preserves the home, office and grounds and landscape design records of America's preeminent landscape architect and his firm. In 1881 Olmsted moved from New York City to Brookline, Massachusetts. He wrote his friend Charles Loring Brace, "I enjoy this suburban country beyond expression and in fact, the older I grow find my capacity for enjoyment increasing."[1] In 1883 at a south Brookline property he called "Fairsted," Olmsted established his home and instituted a full-scale professional office, which extended his landscape ideals, philosophy and influence over the course of the next century.

The Olmsted home and office were designated a National Historic Landmark in 1963 and became part of the National Park Service in 1979. Today, Frederick Law Olmsted National Historic Site preserves and provides public access to original plans, drawings and photographs that document more than 6,000 projects undertaken by the Olmsted firm from the 1850s to 1980. The collection includes approximately 138,000 landscape architectural plans and drawings, 70,000 sheets of planting lists, 60,000 photographic prints, 30,000 photographic negatives, 12,000 lithographs, and financial records, job correspondence, records and reports and models relating to thousands of projects. The collection also includes extensive study materials gathered and used by the Olmsted firm.

In 2004, the National Park Service completed a 15-year processing project to make the collection available for public use. A guide to this collection and to the firm's records and correspondence housed at the Library of Congress is now available through an online database (www.rediscov.com/olmsted). In addition to its active research program, Olmsted NHS offers public programs and exhibits on the firm's work and legacy, and engages young people in learning about the history and contemporary relevance of public parks through curriculum-based

General Plan
for the
Improvement
OF THE
U. S. CAPITOL GROUNDS.

FRED. LAW OLMSTED

programming. Through these varied programs, the National Park Service promotes understanding of the creative process of landscape design and encourages public and private stewardship of our nation's significant landscapes for the benefit of present and future generations.

Left: Frederick Law Olmsted's 1874 plan for the United States Capitol Grounds. Job #2820 – Capitol Grounds (Washington, DC).

Above: A grade three student documents plant material in the Fairsted landscape as part of Good Neighbors: Landscape Design and Community Building, a curriculum-based program that introduces youngsters to the work of the Olmsted firm and the relationship between landscape and quality of life. Job #673 – F.L. Olmsted Estate/ Fairsted (Brookline, MA).

Historic view of Fairsted showing vines on the side of the house, with shrubs and sumac, circa 1904. Job #673 – F.L. Olmsted Estate/Fairsted (Brookline, MA).

Preface to the Second Edition

Lucy Lawliss and Lauren Meier

In 1987, a small and dedicated group of landscape historians, landscape architects and Olmsted enthusiasts compiled and published an unprecedented list of landscape design work accomplished by the Olmsted firm. That guide included approximately 5,000 design commissions throughout the United States and beyond its borders, including projects in Canada, Bermuda, Argentina and Great Britain. Over a century of practice, the Olmsted firm, founded by Frederick Law Olmsted, shaped the American landscape into memorable places in which we live, work, recreate and ultimately repose. The publication of *The Master List of Design Projects of the Olmsted Firm 1857–1950*, compiled by Charles E. Beveridge and Carolyn F. Hoffman with assistance from Shary Page Berg and Arleyn A. Levee, marked the burgeoning interest in the history of the designed landscape in America and brought national recognition to the importance and fragility of the work of the Olmsted firm. The National Association for Olmsted Parks had formed almost a decade earlier through local efforts, such as the Massachusetts Association for Olmsted Parks, and its leaders had an important role in publishing the first *Master List*.

Once again, a small and dedicated group—spearheaded by the National Association for Olmsted Parks and Frederick Law Olmsted National Historic Site—has come together to republish this still awe-inspiring list of master works. Over the decades, interest in these special places of beauty and inspiration has grown, resulting in efforts to identify, understand and ultimately preserve and rehabilitate them. With this updated, expanded (to more than 6,000 projects) and extensively illustrated edition of the *Master List*, we hope to serve and assist all interested people in their efforts to appreciate the *human* component in the creation and con-servation of our built environment.

The second edition of *The Master List of Design Projects of the Olmsted Firm 1857-1979* is an updated and comprehensive inventory of the records of the commissions undertaken by Frederick Law Olmsted and his sons and successors in the Olmsted firm. The list reflects the current knowledge and primary source materials related to the work of the Olmsted firm, housed in the Olmsted Archives at Frederick Law Olmsted National Historic Site in Brookline, Massachusetts, and at the Manuscript Division of the Library of Congress in Washington, D.C. It provides the data for evaluating the Olmsted legacy nationwide, with listings in fourteen thematic categories, including parks, city and regional planning projects, suburban communities, college and school campuses, private estates and exhibitions and fairs. Entries within each category are organized geographically, so that communities can easily understand and initiate interest and support for the Olmsted resources in their area. The *Master List* is truly a collaborative undertaking. It brings together park and open space advocates, public officials, landscape historians and landscape architects, archivists, academics and Olmsted scholars, all of whom volunteered their time to bring the list of Olmsted projects together with introductory essays that place the firm's work in its historic context.

Frederick Law Olmsted from an Olmsted family photograph, date unknown.

Frederick Law Olmsted and his successors contributed significantly to the quality of our designed landscape, and their impact is still experienced each day by millions of individuals. The social, aesthetic, political and environmental principles on which these projects are based are still as valid today as they were a century ago. It is our hope that the second edition of the *Master List* will again inspire appreciation and preservation of the Olmsted legacy for future generations.

Acknowledgments

Many individuals have contributed to this second edition. They include Jerry Arbes, Julia S. Bachrach, Alan Banks, Charles E. Beveridge, Ethan Carr, Lee Farrow Cook, Rolf Diamant, Nancy Pollack-Ellwand, Myra Harrison, Susan L. Klaus, Francis R. Kowsky, Ann Knight, Lucy Lawliss, Arleyn A. Levee, Caroline Loughlin, Lauren Meier, Catherine Nagel, Anthony Reed, Cynthia Sanford, Jamison Spittler, Liza Stearns and Jill Trebbe. Thanks also to various staff of the National Park Service, the Northeast Document Conservation Center, the National Association for Olmsted Parks, the Frederick Law Olmsted Papers editorial project and the Library of Congress who have spent countless hours protecting and documenting the collections and entering the data that contributed to this edition of the *Master List*.

---

*This publication was made possible, in part,
through generous financial support from the following:*

Hubbard Educational Foundation
Central Park Conservancy
Felicia Fund
Pressley Associates

National Center for Preservation Technology and Training, National Park Service
Olmsted Center for Landscape Preservation, National Park Service
Quennell Rothschild and Partners, LLP
Reed Hilderbrand Associates Inc.
Rhodeside & Harwell, Inc.
The Jaeger Company
The Trust for Public Land
Wallace Roberts & Todd, LLC

Left: Olmsted Brothers employees outside of Fairsted, 1898 or 1899, (Shurtleff, later Shurcliff [standing in window], Sawyer, Prey, Kellaway, Reed and Cook [standing]).

Right: Frederick Law Olmsted from an Olmsted family photograph, date unknown.

Background: Detail of plan of the parkway between the Muddy River Gate House and Jamaica Park, 1892. Job #927 – Muddy River (Boston, MA).

INTRODUCTORY ESSAYS

The Olmsted Firm — An Introduction

Charles E. Beveridge

The Olmsted Firm

The Olmsted firm originated in the Fall of 1857, when Frederick Law Olmsted and Calvert Vaux agreed to enter the design competition for Central Park in New York. When their "Greensward" plan was awarded first prize in April 1858, the two men undertook to supervise construction of the park—Olmsted as Architect-in-Chief and Vaux in a subordinate position as Consulting Architect. During the next seven years they collaborated on a few commissions—a cemetery in Middletown, New York, the Hartford Retreat in Connecticut, Bloomingdale Asylum in New York City, a street system for the Fort Washington section of Manhattan and a few private estates, but apparently had no formal partnership arrangement. This situation changed in the fall of 1865, when they formed the firm of Olmsted, Vaux & Co. The partners secured a number of important commissions, including parks and parkways in Brooklyn, a park system in Buffalo, the Chicago South Park and the residential suburb of Riverside, Illinois. Olmsted was also a partner in the architectural firm of Vaux, Withers & Co. Both partnerships dissolved in 1872.

For the next dozen years Olmsted carried on his practice in New York City with the assistance of English-born architect Thomas Wisedell and several other architects and engineers. He also relied on the skills of Swiss-born landscape gardener Jacob Weidenmann. As early as at least 1874 his stepson John Charles Olmsted assisted him in his work, and during some periods his wife, Mary Perkins Olmsted, served as amanuensis. Major projects in this period included the United States Capitol grounds, the park on Mount Royal in Montreal, the park on Belle Isle in Detroit, the Back Bay Fens in Boston and the street and rapid transit system of the Bronx.

After his dismissal from the New York City parks department in 1878, Olmsted began the transition to the Boston area that resulted in permanent change of residence to Brookline, Massachusetts, in 1882. There, at "Fairsted," he began to form the firm that continued to operate from Brookline until 1979, when the property, structures and collections became part of the National Park Service as Frederick Law Olmsted National Historic Site.

In 1884 John Charles Olmsted became a partner in the firm of F. L. & J. C. Olmsted. In 1889 another protégé whom Olmsted had trained, Henry Sargent Codman, became partner. This period ended abruptly and tragically with Codman's death in 1893 at the age of twenty-nine. During this period the firm continued planning of the Boston Emerald Necklace and designed other park systems for Louisville, Kentucky, and Rochester, New York. Other significant commissions were the Niagara Reservation, the World's Columbian Exposition of 1893 in Chicago, Lawrenceville School, Stanford University and the suburban community of Druid Hills in Atlanta.

Following the death of Henry Codman, Olmsted convinced his former student Charles Eliot to join the firm, renamed Olmsted, Olmsted & Eliot. Eliot brought to the firm the planning of the system of metropolitan reservations surrounding Boston, which he had inaugurated during a decade of independent practice. He continued to focus on the parks of the Boston area and played an important role in developing other park systems, notably that of Hartford, Connecticut. Eliot's career was cut short when in 1897 he died from meningitis at the age of thirty-seven. Thus two of Olmsted's three highly promising successors, on whom he relied heavily for perpetuation of his design concepts, died prematurely during his own lifetime.

Olmsted had ceased active practice in 1895, a victim of failing memory and vitality. The new firm formed after Eliot's death had the old title of F. L. & J. C. Olmsted, but the son had replaced the father in it. A year later, in 1898, John Charles and Frederick Law Olmsted Jr. formed the partnership of Olmsted Brothers, a name the firm would retain until 1961, some forty years after John Charles's death in 1920 and four years after his half-brother's death in 1957. In the process, a full century had elapsed during which a man named Frederick Law Olmsted practiced landscape architecture in the firm.

The first three decades of the twentieth century witnessed a great increase in the work of the firm and the size of the staff, which reached forty-seven by 1917 and up to sixty at its height in the 1920s. During the four decades of the elder Olmsted's practice the firm carried out some 500 commissions, many of those coming in the 1890s. By the onset of the Great Depression of the 1930s, that number had increased to 2,500. The years prior to the First World War were the firm's most active period, involving the planning of extensive park systems for a dozen metropolitan areas. The 1920s produced little new park work other than expansion of these metropolitan park systems, but the period marked a significant increase in residential subdivisions and suburban communities, including those of Lake Wales in Florida, Palos Verdes in California and Forest Hills in New York. The decade also accounted for fully one quarter of the 2,000 commissions the firm received for the grounds of private residences and estates. One vast project, Fort Tryon Park in Manhattan, proved to be the principal enterprise for the firm during the Depression of the 1930s, supplemented by extensive work for British Pacific Properties, Ltd., in Vancouver, British Columbia. Few commissions followed the Second World War, and the only major project of the firm following the retirement of Frederick Law Olmsted Jr. from active practice in 1949 was the extension of Rock Creek Park from the District of Columbia into Montgomery County in Maryland.

Olmsted taught his design principles to his pupils and partners: John Charles Olmsted, Henry Sargent Codman and Charles Eliot and, less formally, his son and namesake, Frederick Law Olmsted Jr. They in turn passed on elements of his teachings to later partners and staff members. The list of these landscape designers is long and includes later partners in the Olmsted firm during the period covered by this *Master List* of projects: James Frederick Dawson, Percival Gallagher, Edward Clark Whiting, Henry Vincent Hubbard, William Bell Marquis and Leon Henry Zach. It also includes landscape architects who became partners in the firm after the retirement of Frederick Law Olmsted Jr., including Carl Rust Parker, Charles Scott Riley, Artemas Partridge Richardson and Joseph George Hudak. Others about whose design principles and practice the projects in this list will provide new information are members of the firm's staff who subsequently established their own landscape practices, such as Warren Manning, George Gibbs Jr., Frederick G. Todd, William Lyman Phillips, Emil Mische and Arthur Shurcliff.

Assessing the Work of the Olmsted Firm

During the past three decades, there has been a great increase in public awareness and appreciation of the work of Frederick Law Olmsted and his successors in the Olmsted landscape architecture firm. Beginning with the Olmsted Sesquicentennial of 1972, numerous books and articles, films and exhibitions have appeared on the subject of Olmsted and his design legacy. During these years Olmsted's home and office in Brookline, Massachusetts, became part of the National Park Service, which has conserved and made available to researchers the large volume of material there. At the same time, the Manuscript Division of the Library of Congress in Washington, D.C., has organized and

microfilmed the three hundred linear feet of documentary material—reports and correspondence—that constitutes the principal written record of the work of the firm. Drawing from these resources, eight volumes of the projected twelve-volume series of the Frederick Law Olmsted Papers editorial project have been compiled and published. A collaborative undertaking between the National Park Service and the National Association for Olmsted Parks has created the Olmsted Research Guide Online (www. rediscov.com/olmsted), a comprehensive reference tool for materials at Olmsted NHS and the Library of Congress. The National Association for Olmsted Parks, formed in 1980, has been active in publicizing the work of the firm and encouraging the formation of very active Olmsted-related organizations in several states. Many programs for the preservation and rehabilitation of Olmsted parks and landscapes have been created throughout the country and in Canada.

In the process, a renewed awareness has developed of the significance of the role of the Olmsted firm in the history of landscape architecture in the United States—the extent of its legacy, the quality of its designs and the significant influence it has had on millions of people since the mid-nineteenth century. Particularly important to this awareness has been the rehabilitation and restoration of public parks designed by the firm, a movement that began in New York City in the 1980s and has since spread to include parks in most of the major cities for which the firm planned parks and park systems. Included in this list are Boston, Seattle, Louisville, Atlanta, Montreal, Essex County in New Jersey, Denver, Baltimore and Rochester, New York. Those cities, along with numerous others, have rediscovered the past and future value to their citizens of their Olmsted-firm parks. The special genius of the Olmsteds and their firm has proved to be a priceless resource for many communities.

Still, despite the survey and inventory work done in a few states, the extent of the firm's role in shaping the landscape remains for the most part unexplored. Even the number of designs the firm made and carried out is not known. The general figures we have are impressive: between 1857 and 1979 the firm participated in some way in more than 6,000 projects. The basic records of the firm indicate that it drew at least one plan for more than 4,000 of these, including more than 700 public parks, parkways and recreation areas, more than 2,000 private

View upstream from the Longwood Avenue Bridge, 1920, 28 years after construction. Job #930 – Riverway (Boston, MA).

Inset: View upstream from the Longwood Avenue Bridge, May 7, 1892, under construction. Job #930 – Riverway (Boston, MA).

estates and homesteads, more than 350 subdivisions and suburban communities, more than 250 college and school campuses and the grounds of a variety of buildings—almost 100 residential institutions (hospitals and asylums), 100 libraries and other public buildings, more than 125 commercial and industrial buildings and more than 75 churches. For the vast majority of these projects, research has not been done to determine the role of the Olmsted firm—how extensive the planning by the firm was, how much of the design was carried out, what the present condition is and what additional documentary sources exist to guide the preservation and restoration process.

In addition to clarifying the extent of the work of the Olmsted firm, the research to be done on the basis of this *Master List* should reveal much new information about the design philosophy and professional practices of the firm. It will supply information concerning the approach of Frederick Law Olmsted, his partners and his successors to a whole range of issues—design concepts, construction practices, provision for long-term growth and maintenance of plantings and relations with practitioners in related fields, among others.

Frederick Law Olmsted himself had an ambitious conception of the role that landscape architecture could play in improving the quality of life of Americans. His extensive travels in the antebellum South, his two-year sojourn in California and his travels in the British Isles, Europe and China provided remarkable breadth of experience, while his career as a writer and publisher helped clarify his views on a whole series of questions concerning art, politics, economics and social organization. By the end of the Civil War, he had defined what he hoped American society would become and had chosen the means by which he would promote those ideals during the next thirty years.

Olmsted had great faith in the ability of his art to improve society and in particular to promote a sense of community in the rapidly growing urban centers of the country. His great parks and park systems were to be spaces held in common by all residents of their cities, places where all classes could mingle, free from the competitiveness and antagonisms of workaday life. His plans for residential suburbs, too, provided common ground that would foster both physical health and what he called "communitiveness" —the impulse to serve the needs of one's fellow citizens.

In addition, Olmsted believed that scenery could have a powerful, restorative influence. He was convinced that the spacious, gracefully modulated terrain of his parks provided a specific medical antidote to the artificiality, noise and stress of city life. In this and many other ways he strove to use his skill as an artist to meet the most fundamental of human needs in a comprehensive way. The psychological power of scenery, he felt, could be achieved in landscape design only through subordination of all elements to the creation of a single effect.

There must be no specimen planting or placing of works of architecture or sculpture to be viewed for their individual beauty. In the same spirit, he excluded ornamental and decorative features from the buildings he designed, preferring a simple, organic plan that concentrated on fulfilling a particular function. "So long as considerations of utility are neglected or overridden by considerations of ornament," he taught, "there will be no true Art."

For reasons of function as well as effect, Olmsted carefully separated different activities and different styles of planting. He abhorred an "incongruous mixture of styles," feeling that each designed space should have a single, coherent character. Likewise, he separated potentially con-flicting uses in his parks, creating for each activity a setting carefully designed for it. In his parks and parkways he also separated different kinds of traffic, for reasons of both enjoyment and safety.

How closely Frederick Law Olmsted's successors adhered to his principles, in the face of changing technology, social conditions and recreational needs, has yet to be determined. The research that stems from the publication of this *Master List* will provide a far more complete answer to that question than can be offered at the present time. In the process, much will be learned about the significance of the Olmsted firm for the designed landscape of America, and much practical knowledge will be secured for the process of preserving and restoring the designs of Olmsted and his successors.

People relaxing near the lagoon in Washington Park, circa 1900. Job #1903 – Washington Park (Chicago, IL).

Aerial view of Yosemite Valley, date unknown. Job #8099 – Yosemite National Park (CA). See also Job #8204 and Job #12301.

Background: Topographical map of Acadia National Park, 1931. Job #9138 – Acadia National Park (Mount Desert Island, ME).

The Olmsteds and the Development of the National Park System

Rolf Diamant

Any exploration into the founding philosophy of America's national parks inevitably leads one to the Olmsteds. Frederick Law Olmsted's prescient vision for Yosemite (and all public lands) in 1865 and the timely contribution by Frederick Law Olmsted Jr. of a statement of purposes for the National Park Service's 1916 Organic Act have had profound and lasting consequences for the nation and the world.[1]

Until recently this compelling narrative was obscured by a more romantic creation mythology that associated the birth of the park idea with the 1870 Washburn-Diane expedition along the banks of the Madison River in Yellowstone, the "mother park." As historian Richard Sellars wryly mused in his book *Preserving Nature in the National Parks*, "Surely the national park concept deserved a 'virgin birth' — a night sky in the pristine American West, on a riverbank, and around a campfire, as if an evergreen cone had fallen near the fire, then heated and expanded and dropped its seed to spread around the planet."[2]

It is too ambitious to describe here in detail all the mid-nineteenth century influences that shaped the establishment of America's first generation of parks and in 1864 the progenitor of future national parks —Yosemite. There was certainly a sense of national pride and patriotism associated with monuments of nature.[3] The country was also on the cusp of a nascent parks movement, exemplified by New York City's ambitious and well publicized Central Park, a reflection of the perceived value of parkland to public health and social harmony. Alfred Runte suggests, "Here at last — in the blending of the eastern mind and the western experience — was the enduring spark for the American inspiration of national parks."[4] However, one of the least discussed (in the context of parks) and yet perhaps one of the most potent influences was the near-collapse and reincarnation of American democracy through four years of civil war.

"It was during one of the darkest hours, before Sherman had begun the march upon Atlanta or Grant his terrible movement through the Wilderness," wrote Frederick Law Olmsted in his 1865 report on Yosemite, "when the paintings of Bierstadt and the photographs of Watkins, both productions of the war time, had given to the people on the Atlantic some idea of the sublimity of the Yosemite."[5] It is not an accident of history that it was in June 1864, during the war's costliest year, as the government and its people began to look to a future beyond interminable loss and sacrifice, that Congress enacted and Abraham Lincoln signed into law the legislation that held Yosemite Valley "for public use, resort, and recreation… inalienable for all time." "The creation of a park in far away California," wrote historian Robin Winks, "was a statement about national unity, continental status, and hopes for an optimistic future in the midst of a devastating civil war: Yosemite was a monument to union, democracy, and long-term goals for the nation, the product of a great national need."[6]

Following on his revolutionary 1863 Emancipation Proclamation, Lincoln promised a war-weary nation in his Gettysburg Address "a new birth of freedom." When Olmsted was appointed to draft a charter and plan for Yosemite, he expanded upon Lincoln's vision of a broader, more inclusive interpretation of democracy in post-war America and framed the intellectual foundation for what became the world's first system of national parks. In his report, Olmsted made the case that it is a "political duty" of republican government to set aside "great public grounds for the free enjoyment of the people," forever guaranteeing its citizens "the pursuit of happiness." Olmsted, not by coincidence, referred to the words of the Declaration of Independence, as Lincoln had done at Gettysburg when he used the words "all men are created equal," opening the door to "a new birth of freedom"— one that included emancipation among other freedoms.[7] Access to parks and recreation would be a fundamental entitlement of all Americans.

Almost 50 years later, Frederick Law Olmsted Jr. was called upon to amplify and refine his father's Yosemite legacy by addressing the need for a new bureau to professionally manage more than three dozen national

Carte-de-visite of Frederick Law Olmsted, circa 1893.

Right: "Cathedral Rock, Yosemite" by Albert Bierstadt, 1870. Job #12301 – Yosemite Valley, Mariposa (CA). See also Job #8099 and Job #8204.

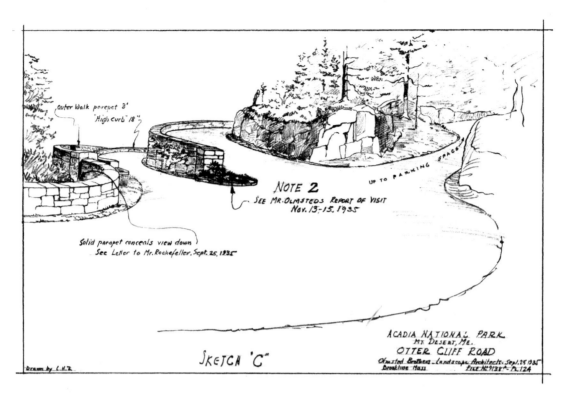

Otter Cliff Road, September 25, 1935. Job #9138 – Acadia National Park (Mount Desert Isle, ME).

parks and monuments scattered across the West. "The present situation in regard to the national parks is very bad," Olmsted Jr. wrote in 1912. "They have been created one at a time by acts of Congress which have not defined at all clearly the purposes for which the lands were to be set apart, nor provided any orderly or efficient means of safeguarding the parks…. I have made at different times two suggestions, one of which was… a definition of the purposes".[8]

In the course of extensive correspondence with park champions such as J. Horace McFarland, President of the American Civic Association, Olmsted Jr. crafted his famous definition of purposes for the 1916 Organic Act that established a unified system of national parks and a professional bureau to manage them:

> To conserve the scenery and the natural and historic objects and the wild life
> therein and to provide for the enjoyment of the same in such manner and by such
> means as will leave them unimpaired for the enjoyment of future generations.

While his father, Frederick Law Olmsted, had argued "that portions of natural scenery be properly guarded and cared for by the government," he had also cautioned that these places not become playgrounds of only the privileged few.[9] There should be a sacrosanct commitment to make them widely accessible "for the free use of the whole body of the people forever."[10]

This theme resonates in the wording of the statement of purposes by Olmsted Jr. in the 1916 Act and also in a letter he wrote to Frank Pierce, Acting Secretary of the Interior, counseling that the national parks be managed "promoting public recreation and public health through the use and enjoyment by the people…of the natural scenery and objects of interest."[11]

If it can be said Olmsted and Olmsted Jr. left their mark on the soul of the National Park Service, it can certainly be said that the Olmsted firm shaped some important parts of its body. The firm was responsible for projects in Acadia, Everglades, Great Smoky Mountains and Yosemite. A partial listing of projects in the nation's capital reads like a guide to the National Park Service managed sites of Washington, D.C., including the Mall, Jefferson Memorial, Roosevelt Island, White House grounds and Rock Creek Park. In his later years, Olmsted Jr. actively worked for the protection of California's coastal redwoods and lived to see Redwood National Park's Olmsted Grove dedicated in his honor.

Embedded in the 1865 Yosemite Report is the phrase "faith in the refinement of a republic." Perhaps there is no more fitting way to sum up the national park legacy of the Olmsteds and their many collaborators than to say their faith lives on in a system of nearly 400 national park areas, reflecting the high purpose and refinement of a democratic nation and its citizenry.

Everglades, January 1932. Job #4022 – Everglades National Park Project (Miami, FL).

View from Mount Royal, Montreal, by John Charles Olmsted, July 1894. Job #609 – Mount Royal Park (Montreal, QC, Canada).

Background: Detail of plan for Mount Royal Park, 1877. Job #609 – Mount Royal Park (Montreal, QC, Canada).

The Olmsted Firm in Canada

Nancy Pollock-Ellwand

In the mid-1870s Frederick Law Olmsted was invited by the City of Montreal to begin work on Mount Royal Park.[1] He considered it a grander natural canvas than Central Park and sought to more fully combine the sublime and the beautiful on a site that he called "the best opportunity…that had ever been presented to my profession."[2] This project began a lengthy involvement (1874-1946) by the Olmsted firm with Canadian clients. It was a body of work that included about 100 projects stretching from Victoria, British Columbia, on the west coast to Truro, Nova Scotia, on the east. The output is small[3] compared to the firm's work in the United States, but the Olmsted effect was large. It penetrated and profoundly influenced late-nineteenth and twentieth century Canadian professional and popular landscape aesthetics.

The firm's Canadian practice was marked by major public projects, most notably town planning and suburban development. In fact, it could be argued that the planning of the extensive Capilano Estates in greater Vancouver (1931-1938, 1944) significantly sustained the Olmsted firm through the difficult years of the Depression and the Second World War. It is also important to note that the majority of Canadian job listings are for private residential commissions where the wealthy demonstrated their status by securing the top landscape architecture firm in North America to design their gardens.

Frederick Law Olmsted began the firm's work in Canada. After 1887, the next generation of the firm led the work. John Charles Olmsted completed designs for a number of major planned communities, including Uplands near Victoria, British Columbia, and South Mount Royal and J. Lonsdale Doupe's Sunalta, both in Calgary, Alberta. Frederick Law Olmsted Jr. concentrated on city planning initiatives, including reports on Montreal's Metropolitan Park System and the Toronto waterfront. Other Olmsted employees involved in Canadian projects included Percival Gallagher, Edward Clark Whiting and Arthur Asahel Shurtleff. However, of all the firm members it was James Frederick Dawson who is credited with much of the work in Canada. Dawson's contributions stretched over a three-decade period, focused in the western provinces of Manitoba, Alberta and British Columbia.

The Olmsted firm played a key role during the formative years of Canadian town planning and landscape architecture.[4] In addition to the influence they exerted through their built projects, written reports and advice, the employees of the Olmsted firm were prolific writers and public speakers. Some of Canada's major land owners and municipal civil servants were listening.[5] In particular, Olmsted Jr. counseled numerous municipalities to adopt formalized planning processes. He insisted that they establish local bureaucracies to facilitate communication so he could work effectively.[6] While many communities may not have achieved an Olmsted-authored plan, the enlightened advice of Olmsted Jr. helped to create a modern planning structure that still exists.

Another legacy of the Olmsted firm was the training and development of landscape architects who went on to form the genesis of the profession in Canada. Three former employees of the firm who were trained in the Olmsted design and planning philosophy helped professionalize landscape architecture and town planning in Canada. They were Frederick G. Todd (1876-1948), Rickson Outhet (1876-1951) and Gordon Joseph Culham (1891-1979).

In 1900 New Hampshire-born Frederick Todd became Canada's first professional landscape architect when he established an office in Montreal. His interest in the city developed while working for the Olmsted firm on Mount Royal Park. He was involved in numerous projects across Canada, most notably producing an influential though unrealized 1901 plan for Ottawa,[7] the nation's capital. Todd became one of Canada's most prominent landscape architects.

A contemporary of Todd's was the Montrealer, Rickson Outhet. Though not formally trained in landscape architecture he learned his trade in the Brookline office of the Olmsted firm. Inspired by his work in the United States, including being draftsman to the McMillan Commission in 1901, he returned to Montreal in 1905 and advertised himself as both a landscape architect and town planner. Outhet became involved in the Province of Quebec Association of Architects' Civic Improvement Committee and the "Plan for the Improvement of Montreal" that included a series of city planning schemes.[8]

The third alumnus was Gordon Joseph Culham, also a Canadian and part of a later generation of Olmsted firm employees. He returned to Canada in the early 1930s after six years of work on various Olmsted projects such as the Cloisters in Fort Tryon Park, New York City, the State Capitol grounds in Olympia, Washington, and most importantly New York City's Regional Plan.[9] Culham returned upon the invitation of Canadian publisher John Bayne Maclean,[10] who was a great admirer of the Olmsteds and had employed the firm on several projects. In the end he decided he needed an Olmsted-trained man closer to home, hence

James Frederick Dawson, Frederick Law Olmsted Jr. and Percival Gallagher,
date unknown.

his proposal to Culham.[11] Maclean's commissions were to become the nucleus of Culham's
Canadian practice.[12] In 1934 Culham was instrumental in creating the Canadian Society
of Landscape Architects and became that organization's first president.[13]

It is worthwhile to distinguish Canadian projects from the broader Olmsted canon
because, as citizens of a younger nation, Canadians chose to engage the more experienced
Olmsted firm to address the challenges of urbanization, open space planning and suburban
expansion. As members of the Empire, the Canadians also turned to influential British town
planners and landscape designers such as Thomas Mawson and Thomas Adams. However,
as the Canadian job list so clearly illustrates, it was the Olmsted firm that had a profound
influence on the development of landscape architecture practice in Canada.

*View of The Cloisters through the arch at Fort Tryon Park, May 1936. Job #529 –
Fort Tryon Park (New York, NY).*

*Background: Preliminary Plan for Volunteer Park, 1908. Olmsted Brothers, Landscape
Architects. Job #2695 – Volunteer Park (Seattle, WA).*

Researching an Olmsted Landscape

Lucy Lawliss, Caroline Loughlin and Lauren Meier

Research is fundamental to understanding the evolution and significance of a historic designed landscape. It can be done for purely academic reasons but more than likely it is undertaken to guide treatment and management decisions for a particular property. These decisions should be grounded in a full understanding of the original design intent, the project's as-built realization and subsequent additions or changes. Researching a landscape for the purposes of treatment includes documenting the development of built features, the use of specific materials, vegetation—both original and planted—and the spaces that make a particular landscape distinct and important. Thus, if the goal is to identify and preserve significant elements as well as the overall character of the historic landscape, the successful implementation of treatment decisions will depend on the adequacy of the research effort.

Designed landscapes associated with the work of the Olmsted firm are important for many reasons, including design, execution, contextual relationship to similar properties, use—past and present—and their place in the local, regional or national environment. Research is essential in determining the historical significance as well as the integrity of the existing landscape. The following steps recommend a tested approach to researching an Olmsted designed landscape.

Defining the Research Scope

For anyone undertaking landscape research—landowners, managers, park officials and design professionals—it is important to define the scope and objectives for the research project. For example, if the goal is to restore a designed landscape to its height of activity or period of significance, the level of research must provide sufficiently detailed information to guide the restoration effort. Therefore, once the scope and objectives of the project are established, the researcher can define research questions both to direct the study of sources and to shape the final outcome.

Considering the following questions will help determine the information needed to meet the project's goals and objectives.

Things to ask about an Olmsted landscape include:

When and why was the property selected/purchased? Who chose the property?

Who are and have been the owners of the property? Did they or others place restrictions on its use or treatment? If so, what are they?

What names have been given the property (historically, colloquially)?

Who hired the Olmsted firm? Was there a prior relationship with the firm?

What was the land's condition or how was it used before the involvement of the Olmsted firm?

Who were the intended users and how was this accomplished? (What was the design intent?)

What was the extent of the design effort of the Olmsted firm and to what degree was it realized?

Who were the subsequent designers, landscape architects and others involved after the Olmsted firm? Are they known locally, regionally or nationally for their work?

What remains from the original design/construction? What is its condition? What is the overall condition of the landscape? Has it been in continuous use or abandoned?

Who actually used (uses) the landscape and in what way?

How will the property be used when this project is completed?

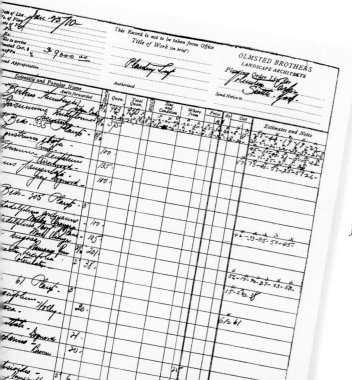

Detail of Planting List, January 23, 1910.
Job #2695 – Volunteer Park (Seattle, WA).

Historic view of Volunteer Park showing reservoir and lily pool. Job #2695 – Volunteer Park (Seattle, WA).

Identifying Sources of Information

The second task in researching an Olmsted landscape is determining how and where to find information needed to answer the research questions. There are a number of local and national sources described below.

Local Sources

For individual landscapes, it is important to check local resources first.

> **Places to look include:**
>
> Historical societies, public libraries, garden clubs;
>
> College and university archives or libraries;
>
> Municipal archives (parks departments, departments of public works, water and sewer departments, court records);
>
> Newspaper files and archives;
>
> Sources cited in footnotes, picture credits and bibliographies of local histories;
>
> State historic preservation offices.

Specific things to look for from local sources include:

Official documents: annual reports, minutes and journals of public agencies or commissions, construction contracts and maintenance records, census records, municipal ordinances and charters, state laws and constitutions, wills, real estate deeds;

Secondary Sources: histories of the municipality, city, state and region; essays; biographies;

Newspapers and periodicals: articles, photographs, editorials, letters to the editor, obituaries;

Unpublished materials: diaries, letters, catalogs of local plant nurseries, seed catalogs;

Visual records and associated documentation: maps, plans, drawings and sketches, photographs, postcards, plant lists;

Transcripts or taped materials of interviews and oral histories;

National Register of Historic Places nominations that describe the building, structure, site or district.

National Sources

The Olmsted firm project lists presented in this publication point to the two primary national sources for information: Frederick Law Olmsted National Historic Site and the Manuscript Division of the Library of Congress. The National Park Service manages the Olmsted Archives as part of the museum collection of Olmsted NHS. The Archives include plans, photographs, plan index cards and planting lists, each associated with a job number assigned by the firm.

The other national repository is the Manuscript Division of the Library of Congress. This source contains most of the firm's written correspondence and administrative files, which support and explain the drawing files. The manuscript collection can be connected to plan and image records in the Olmsted Archives by job number.

Before visiting either of these sources, a researcher can determine a project job number along with preliminary project information by consulting this *Master List* or by using the Olmsted Research Guide Online. Use of these finding aids is a critical step and saves time and expense by providing information that will facilitate contact with either national repository. With the job number(s), and an indication of the quantity and type of materials available, the

Right: Volunteer Park, 1908. Job #2695 – Volunteer Park (Seattle, WA).

Olmsted Research Guide Online
www.rediscov.com/olmsted

Searchable databases:

The Master List of Projects database contains information similar to the information in this book. The Advanced Master List Search allows a search on any combination of fields:

- Keyword
- Project Name/Client Name
- City/Community
- Job Number
- Location (State, Province or Country)
- Project Type

The Archival Records database contains, for each project, a list of the items connected to that job held at the Library of Congress or at Olmsted NHS. The Advanced Archival Records Search allows a search on any combination of several fields:

- Job Number
- Keyword
- Document Title
- Master List Information
- Summary/Notes
- Date
- Location
- Document Type (Correspondence, Map, Photograph, Plan, Scrapbook)

Planting Plan for Volunteer Park, 1910. Olmsted Brothers, Landscape Architects. Job #2695 – Volunteer Park (Seattle, WA).

researcher is ready to consult with the Library of Congress and Olmsted NHS to get a clear understanding of what these sources have and how to access the materials. A trip to both institutions is highly recommended if material of interest is confirmed. Consulting these primary sources is the only way to establish the design and intent of the specific job(s).

Olmsted Research Guide Online

The Olmsted Research Guide Online is an online database of archival records related to the work of the Olmsted firm. ORGO is an expanded list of Olmsted job-related documents, both those at the Library of Congress and those at Olmsted NHS. ORGO contains two searchable databases (see sidebar).

All Library of Congress job-related records are listed in ORGO. However, work continues on data entry of the plans and drawings at Olmsted NHS, and ORGO is updated accordingly. For jobs that do not yet have a detailed inventory of plans in ORGO, more specific information is available from Olmsted NHS.

Frederick Law Olmsted National Historic Site

The National Park Service preserves and protects the Olmsted firm's archives at Olmsted NHS and makes items available for public use with assistance from park staff. Prior to making a research request, individuals should review the information contained in the *Master List* and in ORGO to determine the job number and what relevant information is housed at Olmsted NHS. Once this is established, researchers can contact Olmsted NHS to schedule a research appointment.

Library of Congress

The Manuscript Division of the Library of Congress contains collections of historical papers that support scholarly work in political, cultural and scientific history. This includes two important collections related to the work of the Olmsted firm: the Frederick Law Olmsted Papers and the Olmsted Associates Papers (see Resources), which were acquired by the Library of Congress in several groups from 1947 to 1996. Detailed finding aids for both collections are available online. Individual reels of microfilm, or the full set, may be purchased from the Library of Congress or borrowed through interlibrary loan. The Manuscript Division also houses the papers of Laura Wood Roper, Frederick Law Olmsted's first biographer.

Selected Other National Resources

The John Charles Olmsted Collection at the Harvard Design School in Cambridge, Massachusetts, contains letters, correspondence files and material related to Olmsted firm business or professional associations, as well as family papers, memorabilia and photographs from the papers of John Charles Olmsted (1852-1920). John Charles Olmsted was the nephew, stepson and business partner of Frederick Law Olmsted.

The Archives of American Gardens managed by the Smithsonian's Horticultural Services Division contain documentation for more than 5,500 gardens and landscapes, some of which were designed by the Olmsted firm. This collection includes historic glass lantern slides and 35mm slides donated to the Smithsonian by the Garden Club of America, as well as photographs, plans and papers documenting the work of several important landscape architects, including selected works of the Olmsted firm.

Using Sources

While researchers like to use sources with confidence, some caution should be taken before making assumptions related to the information contained in these sources. Design plans represent the artistic vision of the individual or firm not necessarily the project as it was implemented. Thus, plans should be viewed in concert with historic photographs, correspondence, planting order lists, construction records and, if possible, as-built drawings to determine the built form of the landscape. Detailed inventory of the existing landscape conditions may also reveal information about the execution of the design.

Non-academic publications (including newspapers and memoirs) and personal interviews should be examined for possible bias and misinformation. While they can be informative in communicating popular views at a specific time, they may be unreliable for events distant in time, and thus need to be corroborated through the use of other sources. Often limited involvement of the Olmsted firm in the historic period gained prominence over time as the reputation of Frederick Law Olmsted and the successor firm grew. Design work accomplished by other professionals often gets attributed to the Olmsted firm if the Olmsted firm was involved at any time in the property's history. The work of Frederick Law Olmsted Jr. is often misattributed to the father. Photographs may be misidentified as to date and location. Colors in hand-tinted photographs are unreliable. Even printed material on period postcards may be incorrect and should be verified using other sources.

The Lake Washington Boulevard
and Mount Rainier.

Copyright 1914 by Curtis & Miller.

Section of Boulevard, through Volunteer Park,
with Conservatory in Distance.

Historic postcards of Lake Washington Boulevard and Volunteer Park. Job #2718 – Lake Washington Boulevard and Job #2695 – Volunteer Park (Seattle, WA).

Top: Photographer D. W. Butterfield taking a view of Refectory Hill, October 1892.
Job #918 – Franklin Park (Boston, MA).

Bottom: Volunteer Park Standpipe, 1930. Job #2695 – Volunteer Park (Seattle, WA).

Using Research for Planning and Design

Research should be the foundation for planning and guiding treatment work on the historic landscape, including new design work in the landscape. Without research, the historic design intent as well as the features, materials, character and landscape spaces that contribute to the significance of the property cannot be known or fully understood. The NPS has developed guidance in preparing Cultural Landscape Reports, which can serve as an effective methodology for landscape planning and design in an Olmsted landscape. The scope of a Cultural Landscape Report can be modified to fit the scale, complexity and budget of the project (see Defining the Research Scope).

Olmsted Brothers office cartoon, date unknown.

Four steps are essential to preparing a Cultural Landscape Report and all should be undertaken before making physical alterations to the historic landscape, so that historic features and the overall character are not inadvertently lost or damaged. Each of these steps provides information necessary to the success of a project.

Site history – documents the physical evolution of the landscape;

Existing conditions – records the current condition of the property with site plans and a narrative description;

Integrity and significance – analyzes extant historic features and relevant historic contexts and establishes the significance of the landscape;

Treatment – recommends physical design and work on the landscape necessary to meet the owner's needs and objectives, consistent with the *Secretary of the Interior's Standards*.

Reviewing this *Master List* is a critical first step in the research process, which is essential to protecting Olmsted landscapes and advancing knowledge of the Olmsted legacy.

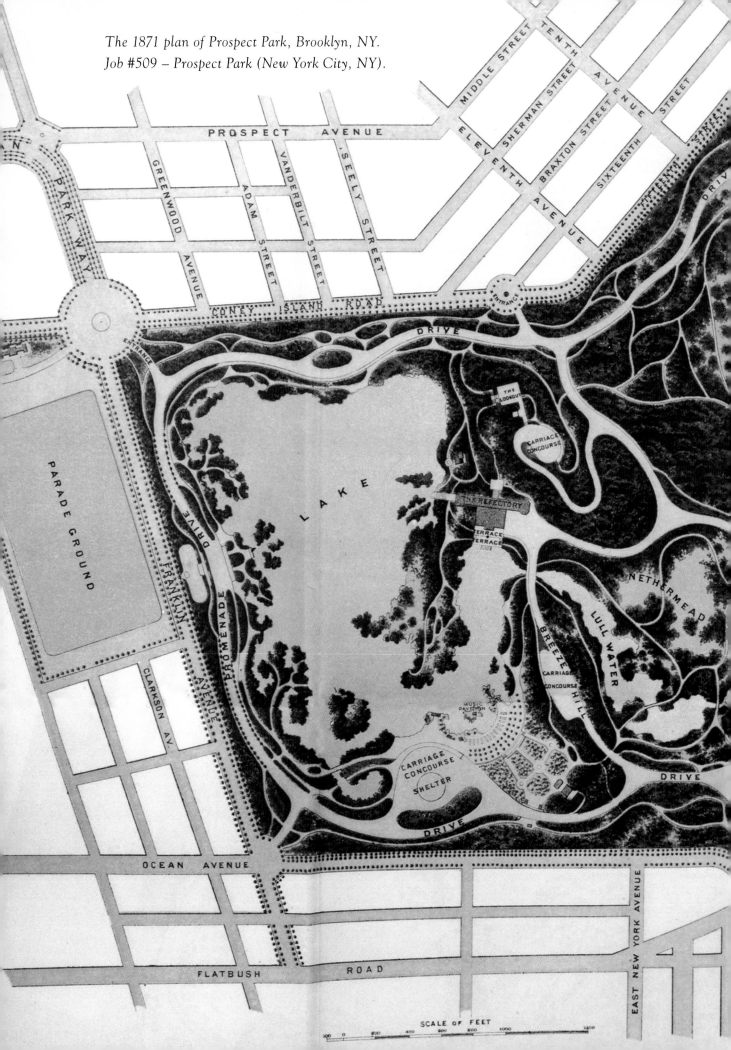

The 1871 plan of Prospect Park, Brooklyn, NY.
Job #509 – Prospect Park (New York City, NY).

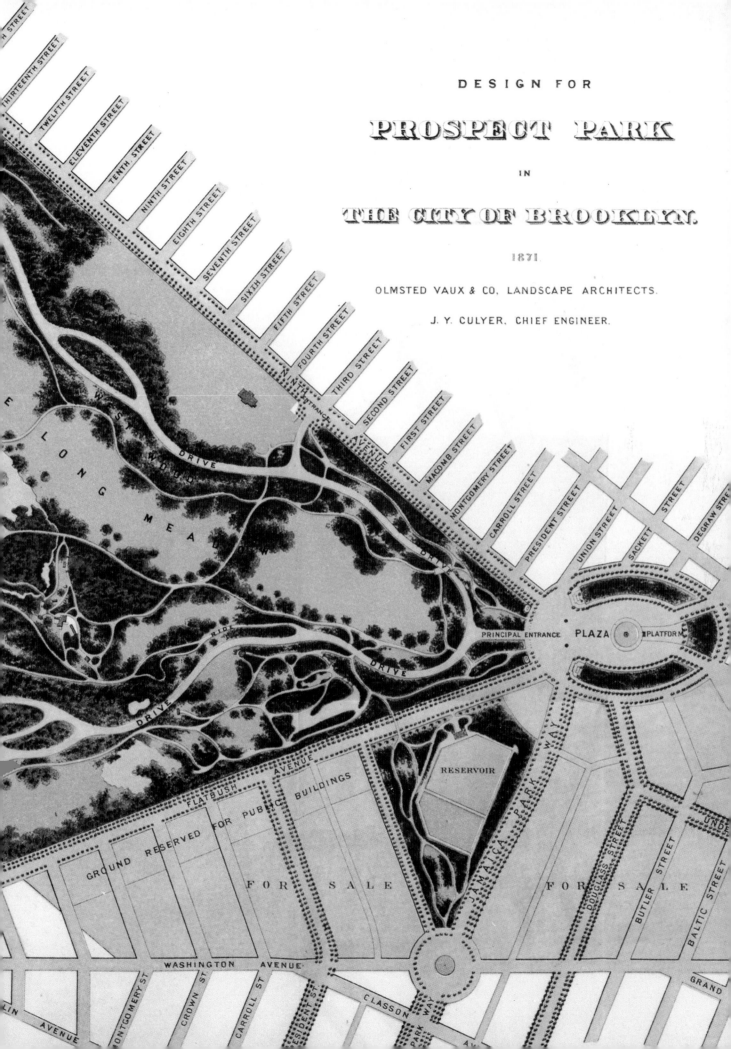

DESIGN FOR

PROSPECT PARK

IN

THE CITY OF BROOKLYN.

1871

OLMSTED VAUX & CO, LANDSCAPE ARCHITECTS.

J. Y. CULYER, CHIEF ENGINEER.

Druid Hill Park, date unknown. Job #2405 – Druid Hill Park (Baltimore, MD).

Background: Detail of plan for the central premises, Stanford University, 1888.
Job #1032 – Leland Stanford Jr. University (Stanford, CA).

THE MASTER LIST OF DESIGN PROJECTS

Introductory Guide

Anthony Reed

The following list is a product of many hands, multiple entities and decades of scholarship and archival processing. Database work accomplished in the 1980s by the editors of the Frederick Law Olmsted Papers led directly to publication of the first edition of the *Master List* in 1987. That edition used the Olmsted firm's "Job Number Books" (handwritten ledgers kept by the firm and organized by job number). Since then the list has grown and changed as information has become available. Other primary sources include the firm's "Vault Book" (organized alphabetically by project name), client card files and plans indices and the individual documents themselves, both those held at Frederick Law Olmsted National Historic Site and those held at the Library of Congress. Files and databases created and used by Olmsted NHS, the Frederick Law Olmsted Papers editorial project and the National Association for Olmsted Parks have also been useful.

In 2002 the consolidation of these data sources premiered as the Olmsted Research Guide Online. For the first time, the Olmsted master list of projects could be searched electronically alongside information about archival records for each individual project. More importantly, the archival records database reunited—in electronic format—a significant archival collection that is physically separated between the Library of Congress and Olmsted NHS. Researchers should use ORGO in conjunction with this *Master List* because it provides additional detail.

The information contained in this *Master List* reflects the total body of work of the Olmsted firm. A job number was assigned by the firm and logged into the Job Number books for every project as soon as a client contact was made. This job number was used on all records relating to a project, even if work never progressed beyond an initial contact, proposal or telephone call. Therefore, the *Master List* reflects all of the firm's work, from initial proposals to decades of paid design consultations, some of which resulted in built projects. Some projects were left unnumbered by the firm, including many of the early projects. For consistency, the editors of the Frederick Law Olmsted Papers and the National Park Service created job numbers for these projects based on their associated thematic category.

The *Master List* is organized into thematic categories and further subdivided by geographic location. Each entry within the thematic category includes the job number, name, location, number and dates of plans in the National Park Service archives at Olmsted NHS and the dates of correspondence held at the Library of Congress or at Olmsted NHS.

Every effort has been made to create a list that is both accurate (useful to contemporary researchers) and authentic (reflective of the historic information). Historic names are retained when they are not misleading and corrected when they are historically erroneous. Inaccurate historic information has been documented and collected as "alternate" information by the National Park Service; outright typographical errors and incorrect interpretations of historical handwriting are corrected. It is important to note here that, as in any data-collection process involving many years and numerous interpreters, errors may still exist in this *Master List*. The authors, editors and data managers responsible for this work would appreciate hearing from users of this guide if an inaccuracy is found. Corrections can be sent to the archives staff at Olmsted NHS.

The following is an explanation of each of the fields in the data.

Thematic Categories

The list is divided into fourteen thematic categories or types of projects that represent a broad range of project types, determined by the editors of the Frederick Law Olmsted Papers and expanded from historic Olmsted Brothers and Olmsted Associates records. Some projects may have dual categories because they changed use or function over time (a private estate that became a public park, for example). These, where known, are listed in more than one category.

Name

The project name is the primary name assigned by the Olmsted firm, usually the client's name or the name of the institution at the time of the Olmsted firm's work. For this reason, historic names and spellings have been retained. Where known, alternate names and names of related jobs have been added when they provide additional information for researchers.

Location

The project location is either the geographic location of the individual project or, in some cases, it may reflect the address of the client or owner. The Olmsted firm worked on projects beyond the United States, and international projects are represented in this list, most notably in Canada with additional projects in Argentina, Great Britain, Bermuda, Panama, Venezuela and the Philippines. These projects are listed with municipality and state or province (if available) and country. In the United States and Canada, the list shows the postal abbreviation used by the country. Country abbreviations used are ARG for Argentina, BER for Bermuda, CUB for Cuba, ENG for Great Britain, PAN for Panama, PHI for the Philippines and VEN for Venezuela.

Plans

Olmsted NHS conserved and cataloged more than 138,000 landscape architectural plans associated with the work of the Olmsted firm. Using data collected from this process, this data field enumerates the number of plans held by Olmsted NHS for each job number, as well as the date range for those plans.

Correspondence

This data field notes the dates of correspondence held at the Library of Congress or Olmsted NHS. This field represents three collections: the Frederick Law Olmsted Papers and the Olmsted Associates Papers (both at the Library of Congress) and correspondence at Olmsted NHS.

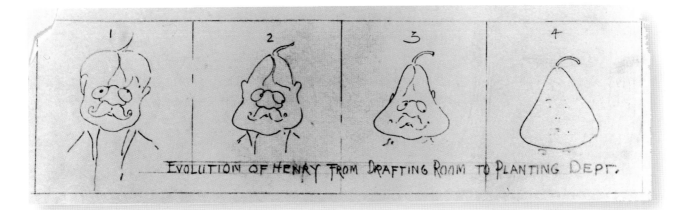

Olmsted Brothers office cartoon, date unknown.

Lawn tennis on the Long Meadow in Prospect Park, Brooklyn, NY, 1885. Job #509 – Prospect Park (New York City, NY).

Background: Detail of plan of a portion of the Boston Park System from the Common to Franklin Park, January 1894. Job #900 – Boston Parks (Boston, MA).

Parks, Parkways, Recreation Areas and Scenic Reservations

Charles E. Beveridge

From the beginning of his career, Frederick Law Olmsted had a clear concept of what constituted a "park," and he devoted much time and energy to explaining the difference between a park and other types of public recreation grounds. The purpose of a park was to provide city dwellers with an experience of extended space that would counteract the enclosure of the city by providing "a sense of enlarged freedom." An expanse of meadow with gracefully contoured terrain, gently curving paths and an indefinite boundary of trees was the central element of the park. Every city, he was convinced, needed such a freely accessible public space. It would provide the most effective antidote to the debilitating artificiality of the built city and the stress of urban life. The park made possible what he termed "unconscious" recreation, whereby the visitor achieved a musing state, immersed in the charm of naturalistic scenery that acted on the deepest elements of the psyche. There the visitor could experience an "unbending" of the faculties that would restore mental and physical energies, renewing strength for the daily exchange of services that sustained the community of the city. This public space would serve a variety of different activities for groups of visitors, with no group or activity monopolizing any part of it. To achieve this, all design details were rigorously subordinated to promote the psychological effect of the park space, by a means that Olmsted called "the art to conceal art."

Olmsted believed that in a park, in addition to restorative landscape, "the largest provision is required for the human presence." He planned extensive systems of walks and drives for visitors, and designed sections of his parks for the gathering and entertainment of crowds. There were places for civic gatherings, for music concerts and for promenades. There were refectories for providing food and beverages and facilities for children's play and gymnastics. Through the years, as team sports became more popular, there was provision for them as well, in separate areas that avoided an "incongruous mixture" of uses and left the landscape experience undisturbed. The separation of interior ways—drives, paths and bridle paths—from each other, and of cross-park city traffic from the park's circulation system, also strengthened the landscape experience.

Singing Tower in the Bok Sanctuary, 1929. Job #7029 – Edward Bok Sanctuary for Birds (Mountain Lake, FL).

A corollary design principle was the provision for active sports and crowd activities in separate spaces at a distance from the principal park of the city. The purpose was to supply a number of all-city uses, not a series of merely local recreation grounds. Such a system of parks and recreation grounds, first clearly accomplished in Buffalo, New York, created a structure of green spaces in advance of the concentrated settlement of residential areas. Completing this system were ribbons of public space in the form of parkways that facilitated movement through the city and served as neighborhood outdoor resting places. Usually two hundred feet wide, the parkways separated the commercial traffic of carts and wagons from private carriages, and provided separate ways for pedestrians and equestrians. Olmsted also advocated creation of linear greenways along urban stream valleys. The classic example is the valley of the Muddy River between the Charles River and Jamaica Pond in Boston and Brookline, Massachusetts.

Olmsted also urged public ownership of areas of special scenic beauty and the creation of scenic reservations where the principal role of the landscape architect was to construct a circulation system that would facilitate enjoyment of the scenery with least intrusion on it.

During the twenty-five years between the retirement of Frederick Law Olmsted and the death of John Charles Olmsted, the firm designed extensive park systems for many cities. After the 1920s, the Olmsted firm created few parks of the size created by the earlier firm, and with more emphasis on utilizing urban stream valleys. In its later years, the firm also placed much greater emphasis on local parks that provided active facilities, including the fieldhouses that marked the Progressive Era, and facilities for team sports. In several instances this involved planning areas for recreational athletic fields adjacent to older city parks. The decades of the 1920s and 1930s saw Frederick Law Olmsted Jr. and other firm members carry out extensive and innovative work in county, state and national park planning and scenic preservation.

Parks, Parkways, Recreation Areas and Scenic Reservations

Job #	Job Name/Alternative Name	Job Location		Plans	Correspondence
04023	National Forests			0	
04016	National Parks/U. S. National Parks			0	1910-1941; 1955-1956
09659	Olmsted, Mr - Services as Collaborator to National Park Service			0	1943-1951

UNITED STATES

Job #	Job Name/Alternative Name	Job Location		Plans	Correspondence
03542	Avondale Park	Birmingham	AL	1 (1924)	1924-1926
03540	Birmingham Alabama City Plan/Birmingham Parks	Birmingham	AL	122 (1924-1925)	1908-1911; 1920-1925; 1938
03544	Ensley Park	Birmingham	AL	2 (1924)	1924-1926
03546	Green Springs Park/Woodrow Wilson Park	Birmingham	AL	0	1925
03089	Rushton Park/Halls Park/Hall's Park/Rushton Memorial Park	Birmingham	AL	20 (1906; 1921-1924)	1905-1906; 1924-1925
03543	Underwood Park	Birmingham	AL	10 (1924)	1924
03545	Woodrow Wilson Park/Capitol Park	Birmingham	AL	37 (1924-1925)	1924-1927
05530	Mobile Alabama Parks	Mobile	AL	0	1912
09613	Dauphin Island	Mobile County	AL	0	1940
07972	Court Street Widening	Montgomery	AL	4 (1929)	1929
09387	Oak Park	Montgomery	AL	24 (1932; 1935-1936)	1934-1936; 1966
01244	Hot Springs Reservation/United States Department of the Interior	Hot Springs	AR	39 (1892-1893)	1877-1878; 1892-1894
05460	Little Rock Arkansas Parkways Association/Parkways Association Parks	Little Rock	AR	0	1893; 1911
02899	Calaveras Big Trees/Calaveras Big Tree Grove		CA	0	1903-1904
08200	Humboldt Redwood State Park		CA	103 (1914-1933)	1925-1947
08333	Huntington Beach & Newport Bay/California State Park		CA	7 (1929-1932)	1932
08335	Master Plan for Redwoods - Save the Redwood League/California State Parks		CA	341 (1944-1955)	1942-1946; 1953-1953
08334	Mill Creek Redwoods		CA	1 (1939)	1939; 1945-1946
08204	Yosemite National Park		CA	8 (N.D.)	
08099	Yosemite National Park		CA	123 (1907-1940)	1927-1954
12301	Yosemite Valley, Mariposa		CA	0	1861-1893
06093	Berkeley Metropolitan Park System	Berkeley	CA	34 (1929-1930)	1914-1915; 1930-1971
08211	Beverly Hills - Roxbury Drive Playground	Beverly Hills	CA	8 (1928)	1928-1929
08212	La Cienega Playground	Beverly Hills	CA	7 (1928)	1928-1929
08232	Pioneer Park	Burbank	CA	7 (1929-1930)	1929-1930
08311	General Bidwell Park/California State Parks	Butte County	CA	0	
08318	Calaveras Big Tree Region	Calaveras County	CA	1 (1946)	

Job #	Job Name/Alternative Name	Job Location		Plans	Correspondence
08313	Mount Diablo Park/California State Parks	Contra Costa County	CA	0	
08072	California State Park Commission	Del Norte	CA	325 (1855; 1879; 1915-1931)	1932-1958
08300	Del Norte Coast Park	Del Norte County	CA	10 (1931-1932)	1925-1932; 1944-1947; 1953
08302	Hiouchi Park/California State Parks	Del Norte County	CA	0	
08101	Hollywood - Palos Verdes Boulevard/ Southwest District Parkways	Hollywood	CA	248 (1914-1928)	1925-1937
08304	Humboldt Lagoons/California State Parks	Humboldt County	CA	0	
08303	Prairie Creek Redwood Park/California State Parks	Humboldt County	CA	0	
08323	Tule Elk Reserve/California State Parks	Kern County	CA	0	
08004	Bluff Park/Gaffey Canyon/Jones, Mr.	Long Beach	CA	0	1922
08009	Bluff Park/The Bluff	Long Beach	CA	30 (1923)	1921-1924
08008	Santa Cruz Park	Long Beach	CA	7 (1922-1923)	1922-1923; 1953-1980
05371	Agricultural Fair Park	Los Angeles	CA	0	1910
08102	Angeles-Mesa Parkway	Los Angeles	CA	0	1926
08202	Leimert Park/Leimert Square	Los Angeles	CA	34 (1927-1934)	1927-1938
05370	Los Angeles Park System	Los Angeles	CA	0	1895
05373	Los Angeles Traffic/Los Angeles Traffic Commission	Los Angeles	CA	39 (1922-1926)	1923-1927; 1935
08260	Malibu Park/Marblehead Land Co.	Los Angeles	CA	26 (1930-1931)	1931-1936
08326	Manhattan Beach Park/California State Parks	Los Angeles County	CA	0	
08309	Mount Tamalpais Park/California State Parks	Marin County	CA	0	
08306	Dimmick Park/California State Parks	Mendocino County	CA	0	
08305	Hickey Grove/California State Parks	Mendocino County	CA	0	
08307	Van Damme Beach Park/California State Parks	Mendocino County	CA	0	
08006	Recreation Park	Monrovia	CA	0	1922-1923
08064	Monterey General Parks/General Park Plan	Monterey	CA	27 (1913-1926)	1925-1926
08327	Doheny Beach Park/California State Parks	Orange County	CA	0	
08328	San Clemente Beach Park/California State Parks	Orange County	CA	0	
08317	Lake Tahoe Bliss Memorial and Rubicon Point Park/California State Parks	Placer County	CA	0	
08316	Lake Tahoe Fish Hatchery Park/California State Parks	Placer County	CA	0	
08083	Point Lobos	Point Lobos	CA	39 (1890; 1913; 1927; 1932-1936)	1927-1954
05410	Redlands California Park System	Redlands	CA	0	1911
08240	Redondo Parks	Redondo	CA	0	1929
08236	Buena Vista Avenue Improvement	Riverside	CA	21 (1929)	1929-1931
05391	Fairmount Park	Riverside	CA	5 (1911)	1911-1912
05390	Riverside Park System	Riverside	CA	0	1913-1914

Job #	Job Name/Alternative Name	Job Location		Plans	Correspondence
08329	Mount San Jacinto Park/California State Parks	Riverside County	CA	0	1930; 1946
05280	Sacramento Park System	Sacramento	CA	0	1910-1911
08331	Mission Bay Park/California State Parks	San Diego County	CA	0	
08330	San Pasqual Battlefield/California State Parks	San Diego County	CA	0	
08332	Silver Strand Park/California State Parks	San Diego County	CA	0	
00291	Golden Gate Park	San Francisco	CA	0	1883-1965
12011	San Francisco Parks	San Francisco	CA	0	1865-1867; 1893-1894; 1952
08322	Morro Strand/California State Parks	San Luis Obispo County	CA	0	
08324	Carpenteria Beach/California State Parks	Santa Barbara County	CA	0	
08319	California Redwood Park/California State Parks	Santa Cruz County	CA	0	
08320	Sunset-Seacliffe Beaches Park/California State Parks	Santa Cruz County	CA	0	
08301	Santa Monica State Park/Santa Monica Beach Park	Santa Monica	CA	0	1931-1932
08267	Kings River Canyon/Sequoia National Forest/Kings River Canyon Region	Sequoia National Forest	CA	20 (1921-1933)	1933-1947
08310	McArthur - Burney Falls Park/California State Parks	Shasta County	CA	0	
08308	Fort Ross Park/California State Parks	Sonoma County	CA	0	
08312	Sonoma Mission Park/California State Parks	Sonoma County	CA	0	
08336	Calaveras Big Trees and Surroundings/California State Parks	Tuolumne County	CA	0	1945-1951
09626	Colorado River Basin Recreational Survey/Department of the Interior		CO	8 (1941-1942)	1938-1950
03304	Lovers Hill	Boulder	CO	0	
03303	Newlands Park	Boulder	CO	0	
05860	Colorado Springs/Park System	Colorado Springs	CO	8 (1905-1906)	1913
05593	Barnum Park	Denver	CO	2 (1911-1913)	
05587	Berkley Park	Denver	CO	5 (1912-1913)	1912-1913
05594	Block 8	Denver	CO	1 (1913)	
05591	Cheeseman Park	Denver	CO	0	1915
05586	City Park/Denver City and County Parks	Denver	CO	17 (1912-1914)	1912-1915
05590	Curtis Park	Denver	CO	2 (1913)	
05580	Denver Parks/Denver Park Commission	Denver	CO	6 (1888-1913)	1912-1920
05585	Marion Street Parkway	Denver	CO	1 (1911-1912)	
05582	Mountain Park/Mountain Parks	Denver	CO	62 (1912-1914)	1911-1914
05592	Platte River Park/Platte River Parkway	Denver	CO	2 (1913-1914)	1914
05589	Rocky Mountain National Park	Denver	CO	1 (1914)	1937
05584	Seventh Avenue Boulevard	Denver	CO	5 (1912-1913)	1913

The Greensward Plan of Central Park,
Frederick Law Olmsted and Calvert Vaux,
issued April 8 and adopted April 28, 1858.
Job #502 – Central Park
(New York City, NY).

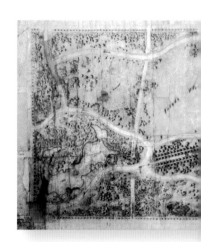

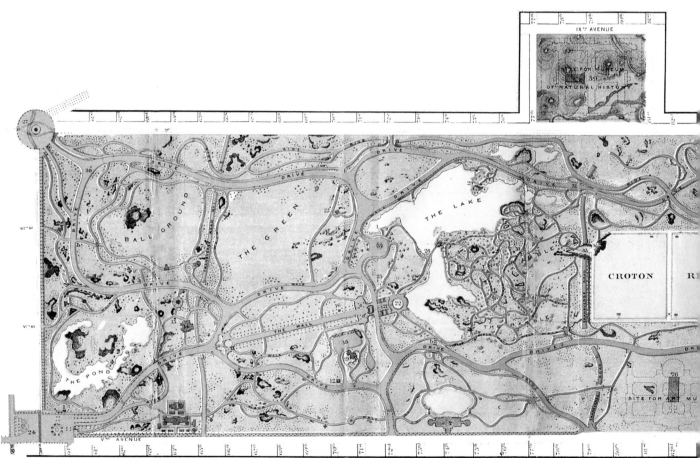

Olmsted and Vaux, Landscape Architects

Scale 400 feet to

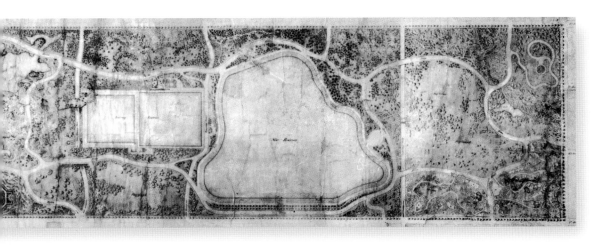

TRAL PARK 1871-2.

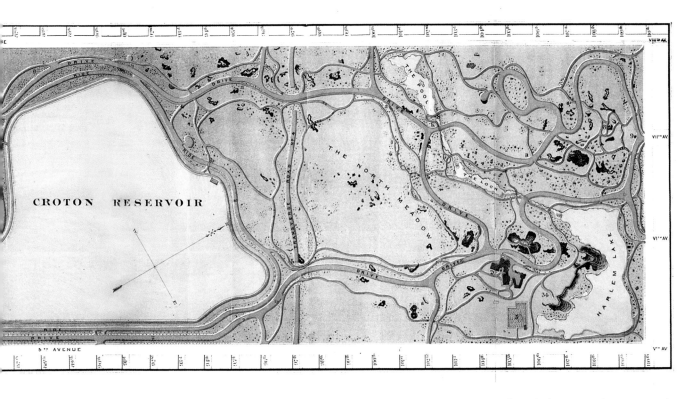

As-built plan of Central Park, 1872. Job #502 – Central Park (New York City, NY).

Job #	Job Name/Alternative Name	Job Location		Plans	Correspondence
05596	Sloan & Coopers Lake/Sloan and Cooper Lake Park	Denver	CO	3 (1913-1914)	1914
05595	Thirty-eighth Street Playground	Denver	CO	1 (1913)	
05588	Washington Park	Denver	CO	3 (1912-1913)	
05597	Welton Street Playground	Denver	CO	4 (1913-1914)	1914
05583	Williams Street Parkway	Denver	CO	11 (1912-1914)	1912-1914
00127	Estes Park	Estes Park	CO	0	
00691	Beardsley Park	Bridgeport	CT	28 (1880-1913)	1880-1892; 1902-1904; 1908; 1913
00692	Beechwood Park	Bridgeport	CT	1 (1917)	1917
00690	Bridgeport Parks/Board of Park Commissioners	Bridgeport	CT	0	1873; 1881-1891; 1903; 1913
00693	Fairchild Memorial Park	Bridgeport	CT	4 (1923-1927)	1924-1930
12021	Seaside Park	Bridgeport	CT	0	1881-1891
02810	Bristol Green	Bristol	CT	0	1896-1899
02283	D.A.R. Chapter Park	East Hartford	CT	5 (1901-1902)	
10091	South End Park	East Hartford	CT	34 (1957-1959)	1958-1960
09850	Sunset Ridge Memorial Park	East Hartford	CT	55 (1949-1951)	1949-1951
07941	Greenwich Park/Shore Front Park	Greenwich	CT	14 (1908-1931)	1928-1932
00801	Bushnell Park	Hartford	CT	435 (1897-1961)	1870-1899; 1916; 1944-1976
00802	Goodwin Park/South Pk	Hartford	CT	133 (1895-1901)	1895-1901
00800	Hartford Park/Hartford Park System	Hartford	CT	3 (1874-1893)	1890-1906; 1920; 1940; 1970
00803	Keney Park	Hartford	CT	98 (1895-1904)	1895-1901; 1920; 1941-1942
00804	North Meadow Drive/Keney Park	Hartford	CT	8 (1899-1900)	1899
00805	Pope Park	Hartford	CT	16 (1886-1901)	1892-1900
00806	Riverside Park	Hartford	CT	22 (1895-1959)	1897-1900; 1959
00807	South Green	Hartford	CT	4 (1896)	1896-1900
00809	South Western Parkway	Hartford	CT	1 (1896)	
00808	Southern Parkway	Hartford	CT	1 (1897)	1896-1897
00810	Washington Green & Others	Hartford	CT	2 (1896-1897)	1897
00811	Western Parkway	Hartford	CT	6 (1897-1898)	1896-1898
07784	Kent Falls, Connecticut State Park Commission	Kent Falls	CT	0	1927
10123	Wickham Park	Manchester	CT	278 (1955-1970)	1960-1972
00283	Hubbard Park	Meriden	CT	0	1898
03359	Long Lane/Wadsworth, C. S./Wadsworth, C. P.	Middletown	CT	11 (1907-1910)	1907-1910
00600	New Britain - Proposed Park/Walnut Hill Park	New Britain	CT	2 (1870; 1912)	1867-1874; 1908; 1920-1921
05314	Beaver Pond Park/Beaver Ponds	New Haven	CT	38 (1917-1921)	1917-1921
05317	Commission of Public Parks/Street Tree Surveys and Study	New Haven	CT	0	1948
05313	East Rock Park	New Haven	CT	128 (1905-1931)	1914-1920; 1926-1931

Job #	Job Name/Alternative Name	Job Location		Plans	Correspondence
05311	Edgewood Park	New Haven	CT	10 (1900; 1911)	1911
05312	New Haven Green/Central Green	New Haven	CT	4 (1912)	1912-1916
05310	New Haven Park System	New Haven	CT	0	1919-1925
05316	Townsend Tract/East Shore Park	New Haven	CT	37 (1922-1945)	1922-1930; 1965
05315	West River Memorial/West River Parkway	New Haven	CT	18 (1919-1937)	1919-1955
01001	Memorial Park	New London	CT	34 (1884-1885)	1884-1885
02248	Hartford Road	South Manchester	CT	11 (1899)	1898-1899
03345	Coe Memorial Park	Torrington	CT	4 (1907)	1907
06643	Fuessenick, Elizabeth Blake Park	Torrington	CT	13 (1919-1921)	1919-1921
10166	Board of Park Commissioners	Waterbury	CT	5 (1953-1961)	1961-1963
06789	Chase Park/Chase, F.S.	Waterbury	CT	23 (1901; 1904; 1919-1921)	1919-1921
06791	Fulton, William S. Mrs./Fulton, W.S./Hayden Homestead Park	Waterbury	CT	30 (1911; 1920-1921)	1920-1921
06847	Hamilton Park	Waterbury	CT	0	
06780	Lewis Fulton Memorial Park/Fulton, William E.	Waterbury	CT	33 (1919-1922)	1920-1924
06677	Library Park	Waterbury	CT	38 (1920-1922)	1919-1923; 1949
06989	Waterbury Parks	Waterbury	CT	0	1921; 1923
07767	Black Rock Forest Inc.	Watertown	CT	0	1926-1927
06695	Waterville Green/F.S. Chase	Watertown	CT	31 (1919-1921)	1919-1922
02824	Cooke Park	Washington	DC	1 (1877)	
02823	District of Columbia, Plaza/U. S. Senate Park Commission	Washington	DC	13 (1903-1906)	1897-1922; 1928-1935
02379	Hornblower, J. C./Hornblower, Joseph C.	Washington	DC	1 (1902)	1902
02830	John Cabin Park	Washington	DC	0	
05507	Klingle Parkway/Chevy Chase Land Company	Washington	DC	6 (1909-1912)	1903; 1912
02829	Lafayette Square	Washington	DC	0	
02828	Mall, The	Washington	DC	37 (1901-1915)	1904-1910
02840	McMillan Park	Washington	DC	42 (1907-1911)	1906-1913; 1968
02822	National Zoo/National Zoological Park	Washington	DC	51 (1889-1905)	1887-1914; 1927; 1936; 1972-1973
02260	Perkins, Henry C.	Washington	DC	2 (1900-1915)	1900; 1909; 1915
02839	Potomac Park/Plans N. of RR/Mall	Washington	DC	0	1907-1910; 1922
02841	Potomac Quay	Washington	DC	0	1907
02837	Rock Creek Park	Washington	DC	113 (1907-1945)	1884-1896; 1906-1934; 1943
02833	The Plaza/Union Station	Washington	DC	0	1904-1907
02846	Washington Rose Garden Project/Potomac Park	Washington	DC	9 (1921)	1920-1923; 1929-1934
01080	Wilmington City Parks	Wilmington	DE	31 (1889-1890)	1883-1895; 1934; 1976
07426	Babson Park		FL	4 (1925)	1925; 1943; 1966
06121	Florida State Parks		FL	0	1930; 1934

Job #	Job Name/Alternative Name	Job Location		Plans	Correspondence
05980	Pinellas County Parks/Pinellas County Park System		FL	13 (1910-1914)	1913-1921
05150	Jacksonville Parks	Jacksonville	FL	0	1910
05151	Memorial Park	Jacksonville	FL	67 (1920-1923)	1921-1925; 1934
05152	Metropolitan Parkway	Jacksonville	FL	0	1934
04022	Everglades National Park Project/Tropic Everglades	Miami	FL	55 (1928-1939)	1929-1947
07029	Bok, Edward Sanctuary for Birds/Mt. Lake Sanctuary/Bok, Edward W./Sanctuary and Singing Tower	Mountain Lake	FL	303 (1922-1959)	1920-1978
06164	Palm Beach Garden Club	Palm Beach	FL	5 (1931)	1931; 1939
06125	Highlands Hammock State Park	Sebring	FL	0	
06167	Hillsborough River Parkway/Hillsborough River Boulevard	Tampa	FL	3 (1932)	1931-1932
02740	Atlanta Parks/Grant Pk/Spring Vale Pk/Mim's Park/	Atlanta	GA	3 (1903-1904)	1892-1895; 1902-1915
02741	Grant, L. P. - Park	Atlanta	GA	19 (1903-1912)	1912

Audubon Park, February 1918. Job #2001 – Audubon Park (New Orleans, LA).

Job #	Job Name/Alternative Name	Job Location		Plans	Correspondence
02743	Mim's Park	Atlanta	GA	4 (1903-1911)	1909-1916
02745	Oakland City Park	Atlanta	GA	0	1910
02744	Piedmont Park	Atlanta	GA	11 (1909-1912)	1909-1912; 1964; 1977
02742	Spring Vale Park	Atlanta	GA	4 (1903)	
02747	Triangle Park and Medical Center/Joel Hurt Memorial Park/Atlanta, GA	Atlanta	GA	0	1939-1940
01731	Estill Park	Savannah	GA	1 (1896)	1896
01730	Savannah Georgia Parks	Savannah	GA	0	1896-1900; 1907
07326	Stone Mountain	Stone Mountain	GA	0	1924
07959	Hawaii National Park		HI	5 (1912-1928)	1929
07202	Des Moines Park System	Des Moines	IA	0	1923-1925; 1935
01916	Armour Square - Park 3/Chicago South Pk Comm./Armour Square	Chicago	IL	8 (1903-1905)	1909
01925	Bessemer Park - Park 12/Chicago South Pk Comm.	Chicago	IL	7 (1904)	
01913	Bond Avenue/Chicago South Pk Comm.	Chicago	IL	3 (1910)	1910
01924	Calumet Park - Park 11/ Chicago South Pk Comm.	Chicago	IL	17 (1904-1908)	1907-1908
03001	Chapin, S. B./Rookery, The	Chicago	IL	0	1904-1905
01904	Chicago Playgrounds/Chicago South Pk Comm./Small Parks	Chicago	IL	2 (1907-1910)	1903-1912
01918	Cornell Square - Park 5/Chicago South Pk Comm.	Chicago	IL	8 (1904)	
01927	Davis Square - Park 14/Chicago South Pk Comm	Chicago	IL	8 (1904)	
01906	Douglas Park	Chicago	IL	0	
01917	Fuller Square - Park 4/Chicago South Pk Comm.	Chicago	IL	6 (1903-1904)	
01905	Garfield Park	Chicago	IL	0	1891-1896
01909	Grand Boulevard	Chicago	IL	0	1907-1910
01928	Grand Crossing Park/Park #15, Chicago Parks/Chicago South Pk Comm.	Chicago	IL	16 (1910-1911)	1911
01901	Grant Park/Lake Front	Chicago	IL	88 (1895-1911)	1895-1896; 1903-1912; 1977
01922	Hamilton Park - Park 9/Chicago South Pk Comm.	Chicago	IL	7 (1904)	
01914	Hardin Square - Park 1/Chicago South Pk Comm	Chicago	IL	14 (1904-1911)	1910-1911
01902	Jackson Park/South Pk/Washington Pk	Chicago	IL	328 (1880-1911)	1891-1915; 1936
01910	Jackson St. [Boulevard]/Jackson Boulevard	Chicago	IL	25 (1908-1909)	1908-1909
01912	Lake Shore Boulevard/Jackson Pk & Grant Pk, between	Chicago	IL	7 (1910)	1893-1895; 1910
01908	Lincoln Park	Chicago	IL	0	1869-1874; 1894
01930	Mann Park/Park #17, Chicago Parks/ Chicago South Pk Comm.	Chicago	IL	27 (1910-1912)	1911
01915	Mark White Square - Park 2/Chicago South Pk Comm.	Chicago	IL	10 (1903-1904)	

Job #	Job Name/Alternative Name	Job Location		Plans	Correspondence
01923	Marquette Park - Park 10/Chicago South Pk Comm.	Chicago	IL	12 (1904)	1908-1910
01911	Normal Avenue/Chicago South Park Commission	Chicago	IL	1 (1908)	
01921	Ogden Square - Park 8/Chicago South Pk Comm.	Chicago	IL	10 (1904)	
01926	Palmer Park - Park 13/Chicago South Pk Comm.	Chicago	IL	10 (1904)	
01919	Russell Square - Park 6/Chicago South Pk Comm.	Chicago	IL	15 (1904-1910)	1909-1911
01920	Sherman Park - Park 7/Chicago South Pk Comm.	Chicago	IL	12 (1903-1909)	N.D.
01900	South Park Commission/Chicago Parks/ Chicago South PK Comm.-Plans	Chicago	IL	11 (1897-1911)	1866-1870; 1891-1912; 1975
01929	Trumbull Park/Park #16, Chicago Parks/ Chicago South Pk Comm.	Chicago	IL	17 (1910-1911)	1911
01931	Tuley Park/Park #18, Chicago Parks/ Chicago South Pk Comm.	Chicago	IL	7 (1910-1912)	1911
01903	Washington Park	Chicago	IL	28 (1880-1910)	1874; 1885-1898; 1907-1911
03492	Danville Illinois Parks	Danville	IL	0	1906-1908; 1978
03113	Lowell Park/Lowell, Carlotta Russell	Dixon	IL	3 (1906-1909)	1906-1908
03761	Mildred Park	Springfield	IL	1 (1909)	
03760	Springfield City Parks	Springfield	IL	0	1909
02300	Indianapolis Parks	Indianapolis	IN	0	1895-1898; 1905-1908
02301	White River Parkway/Indianapolis Parks	Indianapolis	IN	1 (1897)	1957-1958
05230	South Bend Parks	South Bend	IN	0	1911
09214	Blue Licks Battlefield Park		KY	19 (1930-1931)	1930-1931; 1951
07413	Central Park	Ashland	KY	1 (1940)	1907-1908; 1925; 1940-1941
05130	Covington Parks	Covington	KY	0	1910
05722	Peace Park	Hopkinsville	KY	0	
05721	Virginia Park	Hopkinsville	KY	0	1913
05720	Virginia Park/Hopkinsville Park System	Hopkinsville	KY	4 (1912-1913)	1912-1913
03020	Ben Gratz Park	Lexington	KY	1 (1916)	
03021	Douglass Park	Lexington	KY	2 (1915-1916)	
03019	Duncan Park & Playground	Lexington	KY	1 (1914)	
03015	Lexington Parks/Woodland Pk/So. Upper Plgd	Lexington	KY	4 (1902-1904)	1904-1916
10112	Lexington Parkway	Lexington	KY	68 (1955-1960)	1958-1960
03017	South Upper Street Playground	Lexington	KY	6 (1904-1905)	
03016	Woodland Park	Lexington	KY	10 (1904-1907)	1905; 1916
01285	Algonquin Park	Louisville	KY	19 (1928-1935)	1929-1935
01261	Baxter Square	Louisville	KY	5 (1892-1901)	1901
01278	Bear Grass Creek Parkway/Beargrass Creek Park	Louisville	KY	0	1915-1916; 1935
01271	Boone Square	Louisville	KY	32 (1891-1892)	1891-1895; 1909

Job #	Job Name/Alternative Name	Job Location		Plans	Correspondence
07834	Bullitt, William Marshall	Louisville	KY	40 (1924; 1927-1928)	1927-1934; 1946; 1953
01273	Caldwell Playground/Shelby Park	Louisville	KY	9 (1907-1911)	1907-1914
01265	Central Park/Dupont Sq./Central Square	Louisville	KY	26 (1903-1904; 1921-1926)	1899-1910; 1917-1925
01263	Cherokee Park/Southern Parkway	Louisville	KY	404 (1891-1933)	1892-1935; 1947-1961; 1973-1979
01279	Chickasaw Park	Louisville	KY	11 (1923-1930)	1923; 1929-1931
01276	Churchill Park	Louisville	KY	2 (1912)	1911-1913
01277	Clifton Park	Louisville	KY	5 (1914-1917)	1915-1917
01264	Court House Square	Louisville	KY	2 (1896)	
01272	Eastern Parkway	Louisville	KY	15 (1907-1912)	1907-1912; 1935
01274	Elliot Park	Louisville	KY	8 (1908; 1923)	1908-1909; 1923
01275	Elliott Park/Douglas Boulevard	Louisville	KY	0	1915-1916; 1958
01287	Fort Nelson Park	Louisville	KY	12 (1973-1974)	1974
01283	George Rogers Clark Park	Louisville	KY	0	
01266	Iroquois Park	Louisville	KY	20 (1892-1935)	1892-1916; 1923-1935
01267	Kenton Place	Louisville	KY	4 (1891)	
01268	Logan Square	Louisville	KY	5 (1891-1892)	1892
01260	Louisville Parks	Louisville	KY	1 (1898)	1891-1951; 1977
10498	River Fields, Inc.	Louisville	KY	0	1974
01284	Seneca Park/Von Zedtwitz tract/Cherokee Park Extension	Louisville	KY	210 (1928-1948)	1928-1940
01269	Shawnee Park	Louisville	KY	97 (1892-1929)	N.D.; 1893-1902; 1909-1916; 1929-1935
01281	Story Avenue Playground	Louisville	KY	0	
02927	Strater, Charles G./Spotswood	Louisville	KY	12 (1905-1917)	1905-1917; 1924-1926
01270	Third Street Playground	Louisville	KY	5 (1900-1909)	1901
01282	Thrusten Square	Louisville	KY	0	
01262	Tyler Park	Louisville	KY	16 (1907-1911)	1907-1911
01280	Victory Park	Louisville	KY	8 (1923-1924)	1923-1929
06470	Paducah Parks/Paducah Park System	Paducah	KY	0	1916
09150	Cumberland State Park	Pineville	KY	11 (1929-1930)	1929-1931
02001	Audubon Park	New Orleans	LA	508 (1894-1941)	1893-1949; 1965-1975
02003	City Park/Popp Memorial	New Orleans	LA	134 (1929-1937)	1925-1939
02000	New Orleans	New Orleans	LA	0	1885; 1897-1899
01503	Blue Hills Parkway		MA	9 (1892-1903)	1895-1905; 1924
01504	Blue Hills Reservation		MA	56 (1893-1906)	1885-1910; 1924
01546	Charles River Improvement/Metropolitan Park Commission		MA	10 (1893-1894)	1893-1897; 1903-1907; 1928
01505	Charles River Reservation - Sec. A/Charles River Pkwy./E. Camb. Embank		MA	94 (1893-1935)	1895-1916; 1928-1935
01506	Charles River Reservation - Sec. B		MA	24 (1894-1915)	1896-1897; 1904
01507	Charles River Reservation - Sec. C/ Metropolitan Park Commission		MA	21 (1892-1903)	1902-1907

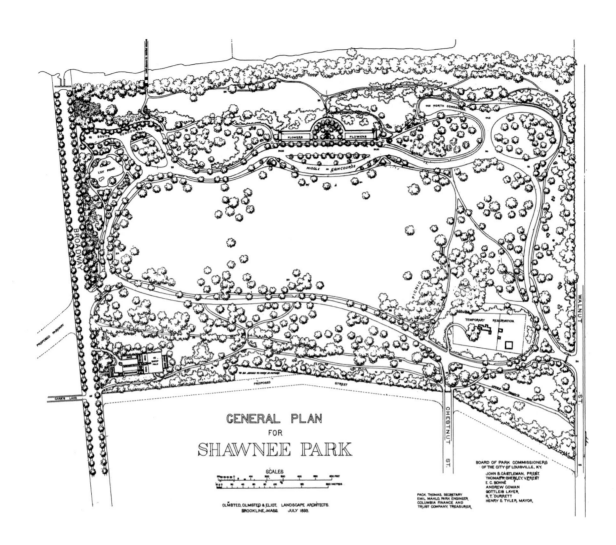

General plan for Shawnee Park, July 1893. Job #1269 – Shawnee Park (Louisville, KY).

Job #	Job Name/Alternative Name	Job Location		Plans	Correspondence
01508	Charles River Reservation - Sec. D/ Metropolitan Park Commission		MA	12 (1897-1915)	1898; 1905
01509	Charles River Reservation - Sec. E/ Metropolitan Park Commission		MA	4 (1898)	1904
01553	Hammond Pond Parkway/Metropolitan Park Commission		MA	0	
01528	Neponset River Parkway - Sec. A/Balster Brook Pkwy/Balster Brook/Metropolitan Park Commission		MA	20 (1899-1908)	1897-1912
01529	Neponset River Parkway - Sec. B/ Metropolitan Park Commission/Paul's Bridge to Stony Brook Bridge		MA	2 (1900)	1896-1901
01530	Neponset River Parkway - Sec. C/Brush Hill Pkwy/Metropolitan Park Commission		MA	3 (1898-1899)	1897-1908
01542	West Roxbury Parkway/Metropolitan Park Commission		MA	0	1894-1898; 1915
01543	Whitmore Brook Parkway/Fells Res.		MA	4 (1898-1899)	1898-1899

Job #	Job Name/Alternative Name	Job Location		Plans	Correspondence
01550	Winthrop Parkway/Winthrop Shore Res		MA	0	1894-1895; 1904
01544	Winthrop Shore Reservation/Revere Beach/Metropolitan Park Commission		MA	0	1893-1904; 1909
01545	Woburn Parkway/Winchester Parkway/ Mystic Valley Pkwy/Winchester-Woburn Parkway		MA	13 (1895-1913)	1894-1908; 1913-1914
09644	Peregrine White Sanctuary/Ames Memorial	Abington	MA	24 (1941-1946)	1941-1946; 1959
00965	Allston Street Playground	Allston	MA	0	1916
06540	Amesbury Public Park/Amesbury Park Commission	Amesbury	MA	0	1917
02250	Arlington Parks/Meadow Park	Arlington	MA	0	1898-1901
02251	Meadow Park	Arlington	MA	20 (1899-1902)	1899-1902
02253	Robbins Farm Park	Arlington	MA	12 (1945-1946)	1944-1946
01547	Spy Pond Parkway/Metropolitan Park Commission	Arlington	MA	8 (1898-1903)	1898-1903
06853	Attleboro Municipal Baseball/Municipal Baseball Park	Attleboro	MA	0	1920
01099	Sandy Neck (sand dunes)	Barnstable	MA	0	
	*See also Allston, Brighton, Charlestown, Dorchester, East Boston, Hyde Park, Mattapan, Readville, Roxbury and South Boston	Boston	MA		
01501	Alewife Brook Parkway/Metropolitan Park Commission	Boston	MA	68 (1907-1910)	1903-1909
00901	Arborway	Boston	MA	86 (1882-1918)	1896-1897; 1978
01502	Beaver Brook Reservation/Metropolitan Park Commission	Boston	MA	27 (1893-1894; 1902-1906)	1893-1919
00903	Bennett Street Playground	Boston	MA	10 (1897)	1897
00950-02	Blackstone Square - Boston Parks/Public Grounds Department	Boston	MA	2 (1913)	
00951-C	Blue Hill Avenue/Boston Public Grounds Dept.	Boston	MA	5 (1911)	1891-1897
00946	Boston Common	Boston	MA	336 (1910-1913)	1895-1927; 1934-1939; 1978
00900	Boston Parks through 950	Boston	MA	70 (1897)	1870-1901; 1909-1936
00906	Brighton Parkway	Boston	MA	7 (1889-1890)	1897
01468	Cambridge Bridge/Cambridge Bridge Approaches	Boston	MA	7 (1900-1901)	1901-1904
05516	Charles River Square	Boston	MA	1 (1913)	1912-1914
00907	Charlesbank/Boston Park System	Boston	MA	178 (1851-1907)	1890-1895; 1908-1909; 1935
00908	Charlestown Heights	Boston	MA	9 (1891-1895)	1892-1896
00909	Charlestown Playground	Boston	MA	11 (1891-1896)	1891-1897
00910	Chelsea Street Playground	Boston	MA	2 (1897)	1895-1897
02071	Chestnut Hill Reservoir Pumping Station	Boston	MA	9 (1899-1900)	1896-1901
12041	City Point	Boston	MA	0	
10554	Clarendon Street Playground	Boston	MA	17 (1977-1978)	1974-1977
02072	Clinton Reservoir	Boston	MA	4 (1903)	1903
00911	Columbia Road Playground	Boston	MA	7 (1897)	1897

Job #	Job Name/Alternative Name	Job Location		Plans	Correspondence
00931	Columbia Road Street Department/So. Boston Pkway/South Boston Parkway/ Strandway and Columbia Rd.	Boston	MA	73 (1890-1898)	1892-1899; 1915-1916; 1930
00951-E	Columbus Avenue/Boston Public Grounds Dept.	Boston	MA	2 (1912)	
00944	Commonwealth Avenue/Massachusetts Avenue	Boston	MA	16 (1907)	1879-1900; 1907-1917
00950-08	Concord Square - Boston Parks/Public Grounds Department	Boston	MA	2 (1913)	
00913	Dorchester Avenue Playground	Boston	MA	0	1897
00912	Dorchester Park	Boston	MA	6 (1893-1896)	1893-1897
00914	Dorchester Playground	Boston	MA	4 (1897)	1897
00954	Dorchester Square & Eaton Square	Boston	MA	3 (1912)	1912
00951-F	Dudley Street/Boston Public Grounds Dept.	Boston	MA	1 (1912)	
00950-11	Egleston Square - Boston Parks/Public Grounds Department	Boston	MA	2 (1921)	
00951-G	Eliot Square/Boston Public Grounds Dept.	Boston	MA	1 (1912)	
00971	Emerald Necklace	Boston	MA	0	1898; 1976-1980
00915	Fellows Street Playground	Boston	MA	4 (1896-1897)	1897
01513	Fells (Middlesex) Reservation/Middlesex Fells Reservation/Metropolitan Park Commission	Boston	MA	88 (1902-1906)	1893-1915
01512	Fells Parkway/Middlesex Fells Parkway/ Metropolitan Park Commission	Boston	MA	34 (1894-1907)	1893-1909; 1916
00916	Fens - Back Bay/Back Bay Fens	Boston	MA	269 (1877-1921)	1878-1897; 1909-1916; 1976-1980
00958	Fort Hill Square	Boston	MA	3 (1912)	N.D.
00917	Franklin Field	Boston	MA	20 (1887-1897)	1892; 1897
00918	Franklin Park	Boston	MA	734 (1881-1917)	1877-1898; 1914-1921; 1933; 1969; 1975-1980
00950-14	Franklin Square - Boston Parks/Public Grounds Department	Boston	MA	2 (1913)	
00951	Freeport St. Triangle, Columbia Rd/Street Department	Boston	MA	0	1894-1898
00919	Freeport Street Triangle	Boston	MA	2 (1897)	
07505	Gillette Safety Razor Company	Boston	MA	15 (1924-1929)	1925-1930; 1937
00951-H	Huntington Avenue/Boston Public Grounds Dept.	Boston	MA	2 (1912)	1898
00920	Jamaica Park/Parkway	Boston	MA	238 (1889-1915; 1967)	1881-1898; 1915; 1973-1979
00940	Jamaica Plain Streets	Boston	MA	3 (1897)	1897
00921	Kemp Street Playground	Boston	MA	2 (1896-1897)	1897
00904	LaGrange Street Playground/Billings Field	Boston	MA	4 (1896-1897)	1897
00923	Leverett Park	Boston	MA	161 (1880-1896)	1895-1897; 1915; 1967-1980
00951-B	Louis Pasteur Avenue	Boston	MA	2 (1911)	1902; 1911-1913
00950-23	Massachusetts Avenue - Boston Parks/ Public Grounds Department	Boston	MA	3 (1913)	

Job #	Job Name/Alternative Name	Job Location		Plans	Correspondence
01500	Metropolitan Parks/Metropolitan Park Commission/Metropolitan Park System	Boston	MA	14 (1893-1899; 1934-1939)	1893-1910; 1915-1923
02070	Metropolitan Water Board - Misc./Spot Pond/Chestnut Hill Resv./Metropolitan Water and Sewerage Board	Boston	MA	0	1892-1906
12031	Middlesex Fells	Boston	MA	0	1880; 1893-1896; 1898
01522	Mother Brook Parkway/Metropolitan Park Commission	Boston	MA	2 (1898)	1898
00951-I	Mount Pleasant Avenue/Boston Public Grounds Dept.	Boston	MA	2 (1912)	
00927	Muddy River	Boston	MA	171 (1882-1893)	1882-1899; 1907; 1970-1980
00928	Neponset Avenue Playground	Boston	MA	7 (1896-1897)	1896-1897
01557	Neponset River Valley Parkway/Metropolitan Park Commission	Boston	MA	111 (1942-1945)	1942-1947
00937	North End Park	Boston	MA	39 (1876-1897)	1893-1897
01552	Old Colony Parkway/Metropolitan Park Commission	Boston	MA	11 (1908-1925)	1908-1915; 1920; 1925

Revised general plan for Jackson Park, 1895. Job #1902 – Jackson Park (Chicago, IL).

Job #	Job Name/Alternative Name	Job Location		Plans	Correspondence
00964	Olmsted Park/Leverett Pk/Jamaica Pond/Jamaica Way/James Park	Boston	MA	23 (1892-1915)	1888-1915; 1946-1947
00929	Parker Hill/Parker Hill Playground	Boston	MA	12 (1892-1917)	1892-1893; 1917
00951	Pasteur, Louis Ave./Louis Pasteur Avenue	Boston	MA	0	1902; 1911-1913
00948	Public Garden/Boston Common	Boston	MA	91 (1911-1912)	1882; 1893-1895; 1911-1917; 1938-1939; 1967
00930	Riverway	Boston	MA	131 (1882-1915)	1878-1922
00961	Ronan Park	Boston	MA	0	1915-1919
00932	Roxbury High Fort	Boston	MA	3 (1895)	1895
00950-27	Rutland Square - Boston Parks/Public Grounds Department	Boston	MA	2 (1913)	
00962	Savin Hill Playground	Boston	MA	10 (1914-1917)	1915-1917
00063	Soldiers Field/Harvard University/Soldiers' Field	Boston	MA	12 (1900-1905)	1896-1912
00951	South Boston Parkway/Strandway	Boston	MA	0	1892; 1896
02073	Spot Pond/Metropolitan Water Board/Spot Pond and Fells Reservoir	Boston	MA	116 (1897-1902)	1897-1906; 1921-1923
01541	Stony Brook Reservation/Stonybrook	Boston	MA	31 (1890-1914)	1894-1906
00951	Strandway/South Boston Parkway	Boston	MA	0	1892; 1896
00951	Street Department/Freeport St. Triangle, Columbia Rd.	Boston	MA	0	1895
00966	Tenean Beach	Boston	MA	3 (1916)	1916
02050	Trustees of Reservations/Bay Circut/Trustees of Public Reservations	Boston	MA	1 (1941)	1890-1914; 1927-1931; 1942-1951; 1970-1977
00950-33	Union Park - Boston Parks/Public Grounds Department	Boston	MA	2 (1913)	
02075	Wachusett Dam	Boston	MA	22 (1894-1905)	1900-1907
00950-35	Waltham Square - Boston Parks/Public Grounds Department	Boston	MA	2 (1913)	
00963	Ward 19 Playground	Boston	MA	9 (1915-1916)	1915-1917
00951-J	Warren Street	Boston	MA	2 (1912)	
00934	West Roxbury Parkway	Boston	MA	23 (1893-1897)	1885; 1895-1897
00933	Western Avenue Playground	Boston	MA	16 (1894-1898)	1897
00935	Wood Island Park	Boston	MA	81 (1882-1896)	1888-1895
00950-38	Worcester Square - Boston Parks/Public Grounds Department	Boston	MA	2 (1913)	
00905	Brighton Park	Brighton	MA	3 (1893)	1894
00950-03	Brighton Square - Boston Parks/Public Grounds Department	Brighton	MA	2 (1913)	
00950-13	Fern Square - Boston Parks/Public Grounds Department	Brighton	MA	1 (1913)	
00950-28	Sparhawk Square - Boston Parks/Public Grounds Department	Brighton	MA	1 (1913)	
01330	Brockton Parks	Brockton	MA	11 (1892-1893)	1892-1896
01332	Field, D. W. Park	Brockton	MA	14 (1935-1936)	1939-1940
01331	Flagg Park	Brockton	MA	3 (1936-1937)	1937
01333	Keith, Myron/Geo. E. Keith Pk	Brockton	MA	77 (1930-1932)	1896; 1940-1953

Job #	Job Name/Alternative Name	Job Location		Plans	Correspondence
10239	Arborway - Jamaicaway - Riverway Complex	Brookline	MA	0	1896; 1968-1970
01172	Beacon Street Widening	Brookline	MA	87 (1886-1887)	1884-1887
01303	Brookline Avenue Playground	Brookline	MA	1 (1897)	1884
12051	Brookline Parkway	Brookline	MA	0	1892
00105	Brookline Reservoir	Brookline	MA	0	1901-1902
03222	Cabot Hill Reservoir/Cabot Hill Res./Cabot, Henry B.	Brookline	MA	41 (1906-1924)	1906-1908; 1916-1922
01306	Chestnut Hill Parkway	Brookline	MA	8 (1892-1902)	1893; 1901-1907
01307	Clyde Street Playground	Brookline	MA	1 (1903-1904)	
10189	Coolidge Playground	Brookline	MA	48 (1918; 1965-1967; 1977)	1965-1967
10122	Griggs Field	Brookline	MA	12 (1948; 1960-1962)	1960-1962
01308	Heath Square	Brookline	MA	4 (1910)	1890; 1910
01314	Larz Anderson Park	Brookline	MA	219 (1939-1970)	1912; 1952-1970
10330	Lawton Playground	Brookline	MA	32 (1969-1971)	1969-1974
10199	Linden Park	Brookline	MA	29 (1893; 1965-1967)	1966-1968
10200	Linden Square	Brookline	MA	22 (1965-1966)	1965-1968
10227	Longwood Playground	Brookline	MA	105 (1891-1970)	1962-1971
00924	Longwood Playground	Brookline	MA	0	1893; 1895
10198	Robinson Playground	Brookline	MA	22 (1939-1940; 1954-1966)	1965-1967
01300	Town of Brookline	Brookline	MA	53 (1884-1922)	1888-1920
10182	Town of Brookline Park Department	Brookline	MA	1 (1965)	1896; 1965
10228	Walnut Place Neighborhood Park	Brookline	MA	1 (1967)	1967
01451	Broadway Square	Cambridge	MA	4 (1894-1895)	1894-1896
01454	Cambridge Embankment or Esplanade	Cambridge	MA	0	1893-1899
01452	Cambridge Field	Cambridge	MA	6 (1894-1901)	1894-1901
01450	Cambridge Parks	Cambridge	MA	0	1893-1907
00047	Cambridge Water Board/Fresh Pond/Fresh Pond Park	Cambridge	MA	53 (1894-1920)	1894-1977
01458	Charles River Parkway	Cambridge	MA	104 (1890-1908)	1893-1909
01459	Common, The	Cambridge	MA	3 (1896-1897)	1895-1896; 1903-1905
01460	Fresh Pond Parkway	Cambridge	MA	6 (1889-1894)	1895-1902; 1908; 1915-1916
01514	Fresh Pond Parkway/Charles River Res. Sec. A/Metropolitan Park Commission	Cambridge	MA	22 (1896-1916)	1897-1907; 1920
01462	Hastings Square	Cambridge	MA	0	1898-1901
01479	Longfellow Park	Cambridge	MA	3 (1887-1912)	1894-1895; 1909-1912; 1922
01463	Porter Square	Cambridge	MA	2 (1901)	1901-1902
01464	Rindge Field	Cambridge	MA	9 (1905-1906)	1894-1898; 1905-1906
01465	Winthrop Square	Cambridge	MA	7 (1897)	1896-1897
09595	Canton Park	Canton	MA	10 (1940)	1939-1940; 1945
09672	Canton Planning Commission	Canton	MA	14 (1944-1946)	1944-1964

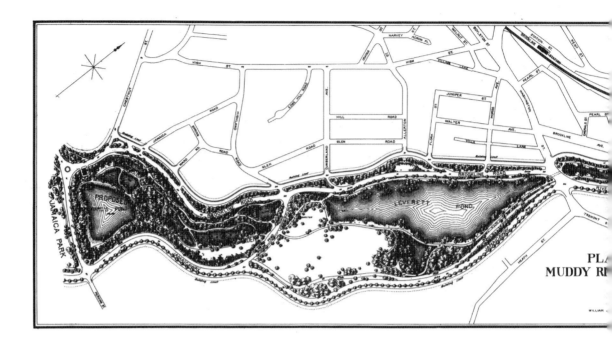

Plan of the parkway between the Muddy River Gate House and Jamaica Park, 1892.
Job #927 – Muddy River (Boston, MA).

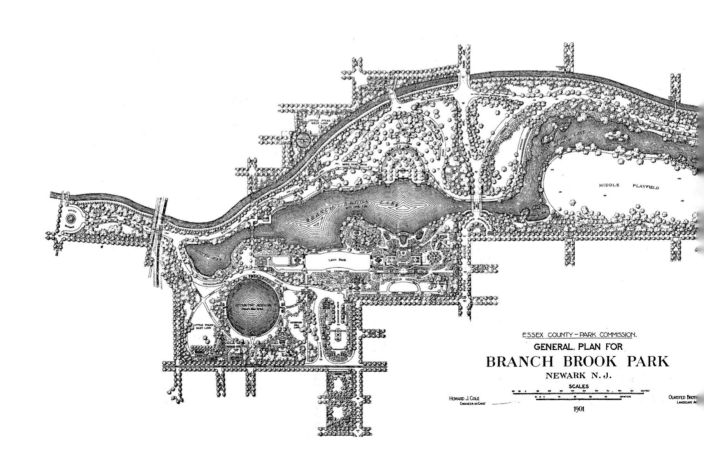

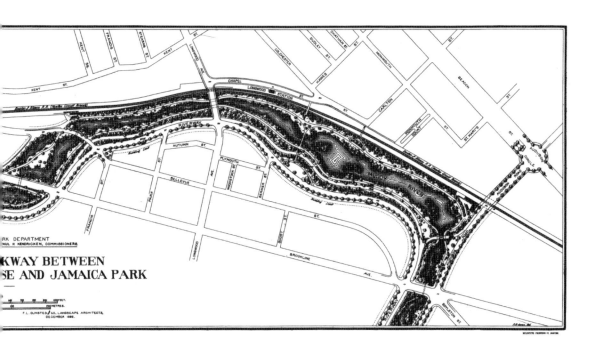

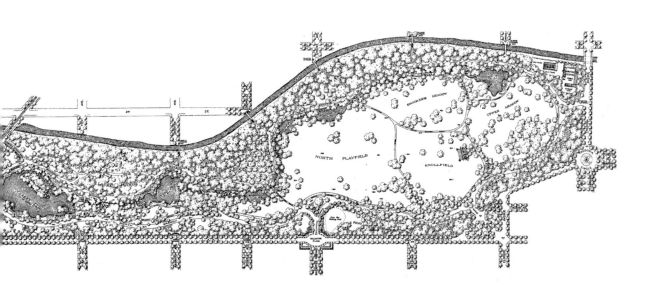

General plan for Branch Brook Park, 1901, part of the Essex County, New Jersey, park system. Job #2121 - Branch Brook Park (listed as Newark, NJ).

Job #	Job Name/Alternative Name	Job Location		Plans	Correspondence
10615	Charlestown Shipyard Park	Charlestown	MA	27 (1977)	1977-1979
00955	City Square - Charlestown/Boston Public Grounds Dept.	Charlestown	MA	5 (1912)	1912
00950-30	Sullivan Square - Boston Parks/Public Grounds Department	Charlestown	MA	2 (1913)	
00950-37	Winthrop Square - Boston Parks/Public Grounds Department	Charlestown	MA	2 (1913)	1897
10434	Fairbanks Park	Dedham	MA	6 (1972)	1972
01510	Dedham Parkway/Metropolitan Park Commission	Dedham/Boston	MA	6 (1913-1915)	1900
00950-07	City Greenhouse Grounds - Boston Parks/Public Grounds Department	Dorchester	MA	1 (1913)	
00950-09	Drohan Square - Boston Parks/Public Grounds Department	Dorchester	MA	2 (1913)	
00950-10	Eaton Square - Boston Parks/Public Grounds Department	Dorchester	MA	1 (1913)	
00922	Kings Mill Pond	Dorchester	MA	25 (1870; 1890-1897)	1891-1893
00950-24	Mount Bowdoin Green - Boston Parks/Public Grounds Department	Dorchester	MA	2 (1913)	
00950-26	Richardson Square - Boston Parks/Public Grounds Department	Dorchester	MA	2 (1913)	
00967	Ripley Playground	Dorchester	MA	3 (1913; 1917)	1916-1917
00950-29	Spaulding Square - Boston Parks/Public Grounds Department	Dorchester	MA	1 (1913)	
00950-32	Tremlett Park- -Boston Parks/Public Grounds Department	Dorchester	MA	2 (1913)	
00950-36	Wellesley Square - Boston Parks/Public Grounds Department	Dorchester	MA	2 (1913)	
00950-01	Belmont Square - Boston Parks/Public Grounds Department	East Boston	MA	2 (1913)	1911-1915
00951-A	Bennington Street/Boston Public Grounds Dept.	East Boston	MA	3 (1911)	1902; 1911-1913
00950-06	Central Square - Boston Parks/Public Grounds Department	East Boston	MA	2 (1913)	
00968	Eagle Hill Reservoir/Eagle Hill Reservoir Playground	East Boston	MA	4 (1911-1917)	1916-1917
00959	Maverick Square	East Boston	MA	1 (1911)	
00950-25	Prescott Square - Boston Parks/Public Grounds Department	East Boston	MA	2 (1913)	
01461	East Cambridge Embankment/Front, The	East Cambridge	MA	11 (1892-1894)	1907
01601	Durfee Green/Jackson Green	Fall River	MA	2 (1902)	1902-1903
01610	Fall River Parks	Fall River	MA	0	1896
01600	Fall River Parks/So. Pk 05/Durfee Green 01/Ruggles Pk 04	Fall River	MA	3 (1891-1896)	1870-1872; 1890-1896; 1902-1914
01602	Grinnell Square	Fall River	MA	7 (1902-1903)	
01603	North Park	Fall River	MA	20 (1902-1910)	1904-1905
01604	Ruggles Park	Fall River	MA	12 (1902-1905)	1903-1904
01605	South Park	Fall River	MA	36 (1893; 1902-1904)	[1896]; 1902-1903; 1914

Job #	Job Name/Alternative Name	Job Location		Plans	Correspondence
00070	Wautuppa Reservior	Fall River	MA	0	1895-1897
03123	Massachusetts Zoological Society	Fells Reservation	MA	3 (1906)	1906-1907
06439	Crocker, Alvah/Crocker, Alva/Crocker Field	Fitchburg	MA	317 (1916-1931)	1916-1931; 1955-1959
06160	Ravenwood Park	Gloucester	MA	0	1915
10489	Stoddard's Neck Park	Hingham	MA	0	1973
02361	Elmwood Park	Holyoke	MA	32 (1902-1909)	1901-1908
02366	Jones Point/Jones Point Park	Holyoke	MA	6 (1908-1910)	1909-1911
02363	Prospect Park	Holyoke	MA	2 (1910)	1910
02364	Riverside Park	Holyoke	MA	14 (1905-1911)	1905-1911
02360	Town Improvement/Riverside Pk/Elmwood Pk/Holyoke Parks	Holyoke	MA	2 (1907)	1901-1913
01527	Nantasket Beach/Nantasket Beach Reservation	Hull	MA	29 (1899-1917)	1898-1908; 1916-1917
01534	Neponset River Reservation - Sec. D	Hyde Park	MA	10 (1894-1903)	
10109	Crane Reservation	Ipswich	MA	30 (1957; 1960)	1959-1960
06999	Kingston Training Green	Kingston	MA	3 (1921)	1921
01850	Lawrence, City of	Lawrence	MA	3 (1895-1896)	1895-1897
10240	Lincoln Street Recreation Camp	Lexington	MA	33 (1968)	1968
09350	Longmeadow Park/Old Town Water Works/ Laurel Park	Longmeadow	MA	27 (1934-1935)	1934-1935
03970	Anne Street/Lowell Massachusetts Parks	Lowell	MA	2 (1910)	1910
01370	Lowell Parks/Board of Park Commissioners	Lowell	MA	0	1893-1894; 1904-1913
01375	North Common	Lowell	MA	0	
01377	Park Garden	Lowell	MA	0	
01373	Pawtucket Boulevard	Lowell	MA	2 (1892-1893)	1893
01378	Proctor Triangle	Lowell	MA	0	
01374	Rogers Park/Rogers Fort Hill Pk	Lowell	MA	13 (1907-1910)	1894; 1900-1905; 1975-1979
01376	South Common	Lowell	MA	5 (1904-1905)	1913
01372	Tyler Park	Lowell	MA	3 (1894)	1896
03315	Elm Street Playground	Lynn	MA	3 (1920-1921)	1920-1921
03311	High Rock/High Rock Reservation	Lynn	MA	0	1907-1908; 1913
03312	Little River Playground	Lynn	MA	5 (1904-1910)	1907-1914
01520	Lynn Shore/Lynn Shore Reservation/ Metropolitan Park Commission	Lynn	MA	20 (1899-1915)	1898; 1904-1907
03314	Lynn Woods	Lynn	MA	1 (1892)	1919
03310	Lynn Woods/Lynn Park Commission	Lynn	MA	0	1889-1896; 1907
03313	Meadow Park	Lynn	MA	19 (1920-1921)	1919-1921
01521	Lynnway/Metropolitan Park Commission	Lynn/Saugus	MA	4 (1898-1915)	1898-1899; 1915
01696	Bell Rock Park	Malden	MA	15 (1908-1911)	1907-1915; 1931
01691	Cotyemore Lea/Coytemore Lea	Malden	MA	15 (1895-1900)	1895-1901
01692	Craddock Field	Malden	MA	27 (1898-1910)	1898-1899; 1906-1910
01693	Fellsmere Park/Fells Pkwy	Malden	MA	7 (1893-1895)	1893-1900

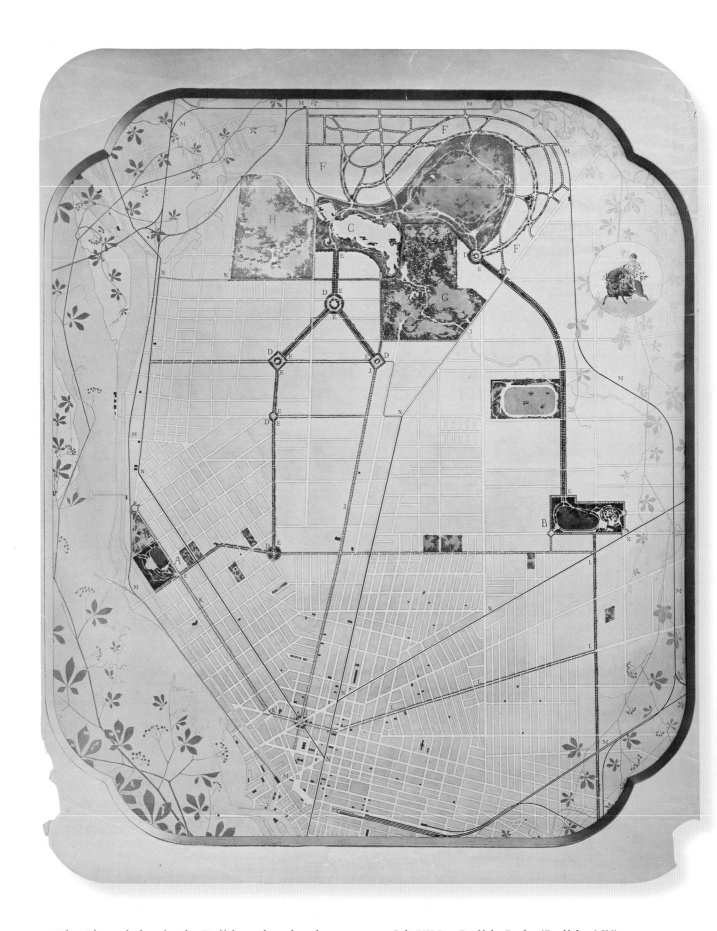

The Olmsted plan for the Buffalo park and parkway system. Job #700 – Buffalo Parks (Buffalo, NY).

Job #	Job Name/Alternative Name	Job Location		Plans	Correspondence
01694	Hitchings Field	Malden	MA	3 (1893)	
01710	Malden Parks	Malden	MA	0	
01690	Malden Parks	Malden	MA	4 (1910-1911)	1893-1900
01695	Oldway Place	Malden	MA	1 (1894)	1894
04062	Manchester Town Common/Manchester Common	Manchester	MA	48 (1919-1945)	1919-1921; 1924; 1944-1945; 1955
04060	Masconomo Park	Manchester	MA	50 (1906-1945)	1910-1916; 1931-1940; 1976-1977
02216	Old Neck Beach	Manchester	MA	0	
01533	Neponset River Reservation - Sec. C	Mattapan	MA	2 (1896-1902)	1898
01523	Mystic River Reservation/Metropolitan Park Commission	Medford	MA	25 (1897-1916)	1895-1923
01524	Mystic Valley Parkway	Medford	MA	29 (1893-1919)	1894-1919
01525	Mystic Valley Parkway, North/Winchester Pkwy/Metropolitan Park Commission	Medford	MA	5 (1898-1900)	1897-1908; 1913-1919
09520	Ell Pond Park	Melrose	MA	0	1937-1938; 1943
06873	Emerson Street Park/Melrose Park/Bowden, F. P.	Melrose	MA	5 (1921)	1920-1924
01519	Lynn Fells Parkway/Metropolitan Park Commission	Melrose/Stoneham	MA	48 (1893-1915)	1898-1908; 1913
01190	Milton Park Commission	Milton	MA	0	1891-1898; 1932
01532	Neponset River Reservation - Sec. B	Milton Station	MA	2 (1898)	1897
07663	Plymouth County Development Company Park/E.B. Davis Park	Montello	MA	7 (1926)	1926-1927
01526	Nahant Beach Parkway/Metropolitan Park Commission	Nahant	MA	11 (1899-1914)	1899-1908; 1913
01810	New Bedford Parks/Buttonwood Park	New Bedford	MA	3 (1895)	1894-1896
05132	Cooper, F. I.	Newton	MA	0	1895-1898
01517	Hemlock Gorge Reservation	Newton	MA	8 (1905)	1894-1906
01061	Newton Centre Playground	Newton	MA	14 (1891)	1890-1894; 1979
01060	Park in Newton Massachusetts	Newton	MA	0	1890-1897
01065	Lowell Avenue Playground/Lowell Avenue Playground School Site	Newtonville	MA	9 (1931; 1946)	1946
00349	Valley Park	North Adams	MA	2 (1903-1904)	1903-1905
00671	North Easton Park	North Easton	MA	36 (1881-1883; 1946-1947)	1882-1887; 1946-1950; 1961-1980
00181	Palmer Massachusetts	Palmer	MA	0	1884
06652	Washington Park/Wright Wire Co.	Palmer	MA	12 (1918-1919)	1918-1919
01535	Neponset River Reservation - Sec. E	Pauls Bridge	MA	1 (1898-1899)	1898
03135	Petersham Massachusetts Park/Brooks, James W.	Petersham	MA	0	1906-1907
06170	Drake Athletic Field/Playground Drake Field	Pittsfield	MA	0	1915
10312	Plymouth 350th Anniversary Fountain	Plymouth	MA	3 (1969-1970)	1970
01150	Plymouth Mass. Parks	Plymouth	MA	0	1889-1898
01151	Plymouth Training Green	Plymouth	MA	17 (1889-1890)	1889-1890

Job #	Job Name/Alternative Name	Job Location		Plans	Correspondence
02052	Trustees of Public Reservations/Holmes Reservation/Trustees of Reservations	Plymouth	MA	6 (1943)	1943-1944
01515	Furnace Brook Parkway/Metropolitan Park Commission	Quincy	MA	39 (1897-1917)	1898-1908
00651	Merrymount Park	Quincy	MA	0	1892; 1900
00650	Quincy Park System	Quincy	MA	4 (1881-1893)	1895-1896
01537	Quincy Shore Reservation	Quincy	MA	19 (1903-1915)	1895-1910; 1915-1916
01467	Quincy Square	Quincy	MA	0	
02288	Racing Beach/Davis, L. Shannon	Quissett, Falmouth	MA	3 (1898-1902)	1899-1902
10600	Reading Commons	Reading	MA	2 (1977)	1897; 1977
09945	Field, General Meigs	Readville	MA	0	1952
01538	Revere Beach Parkway	Revere	MA	48 (1899-1915)	1894-1915
01539	Revere Beach/Metropolitan Park Commission/Revere Beach Reservation	Revere	MA	34 (1893-1919)	N.D.; 1894-1909; 1915-1919; 1977-1978
06792	Rockland War Memorial Park/Terrell, James A.	Rockland	MA	0	1920-1921
00950-04	Bromley Park - Boston Parks/Public Grounds Department	Roxbury	MA	1 (1913)	
00950-05	Cedar Square - Boston Parks/Public Grounds Department	Roxbury	MA	1 (1913)	
00950-12	Elm Hill Park - Boston Parks/Public Grounds Department	Roxbury	MA	1 (1913)	
00957	Fountain Square	Roxbury	MA	2 (1912-1913)	
00950-15	Harold Square - Boston Parks/Public Grounds Department	Roxbury	MA	1 (1913)	
00950-16	Heath Square - Boston Parks/Public Grounds Department	Roxbury	MA	1 (1913)	
00953	Highland Park	Roxbury	MA	3 (1911-1912)	1892-1895; 1912-1913
00950-18	Jackson Square - Boston Parks/Public Grounds Department	Roxbury	MA	1 (1913)	
00950-19	Lewis Park - Boston Parks/Public Grounds Department	Roxbury	MA	1 (1913)	
00950-21	Linwood Park - Boston Parks/Public Grounds Department	Roxbury	MA	1 (1913)	
00950-22	Longwood Park - Boston Parks/Public Grounds Department	Roxbury	MA	2 (1913)	1894
00952	Madison Square	Roxbury	MA	10 (1912)	1912-1913
00938	Orchard Park	Roxbury	MA	4 (1912-1913)	1897; 1913
00950-34	Walnut Park - Boston Parks/Public Grounds Department	Roxbury	MA	1 (1913)	
00956	Washington Park/Washington Square Park	Roxbury	MA	8 (1912)	1897; 1912
02902	Boston Society of Landscape Architects/B.S.L.A/Salisbury Beach	Salisbury Beach	MA	25 (1934-1938)	1911-1980
06706	Lawson Park/Lawson Park War Memorial	Scituate	MA	4 (1919)	1919-1920
01540	Somerville Parkway	Somerville	MA	30 (1897-1900)	1899-1908
00951-D	Dorchester Street/Boston Public Grounds Dept.	South Boston	MA	2 (1911)	1902; 1911-1913

Job #	Job Name/Alternative Name	Job Location		Plans	Correspondence
00950-17	Independence Square - Boston Parks/Public Grounds Department	South Boston	MA	2 (1913)	
00950-20	Lincoln Square - Boston Parks/Public Grounds Department	South Boston	MA	2 (1913)	
00925	M Street Playground	South Boston	MA	5 (1896)	1891; 1897
00926	Marine Park	South Boston	MA	83 (1876-1896)	1889-1896
00950-31	Thomas Park - Boston Parks/Public Grounds Department	South Boston	MA	2 (1912-1913)	
01531	Neponset River Reservation - Sec. A/below Milton Lower Falls	South Milton/Lower Mills	MA	2 (1898-1912)	1896-1899; 1912
02051	Trustees of Public Reservations/Rocky Narrows/Rocky Narrows Reservation	South Sherborn	MA	10 (1896-1901)	1897-1901
05123	Court Square	Springfield	MA	13 (1909-1921)	1914; 1925
05125	Cross-Town Boulevard/Crosstown Thoroughfare	Springfield	MA	13 (1928)	1928
05111	Merrick Park	Springfield	MA	0	1910
05112	Mill River/Proposed Park/North and South Branches of Mill River	Springfield	MA	8 (1923-1928)	1928
05121	Northern Approach	Springfield	MA	36 (1914-1916)	
05122	Southern Approach	Springfield	MA	26 (1914)	1915
05110	Springfield Parks	Springfield	MA	0	
05124	Stearns Square	Springfield	MA	7 (1914)	1914
10546	Village Green	Sudbury	MA	0	1975
01518	King's Beach/King's Beach Reservation	Swampscott	MA	5 (1895-1916)	1895; 1904-1916
05890	Swampscott Park Commission	Swampscott	MA	0	1913
01516	Harts Hill Reservation	Wakefield	MA	2 (1900; 1908)	
01554	Quannapowitt Parkway	Wakefield	MA	3 (1915)	
01782	Central Square	Waltham	MA	0	1913
01781	Prospect Hill Park	Waltham	MA	2 (1892-1895)	1899
02370	Worcester Street Widening	Wellesley	MA	5 (1902)	1902
05512	Crocker, Alvah/Park at Mills/West Fitchburg Park	West Fitchburg	MA	6 (1912)	1911-1913
07061	Connecticut Valley Realty Company/West Springfield Bridge Approach	West Springfield	MA	24 (1922)	1922-1923
02074	Weston Reservoir	Weston	MA	34 (1900-1904)	1897-1910; 1977
09303	Hobart Pond Park/Hobard Pond Swimming Pond	Whitman	MA	3 (1931)	1931-1938
00211	Whitman Park	Whitman	MA	54 (1900-1931)	1900-1935
06963	Winchendon Memorial Park/Winchenden Park	Winchendon	MA	12 (1921-1923)	1921-1924
00108	Tutein/Mystic Valley Parkway Playground/Town of Winchester	Winchester	MA	3 (1920)	1899-1900
01350	Town of Winthrop Recreation	Winthrop	MA	5 (1891-1894)	1893-1898
03895	Beaver Brook Playground	Worcester	MA	4 (1942)	1942
03886	Burncoat Park	Worcester	MA	17 (1909-1941)	1910-1912; 1941
03888	Chandler Hill Park	Worcester	MA	0	

Job #	Job Name/Alternative Name	Job Location		Plans	Correspondence
03891	Common, The/Worcester Common	Worcester	MA	8 (1913-1915)	1911-1915; 1965
03883	Crompton Park	Worcester	MA	6 (1911)	1911
00194	Crompton Park	Worcester	MA	0	1892
03881	Elm Park	Worcester	MA	11 (1909-1940)	1910-1918; 1940-1944
03887	Green Hill Park	Worcester	MA	101 (1910-1942)	1912-1918; 1941-1942
03885	Hadwen Park	Worcester	MA	0	
03892	Institute Park	Worcester	MA	0	1911
03889	Kendrick Park/Kendrick Field	Worcester	MA	4 (1910-1911)	1910-1911
03882	Lake Park	Worcester	MA	0	
03897	Morgan Park	Worcester	MA	13 (1941-1944)	1942-1945
03894	Rockwood Playground	Worcester	MA	4 (1940-1942)	1942
03884	University Park	Worcester	MA	0	
03890	Washington Square	Worcester	MA	11 (1911-1913)	1911-1914; 1968
03893	Worcester City Plan/Chamber of Commerce	Worcester	MA	0	1921
03880	Worcester, Massachusetts Parks/Worcester Parks/Parks and Recreation Commission	Worcester	MA	0	1909-1917; 1939-1944
09637	Rehoboth - Chincoteague Seashore Project		MD	0	1940-1941
02447	Baltimore City Plan/Commission on City Plan/Rehabilitation of Slum Areas	Baltimore	MD	1 (1943)	1937-1947
02401	Baltimore Park System/Report to Municipal Art Society	Baltimore	MD	4 (1915-1924)	1876-1877; 1902-1917; 1923-1924
02400	Baltimore Parks Municipal Art Society/ Baltimore Park System	Baltimore	MD	110 (1877-1945)	1892-1895; 1923-1927; 1934-1947
02444	Baltimore Viaduct/Cross-Town Viaduct	Baltimore	MD	14 (1896; 1914; 1929)	1929
03136	Bancroft Park	Baltimore	MD	4 (1900-1907)	1906-1908
02434	Bay View/Poor Farm	Baltimore	MD	0	1910
02415	Carroll Park	Baltimore	MD	30 (1895; 1904-1919)	1904-1915
02419	City Spring Park	Baltimore	MD	9 (1905-1911)	1905-1908
02407	Clifton Park/Druid Hill/Herring Run	Baltimore	MD	26 (1894-1915)	1877; 1905-1915
02423	Clifton to Patterson Parkway	Baltimore	MD	0	1907-1912
02424	Clifton-Patterson Parkway	Baltimore	MD	4 (1894-1906)	
02405	Druid Hill Park	Baltimore	MD	78 (1898-1915)	1876-1879; 1892; 1904-1908; 1916
02435	Easterwood Park	Baltimore	MD	3 (1912)	1912
02413	Federal Hill Park	Baltimore	MD	3 (1896-1904)	1914
02437	Fort McHenry/Francis Scott Key Monument	Baltimore	MD	14 (1914-1917)	1914-1920
02439	Franklin Square	Baltimore	MD	1 (1916)	
02418	Fulton Avenue	Baltimore	MD	1 (1904)	
02422	Garret Parkway	Baltimore	MD	4 (1906-1911)	1909-1913
02421	Gwynn's Falls Parkway	Baltimore	MD	36 (1894-1915)	1906-1916
02406	Gwynn's Falls Reservation	Baltimore	MD	50 (1894-1915)	1907-1915
02438	Harlem Park	Baltimore	MD	1 (1916)	
02430	Harlem Park	Baltimore	MD	0	1908

Job #	Job Name/Alternative Name	Job Location		Plans	Correspondence
02425	Herring Run Parkway	Baltimore	MD	9 (1908-1909)	1907-1912
02440	Lafayette Square	Baltimore	MD	1 (1916)	
02408	Latrobe Park	Baltimore	MD	10 (1903-1912)	1904-1905; 1911-1912
02446	Leakin Park	Baltimore	MD	0	1939-1940
02445	Litter Louna	Baltimore	MD	1 (1930)	1921-1930
02416	Mount Royal Avenue	Baltimore	MD	0	
02403	Mount Vernon Square	Baltimore	MD	21 (1833; 1902-1903)	1903; 1908; 1917
02431	New Park near Patterson Park	Baltimore	MD	0	
02414	Patterson Park	Baltimore	MD	19 (1899-1915)	1905-1915
02442	Perkins Square	Baltimore	MD	1 (1916)	
02427	Reservoir Site	Baltimore	MD	23 (1907-1909)	1907-1915
02409	Swann Park	Baltimore	MD	6 (1903-1908)	1904-1905
02441	Union Square	Baltimore	MD	1 (1916)	
02426	University Parkway	Baltimore	MD	26 (1904-1910)	1908-1910
02436	Venable Park	Baltimore	MD	8 (1913-1914)	1913-1915
02402	Washington Monument/Washington Place/Mt. Vernon Sq/Washington Monument/North and South Parks	Baltimore	MD	10 (ca. 1900)	1877-1879
02404	Wyman Park	Baltimore	MD	101 (1894-1915)	1903-1911; 1947; 1957-1960
02428	Wyman Park Extension	Baltimore	MD	2 (1908-1909)	1908-1909
07730	Augusta Playground	Augusta	ME	1 (1926)	1926
06857	Macomber Playground	Augusta	ME	43 (1920-1921)	1920-1921
06833	Maine State Park/Park East of the Capitol/Burleigh, Lewis H.	Augusta	ME	55 (1918-1929)	1920-1934
03800	Ocean Drive & Newport Mt.	Bar Harbor	ME	1 (1906)	1909-1910; 1930
03448	Bar Island/Barr Island	Bar Island	ME	5 (1908)	1902; 1908
09709	Memorial Park/War Memorial Park	Brewer	ME	21 (1937; 1945-1946)	1945-1948
09385	Camden Shore Develop.	Camden	ME	41 (1935-1937; 1948-1952)	1935-1969
07997	Camden Shore Front Park	Camden	ME	34 (1928-1931; 1947; 1951)	1927-1969
07808	Camden Village Green/War Monument	Camden	ME	17 (1927-1928; 1948-1949)	1927-1968
09263	Gardiner, R.H. Jr. Mrs/Old Mill Pond Lot/Athletic Field/Playground.	Gardiner	ME	4 (1931)	1931-1933
07219	Portsmouth Bridge/Kittery-Portsmouth Bridge	Kittery	ME	0	1923
09138	Acadia National Park	Mount Desert Island	ME	107 (1929-1939)	1918-1937; 1942
09653	Manson Park/Mary Ann Lancey Manson Park	Pittsfield	ME	13 (1943-1953)	1943-1953
01861	Back Cove	Portland	ME	10 (1870-1896)	1895-1896; 1930-1931
01862	Deering's Oaks	Portland	ME	4 (1902)	1902
01863	Eastern Promenade	Portland	ME	10 (1905)	
01860	Portland, City of/Back Cove/Deering Oaks/Portland Parks	Portland	ME	2 (1904-1905)	1895-1896; 1904-1906; 1911

Job #	Job Name/Alternative Name	Job Location		Plans	Correspondence
01864	Western Promenade	Portland	ME	16 (1904-1905)	
00675	Cushing's Island	Portland Harbor	ME	0	1882-1883; 1974
00661	Belle Isle Park	Detroit	MI	69 (1873-1917)	1881-1889; 1895; 1977-1978
00660	Detroit Parks	Detroit	MI	0	1884-1899; 1914
00663	Palmer Park	Detroit	MI	0	
00092	Marquette Park/Presque Isle Park	Marquette	MI	1 (1895)	1891-1896; 1917
03611	Recreation Park/Huron River/Huron River Improvement	Ypsilanti	MI	8 (1902-1917)	1908-1917
03614	Waterworks Park	Ypsilanti	MI	0	1911
03613	Ypsilanti Parks/Huron River	Ypsilanti	MI	62 (1905-1917)	1916-1917
04024	Quetico Superior International Forest and Park		MN	0	1928-1948
12081	Minneapolis Parks	Minneapolis	MN	0	1885-1887; 1890; 18969-1899
00084	Minnehaha Parkway and Minnehaha State Park	Minneapolis	MN	0	1893-1897
01256	Kansas City Liberty Memorial/Penn Valley Park	Kansas City	MO	212 (1925-1927; 1932-1934)	1926-1935; 1948
01250	Kansas City Parks	Kansas City	MO	21 (1892-1893)	1892-1898; 1908
03996	Saint Joseph Park System/St. Joseph Park Board	Saint Joseph	MO	11 (1925-1926)	1910; 1916; 1925-1928
00090	Forest Park	Saint Louis	MO	0	
00091	Lafayette Park	Saint Louis	MO	0	
00081	Missouri Botanic Gardens/Missouri Botanical Garden	Saint Louis	MO	96 (1896-1905)	1892-1912; 1959-1966
00284	Mount Mitchell		NC	0	
09654	Love Park/Gastonia Park	Gastonia	NC	23 (1943)	1943
06749	Berlin Parks/Berlin Park System	Berlin	NH	0	1919
02800	Dover City Parks/Dover Park System	Dover	NH	8 (1903-1904)	1903-1905
09933	Halfway House	East Jaffrey	NH	2 (1952)	1952
09014	Exeter Shore Parkway	Exeter	NH	127 (1924-1931)	1928-1931
09851	Cohen Foundation/Camp Tel Noar/Cohen, Eli	Hampstead	NH	8 (1949)	1949-1950
00221	Fay Reservation	North Woodstock	NH	1 (1903)	1886-1909
09771	Pierces Island	Portsmouth	NH	6 (1943-1947)	1947; 1955
05719	Presidential Range	White Mountains	NH	0	1927; 1933-1935
02148	Belleville Park	Belleville	NJ	22 (1915-1958)	1899; 1915-1919; 1937
02145	Grover Cleveland Park	Caldwell	NJ	26 (1914-1917)	1912-1922
02157	Mills Reservation	Cedar Grove	NJ	14 (1955-1961)	1954-1961
07761	East Orange Central Playground/Board of Recreation Commissioners	East Orange	NJ	12 (1926-1928)	1926-1932
02123	East Orange Parkway	East Orange	NJ	142 (1899-1932)	1899-1904; 1919-1932; 1950
02130	Watsessing Park	East Orange	NJ	54 (1900-1931)	1900-1931

Job #	Job Name/Alternative Name	Job Location		Plans	Correspondence
02146	Essex County Parkway - Speedway/ Southern Parkway/Speedway/Essex County Speedway	Essex Co. Pk. Comm.	NJ	25 (1918-1931)	1913-1926
02125	Anderson Park/Montclair Park	Essex County	NJ	3 (1903-1912)	1902-1912
02139	Bloomfield Park/Watsessing Pk, addit.	Essex County	NJ	70 (1904-1914)	1908-1915
02154	Brookdale Park/Park #19/Bloomfield-Montclair Pk/Essex County Park Commission	Essex County	NJ	123 (1929-1937)	1928-1937
02142	Cedar Avenue Park	Essex County	NJ	0	1910
02135	Central Avenue	Essex County	NJ	5 (1904)	
02124	Eastside Park/Independence Pk, 1928	Essex County	NJ	62 (1898-1930)	1899-1900; 1928-1933
02143	Edgemont Park	Essex County	NJ	0	
02120	Essex County Park System	Essex County	NJ	227 (1895-1959)	1894-1943; 1953-1967; 1977
02140	Glenfield Park/Montclair Pk/Maple Avenue Park	Essex County	NJ	36 (1903-1931)	1909-1910; 1931
02136	Glenridge Park/Essex County Park Commission/Glen Ridge Park	Essex County	NJ	2 (1906)	1906

Storytelling in the Imagination Playground, Prospect Park, Brooklyn, NY, 2002. Job #509 – Prospect Park (New York City, NY).

Job #	Job Name/Alternative Name	Job Location		Plans	Correspondence
02137	Irvington Park	Essex County	NJ	16 (1908-1930)	1906-1914; 1930
02132	Lake Weequahic Reservation/Weequahic Reservation	Essex County	NJ	378 (1899-1931)	1898-1902; 1912-1922
02151	Murphy Memorial Correspondence/ Weequahic Reservation	Essex County	NJ	0	1922-1924
02126	Orange Park	Essex County	NJ	37 (1898-1912)	1898-1914; 1922-1923; 1929-1933
02127	Park Avenue/Essex County Park Commission	Essex County	NJ	8 (1902-1904)	1903
02153	Passaic River Parkway	Essex County	NJ	61 (1926-1937)	1926-1938
02152	Proposed Parkway North of Branch Brook Park	Essex County	NJ	0	1922
02138	Riverbank Park	Essex County	NJ	17 (1908-1931)	1908-1913; 1927-1931
02128	South Mountain Reservation	Essex County	NJ	259 (1887-1933)	1898-1935
10100	The Loo/Essex County Park Commission	Essex County	NJ	0	1959
02150	Verona Lake Park	Essex County	NJ	40 (1919-1932)	1919-1933
02134	West Orange Park/Essex County Park Commission	Essex County	NJ	1 (1904)	
02133	Westside Park	Essex County	NJ	122 (1899-1921)	1898-1921
10050	Essex Fells	Essex Fells	NJ	12 (1932; 1957-1958)	1956-1958
07406	Glen Ridge Athletic Field/Athletic Field	Glen Ridge	NJ	2 (1925)	1925-1926
04025	Island Beach Park/National Monument Committee	Island Beach	NJ	1 (1946-1949)	1949-1950
07178	Kenilworth Golf Course/Galloping Hill Park/Kenilworth Park	Kenilworth	NJ	11 (1926-1927)	1926-1930
07175	Wheeler Park/Linden Park/John Russell Wheeler Park	Linden	NJ	39 (1925-1931)	1925-1940
10005	White Oak Ridge Park	Millburn	NJ	37 (1953-1961)	1955-1961
02122	Eagle Rock Reservation	Montclair	NJ	207 (1898-1933)	1898-1902; 1908-1911; 1917-1922; 1929-1933
03673	Edgemont Park	Montclair	NJ	3 (1907-1909)	1909
02141	Essex Avenue Park	Montclair	NJ	0	1910
07231	Cheesequake State Park	Morgan	NJ	2 (N.D.)	1937
05400	Morristown Parks/Morristown City Plan Park System	Morristown	NJ	0	1911
05540	New Brunswick New Jersey Parks	New Brunswick	NJ	0	1902; 1912
02121	Branch Brook Park	Newark	NJ	720 (1890-1937)	1898-1914; 1920-1936; [1943]
02156	Ivy Hill Park	Newark	NJ	14 (1929-1937)	1930; 1935-1937
00420	Newark Parks	Newark	NJ	10 (1916-1927)	1867-1870; 1904; 1926-1927
02129	South Orange Parkway	Newark	NJ	1 (1903)	1898-1899
02149	Vailsburg Park	Newark	NJ	63 (1918-1923)	1916-1928
02131	Weequahic Parkway	Newark	NJ	9 (1899-1903)	1922-1931
02144	Yantacaw Park	Nutley	NJ	32 (1912-1957)	1912-1915; 1935
07125	Palisade Interstate Parkway/Palisade Interstate Park Commission	Palisades	NJ	7 (1900-1901)	1923

Job #	Job Name/Alternative Name	Job Location		Plans	Correspondence
09971	Union Building & Construction Corporation	Passaic	NJ	15 (1940; 1947; 1954)	1953-1956
09159	Garret Mountain	Passaic County	NJ	97 (1929-1931)	1929-1934
07687	Passaic County Park System/Passaic County Park Commission	Passaic County	NJ	22 (1916-1927)	1926-1934; 1959
09025	Passaic River Park/Bassett, C.P./Passaic Valley Flood Control	Passaic County	NJ	4 (1928)	1928-1929
09160	Goffle Brook Park	Passaic County Park Commission	NJ	64 (1930-1932)	1930-1932
09161	Weasel Brook/Weasel Brook Park	Passaic County Park Commission	NJ	42 (1930-1931)	1930-1937
09163	Monument Heights/Paterson Stadium and Recreation Field	Paterson	NJ	9 (1919-1931)	1930-1931
07004	Green Brook Park/Union County Park System	Plainfield	NJ	114 (1922-1927)	1921-1927
07176	Kenyon Gardens - extension of Cedar Brook	Plainfield	NJ	0	
07340	Library Square/Library Park	Plainfield	NJ	17 (1924-1925)	1924-1925
09162	Preakness Golf Course/Preakness Golf Club/Preakness Valley Park	Preakness	NJ	107 (1930-1946)	1930-1936; 1945-1954
04076	Grove Park/South Orange Park	South Orange	NJ	1 (1910)	
07045	Maplewood Park	South Orange	NJ	15 (1922-1923)	1922-1925
07230	High Point Park	Sussex	NJ	8 (1923-1924)	1922-1925; 1931-1934
01182	Assanpink Creek Parkway	Trenton	NJ	13 (1904-1907)	1901-1914
01184	Bromley Place/Buttonwood Park/E.C. Hill/Hill, Edmund C./Bromley Tract/Bromley Park	Trenton	NJ	10 (1910)	1892-1894; 1907-1910
01181	Cadwalader Park	Trenton	NJ	4 (1891, 1911)	1890-1895; 1908-1911; 1968-1980
00230	Hamilton Terrace	Trenton	NJ	8 (1899-1900)	1895-1900
01186	Reservoir Playground/The Stadium/Hill, Edmund C.	Trenton	NJ	2 (1912)	1908-1912
12091	Shore Drive	Trenton	NJ	0	1891-1892
01180	Trenton Park/Assanpink Creek Parkway/Trenton Parks	Trenton	NJ	0	1890-1892; 1911
07181	Briant Pond Parkway/Bryant Pond Park	Union County	NJ	18 (1926-1930)	1926-1934; 1939
07174	Cedar Brook Park/Cedar Brook Park - Shakespearean Garden	Union County	NJ	68 (1923-1943)	1923-1953
07183	Echo Lake - Nomahegan Connection/Lenape Park	Union County	NJ	57 (1961-1975)	1961-1976
07171	Echo Lake Park	Union County	NJ	27 (1923-1925)	1924-1927; 1938-1944; 1961
07180	Elizabeth River	Union County	NJ	8 (1926-1958)	1921; 1929; 1958
07177	Mattano Park/Elizabethport Park/Elizabeth Port Park/Mattonao Park	Union County	NJ	64 (1925-1931)	1926-1931; 1976-1977
07173	Rahway River Park	Union County	NJ	265 (1922-1962)	1868; 1923-1962
07179	Roselle Parkway	Union County	NJ	0	
06957	Union County Park Commission	Union County	NJ	44 (1921-1929; 1937; 1958-1965)	1921-1939; 1949; 1955-1956; 1961-1971

Job #	Job Name/Alternative Name	Job Location		Plans	Correspondence
09316	Union County Shade Tree Commission	Union County	NJ	0	1932
07170	Warinanco Park/Elizabeth-Roselle Park/Elizabeth Park	Union County	NJ	215 (1923-1956)	1922-1929; 1934-1939; 1944-1962
07172	Watchung Reservation/Ackerman Lake Reservation	Union County	NJ	112 (1922-1970)	1924-1971
09264	Parvin Park/Union Grove/Parvin State Park	Union Grove	NJ	35 (1931-1932)	1931-1934
07110	Echo Lake Park	Westfield	NJ	0	
07916	Woodbridge Park	Woodbridge	NJ	19 (1927-1928)	1928-1930; 1947
00507	Crotona Park		NY	2 (1892-1898)	
12101	Adirondacks Reservation	Adirondacks	NY	0	1884-1886
00701	Bennett Park	Buffalo	NY	5 (1887)	
00700	Buffalo Parks/Cazenovia/Humboldt/Niag. Sq.	Buffalo	NY	41 (1869-1870)	1866-1879; 1885-1903
00703	Cazenovia Park	Buffalo	NY	12 (1892-1896)	1887-1897
00704	Day's Park	Buffalo	NY	3 (1887)	
00705	Delaware Park	Buffalo	NY	46 (1897-1902)	1897-1908
00702	Delaware Park/Buffalo Park	Buffalo	NY	10 (1878-1879)	1875; 1897-1899
00719	Delaware Park/Buffalo Park/North Park	Buffalo	NY	1 (N.D.)	1863-1897; 1900-1915
07461	Erie County Parks/Park Commission	Buffalo	NY	30 (1925)	1925-1926
00706	Front, The	Buffalo	NY	39 (1870-1899)	1882; 1898
00707	Front, The, Addition to	Buffalo	NY	4 (1891)	1898
00717	Humboldt Park/Parade, The	Buffalo	NY	31 (1895-1907)	1897-1898; 1904-1907
00724	Jones Tract Land/Riverside Pk	Buffalo	NY	19 (1894-1899)	1898-1899
00709	Lafayette Square	Buffalo	NY	2 (N.D.)	
00715	Masten Place/Potter's Field	Buffalo	NY	5 (1887)	
12201	McKinley Parkway	Buffalo	NY	0	
00710	Niagara Square	Buffalo	NY	5 (1876; 1895)	1874; 1879
00712	Parade Refectory	Buffalo	NY	1 (1876)	
00714	Prospect Park	Buffalo	NY	1 (1876)	
12211	Red Jacket Parkway	Buffalo	NY	0	
02417	Riverside Park	Buffalo	NY	0	1870; 1898; 1908-1913
00718	South Park	Buffalo	NY	114 (1887-1895)	1888-1898
00716	Terrace Park	Buffalo	NY	9 (1883-1887)	
06565	Crandall Park	Glens Falls	NY	2 (1917)	1917-1919
00510	Bay Ridge Parkway/Shore Drive/Shore Road	Long Island	NY	13 (1893-1897)	1892-1903
09037	Wheatley Hills/Wheatley Hills Parkway Relocation	Long Island	NY	49 (1924; 1928-1929)	1928-1929
06951	Monroe Park	Monroe	NY	0	1921
00530	Broadway Parking Strip, 87th to 88th Streets/Potter, Mrs. Henry Codman	New York City	NY	0	1908-1910
00517	Bronx Park	New York City	NY	0	1897; 1922
00511	Brooklyn Forest	New York City	NY	11 (1894-1897)	1895-1897
00501	Brooklyn Parks (Addition)	New York City	NY	3 (1895)	1867-1897; 1948

Job #	Job Name/Alternative Name	Job Location		Plans	Correspondence
12171	Brooklyn/King's County	New York City	NY	0	1895; 1897
00514	Bushwick Park	New York City	NY	8 (1892-1895)	1894-1895
00502	Central Park	New York City	NY	46 (1859-1876; 1904-1935)	1857-1941; 1968-1969
00535	Central Park West/New York Railways Co./8th Avenue	New York City	NY	1 (1914)	1914
00527	Claremont Park	New York City	NY	125 (1927-1934)	1927-1936
00520	Corleais Hook Park	New York City	NY	0	
00513	Dyker Beach/Dyker Beach Park	New York City	NY	11 (1895-1897)	1894-1898
12261	East River Park/Harlem River Park	New York City	NY	0	1876; 1884; 1890; 1894-1895
12121	Eastern Parkway	New York City	NY	0	1895
12111	Fort Greene Park	New York City	NY	0	1867
00529	Fort Tryon Park/Rockefeller	New York City	NY	987 (1927-1963)	1920-1939
00512	Highland Park	New York City	NY	0	1874; 1894-1896
00519	Lafayette Boulevard/Riverside Drive Extension	New York City	NY	5 (1900-1905)	1877; 1903
00533	Madison Square	New York City	NY	0	1874; 1896; 1912
12271	Manhattan Square	New York City	NY	0	1877
00503	Morningside Park	New York City	NY	43 (1871-1889)	1873-1889
12221	Mount Morris Park	New York City	NY	0	1896
00508	New York Botanical Garden/Bronx Park	New York City	NY	98 (1896-1930)	1897-1898; 1923-1925; 1930-1931; 1937
00518	New York Parks - Municipal Art Society Schemes	New York City	NY	0	1902-1905
00500	New York Parks/Richmond Borough Park System/W.H.Seward Park	New York City	NY	3 (1902-1906)	1873-1900; 1905; 1913-1914; 1920-1924; 1931
12141	Ocean Parkway	New York City	NY	0	
12151	Parade Ground	New York City	NY	0	1894
00509	Prospect Park	New York City	NY	62 (1868-1901)	1865-1897; 1931-1936; 1967-1969; 1974-1978
12161	Ridgewood Park	New York City	NY	14 (1894)	1894
00504	Riverside Drive Extension	New York City	NY	298 (1903-1917)	1875-1885; 1912-1915; 1927-1931; 1956
00505	Riverside Park/Riverside Drive	New York City	NY	6 (1875-1882)	1867-1889; 1894; 1912-1920
00532	Rockaway Beach	New York City	NY	0	1880; 1910-1912
12281	Spuyten Duyvil Park	New York City	NY	0	1870-1891
12241	Stuyvesant Square	New York City	NY	0	
00516	Sunset Park	New York City	NY	3 (1894)	1894
00534	Telawana Park	New York City	NY	0	1914
12131	Tompkins Park	New York City	NY	0	1870
12251	Tompkins Square	New York City	NY	0	1875-1876
12231	Union Square	New York City	NY	0	1867-1868; 1871; 1873
12311	Zoological Grounds	New York City	NY	0	1873-1879; 1887; 1890

Bird's eye view of Niagara Falls with Niagara Reservation (Goat Island and shore of Am

s), *date unknown. Job #617 – New York State Reservation at Niagara Falls (Niagara Falls, NY).*

Job #	Job Name/Alternative Name	Job Location		Plans	Correspondence
01428	Downing Park	Newburgh	NY	23 (1894-1895; 1916; 1944)	1882-1909; 1922-1924; 1944; 1971
00617	New York State Reservation at Niagara Falls/Niagara Falls Reservation	Niagara Falls	NY	29 (1896-1905)	1867-1899; 1919-1920
03330	Niagara Falls post-1905	Niagara Falls	NY	44 (1900-1926)	1905-1928; 1936-1940; 1950
05560	Niagara Falls/Niagara Falls Park System	Niagara Falls	NY	31 (1901-1917)	1912-1919
05420	Oneonta Parks/Oneonata Park System	Oneonta	NY	0	1911
07381	Roosevelt Bird Sanctuary	Oyster Bay	NY	57 (1924-1926)	1924-1926
01111	Brown Square	Rochester	NY	3 (1904)	1904-1909; 1976
01116	Cobbs Hill Reservoir	Rochester	NY	21 (1908-1909)	1908-1910
01115	Durand Eastman Park	Rochester	NY	0	1893; 1908
01101	Franklin Square	Rochester	NY	3 (1894)	1894
01103	Genesee Valley Parkway	Rochester	NY	9 (1890-1892)	1890-1897
01102	Gennesee Valley Park	Rochester	NY	117 (1889-1893; 1908-1912)	1890-1893; 1908-1914
01104	Highland Park	Rochester	NY	112 (1881; 1889-1893; 1908)	1890-1894; 1908-1911; 1919
01105	Jones Square	Rochester	NY	6 (1895-1901)	1895-1901
01106	Lake View Park	Rochester	NY	2 (1897)	1897-1898
01110	Madison Square	Rochester	NY	3 (1904)	1874
01113	Maple Grove Park	Rochester	NY	2 (1904)	1904
01114	Maplewood Park/Seneca Park West	Rochester	NY	0	
12291	Ononto Park	Rochester	NY	0	1890
01119	Parade Grounds/New York State Armory/Convention Hall Triangle	Rochester	NY	1 (1909)	1873 (?); 1911
01107	Plymouth Park	Rochester	NY	7 (1893)	1892-1894
01112	Riley Triangle	Rochester	NY	4 (1894-1908)	1907-1908
07822	Rochester New Reservoir/Honeoye/Honeoye Reservoir	Rochester	NY	1 (1922)	1927
01100	Rochester Parks/Board of Park Commissioners	Rochester	NY	3 (1884-1895)	1888-1894; 1901-1916; 1924
01108	Seneca Park	Rochester	NY	21 (1890-1902)	1890-1902
01117	Warner Tract	Rochester	NY	1 (1908)	1908
01109	Washington Square	Rochester	NY	5 (1910)	1893-1895
03600	Rye Park/Town Park	Rye	NY	1 (1908-1909)	1908-1909
03563	Southampton Park Committee	Southampton	NY	0	1908
06627	Troy Park/Troy City Park	Troy	NY	0	1918
03181	Baggs Square/Bagg Square	Utica	NY	6 (1906-1907)	1906-1907
03186	Erie Canal Abandonment	Utica	NY	1 (1919)	1915-1919; 1927
03182	Jay Street Playground/Utica Park Board	Utica	NY	1 (1910)	1906-1911; 1930; 1936
03185	Proctor, F. T. Park	Utica	NY	16 (1911-1914)	1912-1914; 1979
03323	Proctor, Frederick T.	Utica	NY	0	1907-1910
03091	Roscoe Conkling Park/Valley View Park	Utica	NY	24 (1906-1913)	1906-1908; 1913-1914

Job #	Job Name/Alternative Name	Job Location		Plans	Correspondence
03130	Utica Parkway/Utica Boulevard/Proctor, Thomas R.	Utica	NY	15 (1906-1926)	1906-1914; 1924-1926
03183	Whitesboro Street Playground	Utica	NY	1 (1909)	
00175	Watertown Park	Watertown	NY	173 (1899-1919)	1899-1919; 1924
00212	Cincinnati Ohio Parks	Cincinnati	OH	0	1873-1899; 1915, 1927
07681	Cincinnati Park Department/Park Commission	Cincinnati	OH	0	1894; 1926
00213	Eden Park	Cincinnati	OH	0	1873-1915; 1922
09926	Cleveland Metropolitan Park System	Cleveland	OH	0	1951-1952
01168	Cleveland Ohio Park Commission	Cleveland	OH	0	1883; 1890-1901; 1919; 1939
00187	Cleveland Parks	Cleveland	OH	0	1890-1891
06200	Cuyahoga County Parks/Cuyahoga County Park System	Cleveland	OH	0	1915-1916
05662	Edgewater Park	Cleveland	OH	0	1912
06201	Euclid Creek	Cuyahoga County	OH	0	
06202	Rocky River Parkway/Rocky River Reservation	Cuyahoga County	OH	1 (1915)	1915-1916
06719	Combination Park	Dayton	OH	11 (1917-1919)	
06729	Dayton Fair Grounds Park/Patterson, J.H./Fair Grounds	Dayton	OH	5 (1920)	1898; 1920
03280	Dayton Parks	Dayton	OH	38 (1902-1919)	1899-1902; 1910-1913
03284	Deeds, E. A. - Carillon/Carillon Park/Deeds Park	Dayton	OH	59 (1934-1954)	1939-1946; 1953-1954
09906	General Motors Frigidaire Division	Dayton	OH	124 (1949; 1951-1952)	1951-1966
03281	Idlewild Park	Dayton	OH	0	
03283	McKinley Park/Dayton Parks	Dayton	OH	0	1912
06701	Miami Conservancy District/Riverpoint Park/Miami Conservancy Commission	Dayton	OH	5 (1919)	1919-1922
09979	Oakwood City Recreation Area	Dayton	OH	3 (1953-1954)	1954
06055	Southern Boulevard/Hills and Dales	Dayton	OH	23 (1914-1920)	1914-1921
06969	Sugar Camp/Hills & Dales/NCR/Patterson, J. H.	Dayton	OH	9 (1912-1921)	1921-1922
01440	Van Cleve Park	Dayton	OH	2 (1896)	1896
09519	Wright Brothers Hill/Wright Memorial Park	Dayton	OH	182 (1938-1940)	1938-1948
06767	Harmon Park/Civic Trust of Lebanon, Ohio	Lebanon	OH	5 (1920-1922)	1919-1922; 1961
06902	Mound Builders Fort/Patterson, J. H./Mound Builders' Fort	Montgomery County	OH	2 (1920)	1920-1921
06397	Oakwood Playground/Parrott, Francis	Oakwood	OH	0	1916
05840	Steubensville Ohio Park System	Steubensville	OH	0	1913
07283	Summit County Metropolitan Park Board	Summit County	OH	70 (1925)	1924-1926; 1934-1937; 1965-1974
06668	Campbell Park	Youngstown	OH	0	
09779	Mill Creek Park	Youngstown	OH	586 (1899; 1923-1962)	1919-1920; 1947-1961
06879	Youngstown Park	Youngstown	OH	0	1919-1921

Job #	Job Name/Alternative Name	Job Location		Plans	Correspondence
08234	Mount Hood National Forest		OR	12 (1926-1929)	1924-1932
03650	Public Park	Baker City	OR	0	1909
02641	Hillside Parkway	Portland	OR	1 (1908)	
02640	Portland Parks/Park System	Portland	OR	21 (1897-1909)	1895-1921
02642	Terwilliger Boulevard/Terwilliger Parkway	Portland	OR	2 (1902)	1909
09774	Pennsylvania State Park System		PA	0	1944-1950
06976	Charleston Parks	Charleston	PA	0	1921
05951	Creisheim Creek Parkway	Chestnut Hill	PA	0	1913
06794	Harrisburg City Plan/Market Square/Market Square Association	Harrisburg	PA	51 (1915; 1919-1920)	1920
02270	Carnegie Land Company/Carnegie Steel Co. Ltd	Homestead	PA	12 (1900)	1886-1890; 1898-1900
02068	Carnegie Steel Company Ltd./Library Park and Library Place	Homestead	PA	0	1898-1900
07303	Lancaster Park	Lancaster	PA	0	1924
00121	Fairmount Park	Philadelphia	PA	0	1866-1898
05942	Fairmount Park Extension/Woodward, George	Philadelphia	PA	8 (1914-1929)	1913-1914; 1929
02948	Fairmount Park/Fairmount Park Art Association	Philadelphia	PA	0	1904-1905
03822	League Island Park/Southern Blvd., Inc	Philadelphia	PA	77 (1912-1921)	1912-1925; 1968-1974
03824	Northeast Boulevard	Philadelphia	PA	30 (1910-1913)	1910-1915; 1920
06955	Pastorius Park Extension	Philadelphia	PA	14 (1916-1921)	1921-1922
02939	Philadelphia Park System	Philadelphia	PA	0	1895; 1904-1905
03820	Philadelphia Parks/Philadelphia Pennsylvania	Philadelphia	PA	0	1909-1916
03826	South Broad Street Boulevard/League Island	Philadelphia	PA	60 (1910-1915)	1915
03825	Washington Square	Philadelphia	PA	6 (1913)	1912-1913
00102	Willow Grove	Philadelphia	PA	0	
00126	Wissahickon Drive	Philadelphia	PA	0	1868-1873
03461	Arsenal Park	Pittsburgh	PA	0	1908
03465	Frick Park	Pittsburgh	PA	2 (1931)	1931
03460	Pittsburgh Pennsylvania Parks	Pittsburgh	PA	0	1892
00021	Public Square/Punxsutawney Iron Company	Punxsutawney	PA	8 (1901-1902)	1900-1905
02247	Punxsutawney Iron Company	Punxsutawney	PA	1 (1900)	1903
07605	Pendora Park	Reading	PA	11 (1923-1926)	1926
07570	Scranton Park/Scranton Playground	Scranton	PA	0	1925
05386	Sharon Park	Sharon	PA	0	1911
09612	Drake Park	Titusville	PA	7 (1940-1941)	1940-1941
06935	Kirby Park, (F. M.)	Wilkes-Barre	PA	270 (1916-1924)	1921-1927; 1936
09156	Market Street Bridge	Wilkes-Barre	PA	16 (1919-1929)	1929
09502	River Common	Wilkes-Barre	PA	4 (1939)	1936-1940
07578	Weiser, Conrad Park	Womelsdorf	PA	18 (1925-1927)	1925-1926

Cross section and perspective of culvert parapets and auto guard rail, Acadia National Park, June 1933. Job #9138 – Acadia National Park (Mount Desert Isle, ME).

Job #	Job Name/Alternative Name	Job Location		Plans	Correspondence
09308	Trent Avenue Steps	Wyomissing	PA	1 (1932)	1932
06947	Wyomissing Park	Wyomissing	PA	1 (1921)	1921
03253	Codorus Creek	York	PA	5 (1894-1907)	
03255	Farquahar Park	York	PA	2 (1903-1906)	
03254	Old Reservoir Site	York	PA	2 (1907)	
03256	Penn Park	York	PA	1 (1898)	
06320	York Recreation Grounds	York	PA	0	1915-1917
03252	York/Codorus Creek/York City Plan/ Farquhar Park	York	PA	3 (1906-1907)	1907-1909; 1915-1919
09628	Narragansett Bay Forts (general)	Narragansett Bay	RI	0	1941
01211	Easton's Beach	Newport	RI	1 (1883)	1883-1887
01821	Leamington Beach/Harborview Playgrnd/ Harbor View	Newport	RI	3 (1897)	1896-1897
01822	Mall, The	Newport	RI	3 (1895)	
06775	Miantonomi Memorial Park/Memorial Park at Miantonomi Hill	Newport	RI	1 (1921)	1919-1921; 1929
01823	Morton Park	Newport	RI	5 (1894-1896)	1894-1896; 1955-1956
01826	Newport Market Square	Newport	RI	0	1914-1915
01820	Newport Parks/Mall 22/Morton Pk 23/Leamington Beach 21/Newport Improvement Association	Newport	RI	0	1894-1897; 1912

Job #	Job Name/Alternative Name	Job Location		Plans	Correspondence
01210	Newport Rhode Island Parks	Newport	RI	0	1894; 1925
01059	Pawtucket Park	Pawtucket	RI	49 (1888)	1888-1889
06510	Pawtucket Parks/Pawtucket Park System	Pawtucket	RI	0	1917
06512	Peoples Park	Pawtucket	RI	30 (1921)	1921-1924
06511	Slater Park	Pawtucket	RI	11 (1917)	1917
07277	U.S. Finishing Company	Pawtucket	RI	51 (1924)	1924
03506	Barrington Boulevard/Barrington Parkway	Providence	RI	10 (1910-1921)	1911; 1920-1921
02601	Blackstone Boulevard Parkway	Providence	RI	8 (1903-1904)	1895; 1901-1904
03510	Goddard Memorial Park	Providence	RI	4 (1928)	1928; 1956
03501	Meshanticut Parkway/Providence	Providence	RI	0	
03503	Pleasant Valley Parkway	Providence	RI	0	
03507	Providence City Plan/Providence City Plan Commission	Providence	RI	10 (1884-1914)	1911-1914; 1921; 1938-1947
03500	Providence Metropolitan Park Commission	Providence	RI	15 (1905-1909)	1869; 1905-1913; 1975
02600	Providence Parks/Blackstone Blvd. 2601etc./Providence Park System	Providence	RI	0	1868; 1875; 1889-1905
02603	Roger Williams Park	Providence	RI	4 (1869; 1904)	1869; 1874; 1895; 1904
03505	Ten Mile Reservation	Providence	RI	0	
03504	West River Park	Providence	RI	1 (1908)	
03502	Woonasquatucket Parkway	Providence	RI	0	
06934	Warren Park	Warren	RI	2 (1921)	1921
09129	Beaufort Shores/Christensen Realty Company	Beaufort	SC	0	1928-1929
02324	Battery Park	Charleston	SC	3 (1909-1912)	1873; 1906-1909
02321	Cannon Park	Charleston	SC	5 (1896-1897)	1896-1897
02320	Charleston Parks/Cannon Pk - 2321/ Chicora/So. Carolina Pk 22	Charleston	SC	4 (1918-1938)	1893-1912
02325	Charleston, SC/Special Committee of Council/Development of Waterfront/ Charleston, SC	Charleston	SC	22 (1896-1911)	1908-1911; 1930
02322	Chicora Park	Charleston	SC	48 (1895-1900)	1896-1900
02323	Hampton Park	Charleston	SC	19 (1906-1912)	1899; 1906-1925
09063	Lookout Mountain Park	Chattanooga	TN	4 (1925; 1928-1929)	1928-1929; 1941
09546	Great Smoky Mountains National Park	Gatlinburg	TN	0	1938-1950
02200	Memphis Park System	Memphis	TN	4 (1877-1898)	1898-1901; 1972-1978
07530	Fort Worth Parks/Park System	Fort Worth	TX	0	1925
01120	Garfield Park/Union Pacific Railway Company	Salt Lake City	UT	2 (1886-1887)	1882-1891
05180	Richmond Parks	Richmond	VA	0	1910
12508	Unnamed Parkway	Richmond	VA	1 (1890)	
03680	Washington's Birth Place/George Washington's Birthplace/Wakefield	Wakefield	VA	1 (1926)	1928-1935
09624	Fort Ethan Allen	Burlington	VT	64 (1940-1941)	1941-1942
05495	Green Mountain Parkway	Burlington	VT	16 (1898-1933)	1933-1937
03213	Fairhaven Park	Bellingham	WA	0	1906-1910

Job #	Job Name/Alternative Name	Job Location		Plans	Correspondence
03579	Everett Washington Parks/Everett Park System	Everett	WA	0	1908
02705	Admiral Phelps Park	Seattle	WA	3 (1904)	
02739	Alaska-Yukon Pacific Exposition	Seattle	WA	43 (1906-1910)	1961
02701	City Park	Seattle	WA	0	
02721	Colman Park	Seattle	WA	3 (1910)	1910
02726	Columbia Park	Seattle	WA	0	
02707	Cowen Park	Seattle	WA	7 (1907-1909)	1906-1909
02717	Delmar Park/Green Lake Low Service Reservoir	Seattle	WA	2 (1908)	
02704	Dewey Park	Seattle	WA	0	
02720	Fort Lawton	Seattle	WA	4 (1909-1910)	1908-1911; 1977
02708	Frink Park	Seattle	WA	21 (1906-1912)	1906-1912
02690	Frink Park/Seattle Park System	Seattle	WA	81 (1894; 1901-1911)	1902-1935; 1972-1979
02714	Green Lake Boulevard	Seattle	WA	32 (1907-1912)	1905-1912
02710	Hill Tract Playground/Park in the Hill Tract	Seattle	WA	2 (1907)	1906
02713	Interlaken Boulevard	Seattle	WA	1 (1908)	1908-1909
02725	Jefferson Park	Seattle	WA	6 (1911-1912)	1911-1913
02692	Kinnear Park	Seattle	WA	5 (1909)	
02706	Lake Washington	Seattle	WA	0	
02718	Lake Washington Boulevard	Seattle	WA	1 (1909)	
02700	Leschi Park	Seattle	WA	0	
02691	Lincoln Park	Seattle	WA	9 (1904)	
02703	Madison Park	Seattle	WA	0	
02702	Madrona Park	Seattle	WA	0	1908-1912
02697	Magnolia Bluff	Seattle	WA	0	
02727	McGraw, John H. Monument	Seattle	WA	3 (1919)	1918-1919
02698	Mercer Street Playground/Columbia Road	Seattle	WA	0	1897
02722	Montlake Boulevard	Seattle	WA	2 (1910-1914)	1911
02709	Pendleton Miller Playground	Seattle	WA	3 (1907)	1906
02693	Ravenna Park	Seattle	WA	0	1908-1909
02719	Schmitz Park	Seattle	WA	19 (1909-1912)	1908-1912
08218	Seattle Parks	Seattle	WA	0	
02724	Seward Park	Seattle	WA	4 (1911-1912)	1911-1912; 1925-1927
02695	Volunteer Park	Seattle	WA	12 (1904-1910)	1904-1913; 1970
02711	Washington Park Addition	Seattle	WA	2 (1895; 1907)	
02728	West Seattle Park	Seattle	WA	0	1910; 1922
02723	West Seattle Parkway	Seattle	WA	1 (1911)	1911
02715	West Seattle Playground/Hiawatha Park/ Green Lake Intermediate Service Resevoir	Seattle	WA	11 (1910-1911)	1910-1911
02694	Woodland Park	Seattle	WA	54 (1909-1912)	1907-1912
05790	Sedro-Wooley Washington Park/Sedro Woolley Park	Sedro-Woolley	WA	0	1912
03101	Adams Tract/Adams Park	Spokane	WA	11 (1909-1911)	1908-1911

Cherry trees in Branch Brook Park, part of the Essex County, New Jersey, park system. Job #2121 – Branch Brook Park (listed as Newark, NJ).

Job #	Job Name/Alternative Name	Job Location		Plans	Correspondence
03099	Corbin Park	Spokane	WA	7 (1909)	1908-1910
03100	Down River Parkway/Northwest Boulevard	Spokane	WA	2 (1908)	1908
08040	Lake Coeur d'Alene/Roomey, Francis P.	Spokane	WA	0	1924
03096	Liberty Park	Spokane	WA	12 (1908-1911)	1908-1913
03102	Manito Park	Spokane	WA	0	1909-1910
03095	Spokane Parks	Spokane	WA	14 (1906-1909)	1905-1915; 1931; 1937
04074	Williamson, V. D./Volney/Williamson, Volney	Spokane	WA	1 (1909)	1910-1911
03230	Walla Walla Parks/Walla Walla Park System	Walla Walla	WA	1 (1906)	1906-1907
02716	Alki Point Beach/Seattle Park Commission/ Aiki Point Bathing Beach	West Seattle	WA	7 (1910-1911)	1910-1911; 1925
06270	Kenosha Wisconsin Park Sysyem	Kenosha	WI	0	1915-1916
01653	Lake Park	Milwaukee	WI	37 (1892-1895)	1893-1898; 1974-1980
01655	Lake Shore Drive	Milwaukee	WI	0	1909
01680	Milwaukee Parks	Milwaukee	WI	0	
01670	Milwaukee Parks - Metropolitan Park Commission	Milwaukee	WI	0	
01660	Milwaukee Parks - Metropolitan Park Commission	Milwaukee	WI	0	1890-1893; 1907-1911
01650	Milwaukee Parks/Lake Park/River Park/ West and Westside Parks	Milwaukee	WI	0	1889-1896
01651	River Park	Milwaukee	WI	11 (1891-1895)	1895
01652	West Park	Milwaukee	WI	27 (1892-1894)	1894-1895
01654	West Side Park	Milwaukee	WI	2 (1892)	
02214	West Virginia University	Morgantown	WV	8 (1898-1901)	1899-1908; 1930

CANADA

Job #	Job Name/Alternative Name	Job Location		Plans	Correspondence
09348	British Pacific Properties Ltd./1st Narrows Bridge Approach/Lion's Gate Bridge	Vancouver	BC	29 (1934-1937)	1933-1935; 1941; 1953
04020	Olmsted Park	Winnipeg	MB	3 (1910)	1910
02969	Winnipeg Public Parks Board	Winnipeg	MB	0	1904-1909
06059	Victoria Park	Truro	NS	2 (1901-1914)	1914
06054	Queen Victoria Niagara Falls Park	Niagara Falls	ON	18 (1903-1927)	1887; 1897; 1914-1919; 1927-1928
00643	Montebello Park	Saint Catherine's	ON	8 (1875; 1887)	1887-1891
05000	Montreal City Improvement/Metropolitan Park System	Montreal	QC	1 (1910)	1910-1912
00609	Mount Royal Park	Montreal	QC	100 (1876-1905)	1874-1895; 1903-1908; 1965-1966
02217	Westmount Park	Westmount	QC	0	1899

OTHER COUNTRIES

Job #	Job Name/Alternative Name	Job Location		Plans	Correspondence
09363	Albuoy Point/Corporation of Hamilton		BER	2 (1934)	1934
06785	Public Park/Moenck, M. A. New Orleans, LA	Havana	CUB	0	1919-1920

Bird's eye study for the Pittsburgh Civic Centre, June 1, 1910. Job #3462 – Pittsburgh Civic Commission (Pittsburgh, PA).

Background: Detail of general plan for Manito Park's second addition and Rockwood addition, January 1910. Job #3471 – Spokane Improvement Company (Spokane, WA).

City and Regional Planning and Improvement Projects

Ethan Carr

No aspect of the Olmsted firm's work is more important — and more often overlooked — than its contribution to the history of city and regional planning in the United States. Landscape architecture, as Frederick Law Olmsted and Calvert Vaux first defined the term, was itself a new form of American urbanism. As Lewis Mumford wrote in 1931, "By 1870, less than twenty years after the notion of a public landscape park had been introduced in this country, Olmsted had imaginatively grasped and defined all the related elements in a full park programme and a comprehensive city development."[1] By the 1880s, as the Boston park system was taking shape, the apprentice Charles Eliot was already responding to Olmsted's suggestions of how park planning could extend to the regional scale. Regional planning in the United States subsequently developed from its roots in regional park plans (such as Eliot's metropolitan Boston parks) just as city planning had origins in municipal park design.

City and regional planning demanded legal expertise, statistical analysis and other skills unfamiliar to traditional landscape designers. By the early twentieth century landscape architects were expected to collaborate with engineers, architects, lawyers and others to devise a range of regulatory and design solutions to the problems of urban growth. The 1893 World's Columbian Exposition in Chicago was an influential example of multidisciplinary collaboration, as was the 1901 effort to replan Washington, D.C., for which Frederick Law Olmsted Jr. assumed his father's role.[2] Between 1907 and 1917, a new profession was born as more than one hundred American towns and cities established comprehensive city plans.[3] A full partner in the firm since 1897, Olmsted Jr. was a leading practitioner and, as historian Susan L. Klaus notes, the "chief spokesman of the planning movement during its formative years."[4] In 1910, for example, he was working with the architect Cass Gilbert on a plan for the city of New Haven that utilized extensive data on demographics, tax rolls and industrial trends. The next year he published similar surveys of Pittsburgh and Rochester that also assembled unprecedented statistical information for those cities.[5] In 1909 the Harvard School of Landscape Architecture (begun under Olmsted Jr. in 1900) offered the country's first professional instruction in "City Planning," and in 1917 Olmsted Jr. and the lawyer Flavel Shurtleff founded what became the American Institute of Planners.[6]

By the 1920s city planning necessarily expanded to address entire metropolitan regions, a development presaged by the Olmsted firm's work not only in Boston, but also for clients such as Essex County, New Jersey, beginning in 1898. The first county park system in the country, this regional park plan integrated municipal and county parks and parkways. Olmsted associates of the period, especially Warren Manning, continued and expanded the regional planning ideas of the Olmsted firm, and so the full significance of the firm's city and regional practice is not to be found in this *Master List* alone. Many of the regional and even national park planning projects of the New Deal of the 1930s, for example, were the fruition of ideas that traced their origins back to the Olmsted firm office in Brookline, Massachusetts. It was especially appropriate, then, that Franklin Delano Roosevelt's National Resources Planning Board, which oversaw federal park and resource planning, had as its executive the landscape architect Charles W. Eliot II, Charles Eliot's nephew.

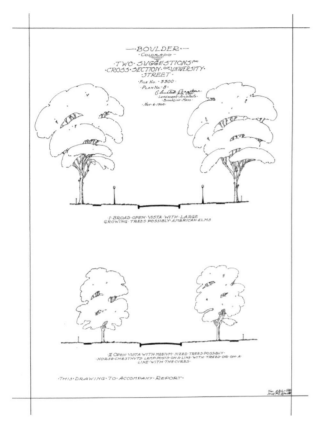

Two suggestions for the cross section of University Street, November 6, 1908. Job #3300 – Boulder Colorado Improvement Association (Boulder, CO).

City and Regional Planning and Improvement Projects

Job #	Job Name/Alternative Name	Job Location		Plans	Correspondence
03812	City Board Regional Planning (General)			0	1905-1931
07091	City Planning Advisory Commission/City Planning Associates			0	1922
00606	Town of West Chester			0	

UNITED STATES

Job #	Job Name/Alternative Name	Job Location		Plans	Correspondence
06877	Birmingham Chamber of Commerce	Birmingham	AL	0	
03541	Birmingham City Plan	Birmingham	AL	0	1908-1913
03913	Corey Land Company	Corey	AL	1 (1909)	1909-1910
06091	Berkeley City Planning Commission	Berkeley	CA	11 (1914-1916)	1914-1915
06090	Berkeley City Planning Committee	Berkeley	CA	0	1915-1917
06092	Berkeley Civic Art Commission	Berkeley	CA	0	1915-1916; 1972
05995	Study for Sloat Boulevard and Corbett Avenue Junction	Berkeley	CA	0	1914-1916
06157	Bath Square	Berkeley Springs	CA	0	
06257	Burlingame City California Garden City/ Garden City Development/Cheney, Charles H.	Burlingame	CA	1 (1915)	1915
08072	Columbia California	Columbia	CA	0	
08010	City of Long Beach/Long Beach Park	Long Beach	CA	0	1922-1924; 1933
05372	City Plan Commission	Los Angeles	CA	0	1910-1914; 1926-1928
05354	Dominguez Estate/Torrance/Dominiquez Estate Company	Los Angeles	CA	21 (1910-1912)	1910-1938; 1974
05374	East Side Organization	Los Angeles	CA	0	1923
08103	Los Angeles City and County Parkway/ Los Angeles County and City Park System	Los Angeles	CA	63 (1893-1933)	1929-1930
08100	Los Angeles County - General	Los Angeles	CA	75 (1901; 1910-1928)	1926-1960
08022	Monterey Peninsula Regional Plan	Monterey	CA	5 (1923-1930)	1923
03370	San Diego Chamber of Commerce/San Diego Art Association	San Diego	CA	2 (1911)	1889-1895; 1902; 1907-1913
06467	San Jose City Plan	San Jose	CA	0	1916
08034	Santa Barbara	Santa Barbara	CA	0	
08031	Santa Barbara Plaza/De La Guerra Plaza	Santa Barbara	CA	19 (1923-1924)	1924
08028	Town Planning/Santa Barbara, City of	Santa Barbara	CA	145 (1898-1924)	1923-1925
08267	Kings River Canyon/Sequoia National Forest/Kings River Canyon Region	Sequoia National Forest	CA	20 (1921-1933)	1933-1947
03300	Boulder Colorado Improvement Association/City of Boulder Improvement Association	Boulder	CO	31 (1906-1924)	1907-1931
03301	Seventeenth Street Subway	Boulder	CO	0	
03302	Boulder Creek and Vicinity	Boulder Creek	CO	0	1919-1924

Job #	Job Name/Alternative Name	Job Location		Plans	Correspondence
05052	Colorado Springs City Plan	Colorado Springs	CO	0	1910
05600	Denver City Plan	Denver	CO	0	1906-1921
03480	Denver Colorado Civic Center	Denver	CO	0	
00699	Bridgeport City Plan	Bridgeport	CT	11 (1912-1914)	1884-1890; 1912-1915
00820	Hartford City Plan	Hartford	CT	0	1898; 1942
06144	Milford Civic Center	Milford	CT	0	1915
03352	New Haven/Commission on Improvement of the City	New Haven	CT	14 (1907-1909; 1922)	1908-1924; 1931
01000	New London Connecticut	New London	CT	0	1884
03112	Waterbury Common	Waterbury	CT	0	1906
02821	Commissioners (Street System)/District of Columbia	Washington	DC	48 (1894-1902)	1891-1904
02844	U. S. Department of Agriculture/City of Washington	Washington	DC	91 (1904-1931)	1922-1935
02836	Washington Consultative Board	Washington	DC	0	1905-1908; 1918
07648	Daytona Beach City Planning/City Plan Commission	Daytona	FL	0	1926
07398	Daytona River Front Improvement/City River Front Inprovement	Daytona	FL	1 (1925)	1924-1925
06724	Triple Cities Chamber of Commerce	Daytona/D. Beach/ Seabreez	FL	1 (1912)	1919-1923
10588	Knight Foundation Highway Beautification Design	Fort Lauderdale	FL	14 (1959-1977)	1977
06998	Lakeland City Plan/Lakeland Chamber of Commerce	Lakeland	FL	1 (1918)	1921-1923
07879	Lake Wales City Plan	Mountain Lake	FL	32 (1925-1931)	1931
06360	Saint Augustine/City Plan Board	Saint Augustine	FL	2 (1912-1916)	1915-1916; 1970
06010	Saint Petersburg City Plan/Saint Petersburg Florida	Saint Petersburg	FL	0	1914-1921
05903	Saint Petersburg Florida City Plan	Saint Petersburg	FL	0	
07942	Tallahassee City Plan	Tallahassee	FL	0	1928; 1975
05360	Tampa Civic Association	Tampa	FL	0	1911
07021	West Palm Beach City Plan	West Palm Beach	FL	0	1922
07625	Winter Haven Subdivision/City Plan	Winter Haven	FL	2 (1921)	1926
06834	Winter Park Florida Board of Trade	Winter Park	FL	0	1920; 1936
02746	Atlanta City Plan	Atlanta	GA	1 (1921)	1912; 1920-1921
06545	Cartersville Improvement	Cartersville	GA	0	1917
03713	Des Moines Women's Club - The City Plan	Des Moines	IA	0	1909
05497	Boise Board of Education/Board Of Education School Park	Boise	ID	0	1911
05934	Alton/Board of Trade	Alton	IL	0	1913
06381	Bloomington and Normal City Plan/ Bloomington Civic League and City Plan	Bloomington and Normal	IL	0	1916
01907	Drexel Boulevard	Chicago	IL	0	1869-1875; 1893
05979	Freeport City Plan	Freeport	IL	0	1914
07151	Hinsdale City Plan	Hinsdale	IL	0	1923

Job #	Job Name/Alternative Name	Job Location		Plans	Correspondence
06626	Joliet Association of Commerce	Joliet	IL	0	1918
06837	Rock Island City Planning Commisssion	Rock Island	IL	0	1920
02946	Evansville	Evansville	IN	0	1904
05053	Richmond City Plan	Richmond	IN	0	1910
07289	Valparaiso City Plan	Valparaiso	IN	0	1924
05443	Kansas City Plan	Kansas City	KS	0	1911
05524	Wichita City Plan	Wichita	KS	0	1913; 1920
04075	Anchorage Town Plan	Anchorage	KY	4 (1915)	1910-1919
06772	Lexington City Planning Survey	Lexington	KY	0	1919-1923
06931	Baton Rouge City Plan	Baton Rouge	LA	0	1921
07688	Monroe and West Monroe City Plan	Monroe	LA	0	1926
10676	MBTA Red Line Extension from Davis Square to Alewife Brook		MA	0	1978
00067	Amherst Improvement Association - South Green	Amherst	MA	3 (1874)	1870; 1901; 1917
02284	Andover, Town of	Andover	MA	1 (1901)	1901
09340	North Main Street Improvement	Attleboro	MA	0	1933
04008	Becket Town Improvement/Harris, N. W.	Becket	MA	0	1910
03496	Auburndale Improvement Society	Boston	MA	0	1908
02897	Beacon Street Tree Planting/ Metropolitan Improvement League	Boston	MA	3 (1902-1910)	1900-1915
06062	Boston City Planning Board	Boston	MA	0	1914-1915
00970	Boston City Planning Board	Boston	MA	0	1942-1945
00943	Boston Transit Commission	Boston	MA	16 (1895)	1891-1897
00960	Copley Square	Boston	MA	4 (1891)	1893-1897; 1912-1913; 1934; 1943-1944
01556	Metropolitan Planning Board	Boston	MA	0	1922-1925
10201	Beacon Street Improvements	Brookline	MA	31 (1953; 1966-1967)	1966-1967
01301	Boylston Street Widening	Brookline	MA	19 (1882-1896)	1891-1901
09371	Brookline Cooperative Civic Progress Association/School Street Improvement	Brookline	MA	1 (1935)	1935
12042	Brookline Streets	Brookline	MA	1 (1894)	1884; 1891; 1895-1896
01310	Brookline Town Planning Board	Brookline	MA	3 (1915-1920)	1894-1896; 1913-1943
01304	Brookline Village Square/Brookline Village	Brookline	MA	4 (1894-1895)	1904-1905
01311	Brookline Water Board/Brookline Reservoir	Brookline	MA	11 (1938-1939)	1899; 1938-1940
01078	Chestnut Hill Ave. Widening	Brookline	MA	40 (1886-1891)	1891-1892
09603	Cambridge Housing Authority/ Cambridge Housing Project/Project Number Mass. 3-1	Cambridge	MA	119 (1940-1959)	1940-1943; 1956-1961
05342	East Walpole Town Plan	East Walpole	MA	0	1911
07025	Town of Framingham Street Survey	Framingham	MA	0	1922
10082	Haverhill Municipal Parking Lot	Haverhill	MA	0	

Job #	Job Name/Alternative Name	Job Location		Plans	Correspondence
09717	Hingham Planning Board	Hingham	MA	0	1945-1946
02365	City Plan for Improvement	Holyoke	MA	0	1907-1915
05935	Lenox Village Improvement Society/ Village Improvement Association	Lenox	MA	21 (1907-1914)	1888; 1913-1914
03434	Longmeadow Street Improvement Association	Longmeadow	MA	0	1908
04061	Beach Street	Manchester	MA	0	
00272	Manchester, Town of	Manchester	MA	1 (1906)	
05552	Civic Improvement/Women's Club	Melrose	MA	0	1894; 1912
09476	Town of Milton - Property south of Houghton's Pond	Milton	MA	15 (1946-1947)	1893; 1936
06985	Mount Hope Finishing Company	North Dighton	MA	193 (1922-1944)	1921-1934; 1944-1946
03940	Norwood City Plan	Norwood	MA	0	1895-1898; 1939
05872	Oxford Village Improvement	Oxford	MA	9 (1913-1914)	1913-1915
03918	City Improvement	Salem	MA	0	
06030	Town of Southbridge/Southbridge, Massachusetts/Wells, A. B.	Southbridge	MA	0	1914
09890	Committee to Beautify Springfield	Springfield	MA	0	1950-1951
05120	Springfield Planning Commission/ Springfield City Plan	Springfield	MA	74 (1914-1926)	1911-1974
05929	Stockbridge Village Improvement/Laurel Hill Association/Town Improvement	Stockbridge	MA	14 (1913-1918)	1913-1917
06130	Improvement of Taunton/Planning Board	Taunton	MA	0	1915
01782	Central Square	Waltham	MA	0	1913
01780	Waltham Parks	Waltham	MA	0	1894-1896
10608	Noanett Parking Lot	Wellesley	MA	0	1976-1977
10607	River Street Parking Lot	Wellesley	MA	0	1977
02371	Wellesley Town Planning Board	Wellesley	MA	19 (1929-1931)	1889; 1897; 1929-1931
10686	Civic Beautification Committee	Winchester	MA	0	1893-1899; 1979
09787	Maryland State Planning Board		MD	0	1945-1947
02410	Baltimore Fire, 1904/Baltimore Pk. System/Burnt District (Waterfront)	Baltimore	MD	7 (1904)	1904
02389	Bouton, E. H./Roland Park/Bouton, Edward H.	Baltimore	MD	19 (1902-1905)	1904-1905; [1915]
02433	City Plan Commission (1910)	Baltimore	MD	0	
02420	Howard Street Extension/Baltimore Improv./Municipal Art Society (City Plan)	Baltimore	MD	75 (1905-1910; 1926)	1905-1921; 1939; 1947
10058	Patapsco Tunnel Project	Baltimore	MD	1672 (1954-1958)	1954-1959
09696	Towson Area/Goucher College Neighborhood Plan	Baltimore	MD	33 (1931-1946)	1945-1948
06954	Cumberland City Plan	Cumberland	MD	0	1921
09970	Maryland National Capitol Park & Planning Commission/Rock Creek Park	MD-Wash. Reg. Dist.	MD	2084 (1922-1968)	1879; 1954-1975
03561	Pikesville Maryland Improvement Association	Pikesville	MD	0	1908
00183	Whitehall Maryland	Whitehall	MD	0	

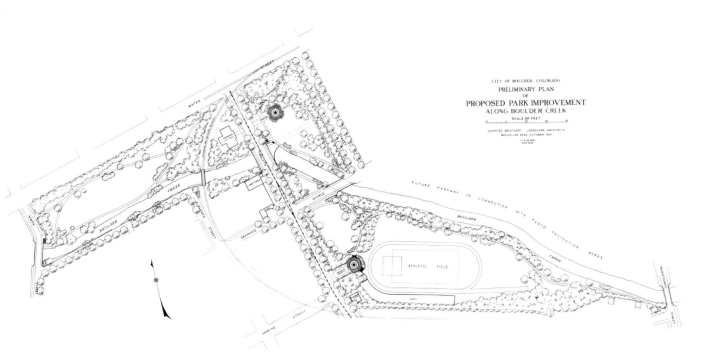

Preliminary plan of proposed park improvement along Boulder Creek, October 1923. Job #3300 – Boulder Colorado Improvement Association (Boulder, CO).

Job #	Job Name/Alternative Name	Job Location		Plans	Correspondence
07246	City of Auburn - Park, Pettingill and Gully Tract/Auburn Park Project	Auburn	ME	0	1923
10078	Camden Shipyard Development	Camden	ME	53 (1958-1959)	1958-1959; 1968-1969
07989	Northeast Harbor Village Improvement Assoc./Northeast Harbor Park Project	Northeast Harbor	ME	12 (1927-1928)	1928-1930
01865	City Plan	Portland	ME	0	1913; 1941-1942
09229	Rockport Harbor Improvement/Rockport Shore Improvement	Rockport	ME	138 (1930-1948)	1930-1977
06558	Waterville City Plan	Waterville	ME	0	1917
03629	Ann Arbor Michigan Improvement/ Huron River Improvement/Ann Arbor City Plan	Ann Arbor	MI	54 (1905-1921)	1914-1922; 1938
00662	Detroit Chamber of Commerce/Palmer Park/Metropolitan Park Commission	Detroit	MI	11 (1904-1905)	1905-1907; 1915
06043	Detroit City Plan and Improvement Commission/Scott Memorial Fountain Commission	Detroit	MI	0	1913-1919
00664	Detroit City Plan Commission	Detroit	MI	0	1919
06067	Lincoln Highway Association	Detroit	MI	0	1914-1915
03450	Grand Rapids/Comprehensive City Plan Commission	Grand Rapids	MI	1 (1906)	1908; 1920-1923
06375	City Plan	Lansing	MI	0	1916
03665	Wayne Michigan/Huron River	Wayne	MI	4 (1908-1914)	1914
03048	Huron River Improvement/Geddes Power Plant/R.W. Hemphill/Huron River Development	Ypsilanti	MI	31 (1905-1916)	1905-1916; 1925

Job #	Job Name/Alternative Name	Job Location		Plans	Correspondence
03623	Ypsilanti City Report/Huron River/ Ypsilanti City Plan	Ypsilanti	MI	1 (1913)	1912-1917
05620	City Plan	Minneapolis	MN	0	1906-1921
07005	City Plan	Rochester	MN	0	1922
06793	Saint Paul City Planning Board	Saint Paul	MN	0	1920
10195	Southeastern Development Corporation	Hattiesburg	MS	0	1965
05457	Billings Montana City Plan	Billings	MT	0	1911-1912
06953	Helena City Plan	Helena	MT	0	1921-1923
06480	Asheville City Plan	Asheville	NC	0	1916
06464	Charlotte City Plan, Charlotte Chamber of Commerce	Charlotte	NC	0	1916
06494	Greensboro City Plan, Greensboro Chamber of Commerce	Greensboro	NC	0	1917
05783	Street Improvements/Southport North Carolina/White, H. K.	Southport	NC	0	1912
03676	Southern Assembly	Waynesville	NC	5 (1910)	1910-1911
06667	Winston-Salem City Plan	Winston-Salem	NC	0	1919
05220	Lincoln City Plan	Lincoln	NE	0	1911-1912
05511	Omaha City Plan	Omaha	NE	0	1912
02598	Nelson New Hampshire	Nelson	NH	0	1939-1940
10680	Portsmouth Industrial Park Extension	Portsmouth	NH	0	1978-1980
03726	Grover Cleveland Memorial Road	Tamworth	NH	0	1909
02633	Asbury Park/Asbury Beach	Asbury	NJ	1 (1893; 1903)	1902-1904
03999	Jersey City Improvement Association	Jersey City	NJ	0	1910-1911
03459	Municipal Art Commission	Montclair	NJ	0	1908-1910
03431	Madison, Borough of/Madison Civic Association	Morris County	NJ	1 (1895)	1908
04097	Newark City Plan	Newark	NJ	0	1910-1911
06756	Village of South Orange/Planning Commission	South Orange	NJ	0	1919
05974	Spring Lake/City Plan	Spring Lake	NJ	0	1914
12052	Summit New Jersey Village Improvement Society	Summit	NJ	0	1882; 1886
05437	Lakewood City Development Plan	Trenton	NJ	0	1911
01187	Trenton City Plan	Trenton	NJ	0	1891-1892; 1911-1914; 1925-1926
05551	Santa Fe	Santa Fe	NM	1 (1912)	1912-1913
12092	Westchester County/23-24 Wards Westchester County		NY	61 (1873-1877)	1860-1878
00708	Improvement of Batavia Street	Buffalo	NY	1 (N.D.)	
00711	North Street Circle	Buffalo	NY	4 (1874)	
03453	City of Elmira Chamber of Commerce	Elmira	NY	0	1908
07200	Garden City, City Plan for Long Island	Long Island	NY	0	1923
07751	Greenhaven/Subdivision	Mamaroneck	NY	0	1926
00531	Borough of Bronx	New York City	NY	0	1908-1910

Job #	Job Name/Alternative Name	Job Location		Plans	Correspondence
12102	Brooklyn Street Plans	New York City	NY	0	1868; 1892
12112	Manhattan Street System	New York City	NY	0	
00521	New York City Improvement Commission	New York City	NY	0	1892; 1905-1908; 1911; 1921
00536	New York Regional Plan	New York City	NY	113 (1922-1924)	1929-1931
00522	Queens Borough	New York City	NY	7 (1905-1922)	1888; 1905; 1910-1913
06425	Riverdale	New York City	NY	0	1916
00536a	Sage Foundation/Rockefeller Property	New York City	NY	14 (1922)	1921-1929
12062	Staten Island Improvement Commission	New York City	NY	0	1866-1868; 1870-1888
03701	West Side Improvement Society	Oswego	NY	0	1909
09375	Lattingtown Village Improvements	Oyster Bay	NY	2 (1931; 1935)	1935; 1940
06120	Rome City Plan	Rome	NY	0	1914
07295	Scarsdale Village Plan	Scarsdale	NY	0	1924
03435	Schenectady Chamber of Commerce	Schenectady	NY	0	1908
06501	Tarrytown Village Improvement	Tarrytown	NY	0	1917
03180	Utica City Improvement	Utica	NY	14 (1810-1925)	1906-1919
05879	Westchester County	Westchester County	NY	0	1913; 1931
05348	Cincinnati Chamber of Commerce/City Plan Project	Cincinnati	OH	0	1911
05667	Cleveland Superior Viaduct/Superior Viaduct	Cleveland	OH	35 (1912-1915)	1912-1915
06520	Columbus City Plan	Columbus	OH	0	1917
06370	Moraine Industrial Village/Industrial Community/Moraine Village	Dayton	OH	25 (1915-1919)	1916-1919
06385	Patterson, Miss Dorothy - tract, 7 houses, grounds	Dayton	OH	0	1916-1917
06782	Schafer Boulevard Extension (J. H. Patterson)	Dayton	OH	0	1921
06421	Mansfield Ohio City Plan, City Planning Commission	Mansfield	OH	0	1916
06748	Nowata Chamber of Commerce	Nowata	OK	0	1919
03958	Tulsa Civic Improvement Committee/Tulsa Commercial Club	Tulsa	OK	0	1910
06597	Bethlehem City/Bethlehem Park System/Boroughs of Bethlehem	Bethlehem City	PA	3 (1912-1917)	1917
06416	Butler City Improvement/Butler Chamber of Commerce	Butler	PA	0	1916
06912	Chester City Plan	Chester	PA	0	1921
05700	Easton Pennsylvania City Plan	Easton	PA	0	1912
05823	Conneautee Brotherhood Civic Committee	Edinboro	PA	0	1913
05484	Erie City Planning Committee, Erie Chamber of Commerce	Erie	PA	0	1912; 1916
06148	Huntington City Plan, Chamber of Commerce	Huntington	PA	0	1915

Job #	Job Name/Alternative Name	Job Location		Plans	Correspondence
05269	Johnstown Civic Improvement/City Planning Commission	Johnstown	PA	0	1911-1916
03821	Commission for City Plan	Philadelphia	PA	0	
06702	Philadelphia Main Line Citizens Association/Main Line District/Main Line Communities/Philadelphia	Philadelphia	PA	14 (1919)	1919-1929
03463	Department of City Planning, Pittsburgh	Pittsburgh	PA	0	1910-1912
05256	Edgeworth, Borough of Pittsburgh	Pittsburgh	PA	0	1911
06063	Pittsburgh Art Commission/Institute of Architects Competition	Pittsburgh	PA	0	1914
03464	Pittsburgh Citizens Committee on City Plans/Citizens Committee on City Plan of Pittsburgh	Pittsburgh	PA	1 (1924)	1924
03462	Pittsburgh Civic Commission	Pittsburgh	PA	32 (1906; 1910-1911)	1898-1899; 1907-1921
03920	Scranton City Improvement Association	Scranton	PA	0	1910
04056	Warren Civic Improvement League	Warren	PA	0	1910
06681	Williamsport City Plan	Williamsport	PA	0	1914-1919
07008	Borough of Wyomissing/Trent Avenue	Wyomissing	PA	6 (1921-1922)	1921-1922
07228	Esmond Mills	Esmond	RI	21 (1923)	1923-1924
01824	Newport Improvement Association	Newport	RI	53 (1897-1914)	1883; 1895-1896; 1912-1919
01827	Touro Street Widening	Newport	RI	0	
07868	City of Pawtucket	Pawtucket	RI	0	1927
03508	Area between Capitol and Station	Providence	RI	0	
02610	Providence Rhode Island	Providence	RI	0	
03511	Report on City Planning/Providence Chamber of Commerce	Providence	RI	0	1943-1945
09323	South Kingston Park/Saugatucket Park	Wakefield	RI	11 (1909; 1932-1935)	1932-1935
00093	Woonsocket/Fortnightly Club	Woonsocket	RI	6 (1900)	1900-1904; 1919
06247	Beaufort South Carolina Improvement	Beaufort	SC	0	1915
02326	Charleston City Planning/City Plan	Charleston	SC	0	1931-1940
06975	Spartansburg City Plan	Spartansburg	SC	0	1921
05917	Sioux Falls/City Improvement	Sioux Falls	SD	0	1913
03808	Chattanooga City Plan & Parks	Chattanooga	TN	0	1909-1910; 1922
09904	Green Acres Shopping Center	Kingsport	TN	35 (1951-1955)	1951-1957
06486	Knoxville Board of Commerce City Improvement	Knoxville	TN	0	1916-1917
02201	Memphis Chamber of Commerce City Plan/City Planning Commission	Memphis	TN	0	1899; 1920
03533	Fort Worth City Plan	Fort Worth	TX	0	1906-1908; 1922
05740	San Antonio Texas/Civic Improvement	San Antonio	TX	0	1912
00184	Arlington Virginia	Arlington	VA	0	1865-1871
04089	Fort Monroe	Fort Monroe	VA	0	1910
05952	Newport News Chamber of Commerce	Newport News	VA	0	1913
06750	Norfolk City Planning	Norfolk	VA	0	1919
03240	City of Richmond/Richmond City Plan	Richmond	VA	0	1906-1907

Job #	Job Name/Alternative Name	Job Location		Plans	Correspondence
06747	Winchester City Plans	Winchester	VA	0	1894; 1919
05482	Burlington City Plan	Burlington	VT	0	1912
05932	Village Improvement Society/Thetford	Thetford	VT	0	1913
03743	Aberdeen Improvement Association	Aberdeen	WA	0	1909
03735	Everett Improvement Company	Everett	WA	5 (1907-1909)	1909
02712	City of Seattle, Improvement of/City Planning Commission	Seattle	WA	0	1907-1911
03097	East Latah Parkway	Spokane	WA	0	1908-1909
03357	Spokane and Washington Improvement Company	Spokane	WA	0	1907
03107	Spokane City Plan Committee	Spokane	WA	0	1918-1920
03471	Spokane Improvement Company/White, A. L. & Associates/Manito Park/Rockwood	Spokane	WA	14 (1908-1910)	1908-1910; 1937
03098	Summit Boulevard	Spokane	WA	0	1908
12082	Tacoma Land Co. (city plan)/Takoma Land Company	Tacoma	WA	0	1873
07384	Kohler Village/Kohler, WI/Town of Kohler	Kohler	WI	743 (1920-1949)	1913; 1924-1954
01656	Milwaukee City Plan	Milwaukee	WI	7 (1922)	1921-1922
07216	Oshkosh City Plan	Oshkosh	WI	0	1923; 1930-1939
06496	Racine City Plan	Racine	WI	0	1917
06762	Fitzpatrick, Campbell, Brown and Davis	Huntington	WV	0	1919

CANADA

Job #	Job Name/Alternative Name	Job Location		Plans	Correspondence
03952	Bridgeland/Addition, Calgary/Doupe, J. Lonsdale/Bridgeland Addition	Calgary	AB	5 (1910)	1909-1910
05525	Calgary Alberta City Planning Commission	Calgary	AB	0	1912
06286	Tuxedo Town Plan	Tuxedo	MB	0	
04096	South Winnipeg/Heubach Indust. Village/Heubach's Industrial Village	Winnipeg	MB	5 (1905-1911)	1910-1913
06311	Winnipeg City Plan	Winnipeg	MB	0	
05451	Halifax City Improvement/City Plan Civic Improvement League	Halifax	NS	0	1912
06676	London Chamber of Commerce	London	ON	0	1919-1921
05070	Ottawa City Plan	Ottawa	ON	0	1913-1914
05680	Toronto Water Front	Toronto	ON	19 (1912)	1902; 1912
12032	Cote St. Antoine	Montreal	QC	0	1891
06239	Shawinigan Water & Power Company/Shawinigan Falls	Shawinigan	QC	15 (1915-1916)	1915-1916

OTHER COUNTRIES

Job #	Job Name/Alternative Name	Job Location		Plans	Correspondence
07163	Argentine Republic	Buenos Aires	ARG	0	1923
02935	Manila, Improvement of/Manila City Plan	Manila	PHI	0	1901-1904; 1925
00436	Manila Phillipine Island Improvement/Municipal Improvement	Manila	PHI	0	1902

House in Forest Hills Gardens, 1914. Job #3586 – Sage Foundation -
Forest Hills (Forest Hills, NY).

Background: Detail of bird's eye view of Forest Hills Gardens, 1910. Job #3586 – Sage
Foundation - Forest Hills (Forest Hills, NY).

Subdivisions and Suburban Communities

Susan L. Klaus

"No great town can long exist without great suburbs," wrote Frederick Law Olmsted in 1868. At the time Olmsted and his then partner Calvert Vaux were designing Riverside, a 1600-acre suburb of Chicago. The suburban and town planning work of Olmsted and his sons clearly demonstrates the full range of social, economic and environmental concerns that their designs addressed. More than 475 proposals for or inquiries about subdivisions and suburban communities had a job number assigned to them by the Olmsted firm. These projects varied greatly in the degree of the firm's involvement, with many showing no activity beyond initial correspondence. It is estimated that one or more plans were prepared for only 370 of these projects. The undertakings in this category also varied greatly in scale, from the modest estate of a single landowner seeking to subdivide his holdings, to a twenty-five square mile area on the Palos Verdes peninsula near Los Angeles.

While much of the subdivision work took place in the northeast, the firm was active across the country and in Canada, particularly in cities in which it would have been familiar to clients through its work on urban parks and regional or state park systems. The 1890s and the first decade of the twentieth century were a time of growing activity in this field for the firm. By the 1920s, when suburban America was growing at twice the rate of its central cities, the design of residential communities represented a significant portion of the firm's overall business. After World War II, the number of such projects dwindled.

Frederick Law Olmsted's suburban work reflected his romanticized nineteenth century view that a suburb, if well planned, would combine the charm of the country with the convenience of the city. It would provide "the most soundly wholesome forms of domestic life," and demonstrate "the best application of the arts of civilization to which mankind has yet attained."[1] The planning work of his sons reflected an early twentieth century confidence that technology and the expertise of planners, administrators and design professionals could be harnessed to shape well-ordered, functional communities. Suburbs, Frederick Law Olmsted Jr. held, required the kind of professional planning heretofore only seen in urban design and large-scale landscapes like Central Park. It was crucial to apply the emerging science of city planning to these suburban additions.

As with their park plans and other landscape designs, there is no formulaic "Olmsted style" that can be associated with residential communities: each plan is sensitive to its locale and topography. The articulation of boundaries; differentiation of street width according to type of traffic; provision of common spaces and other amenities that enhance the character of a place and encourage social interaction; and use of deed restrictions to enforce maintenance and preserve architectural and other community standards are hallmarks of the firm's suburban work that continue to influence suburban design today.

The Olmsteds believed the residential suburb was deserving of the best efforts of planning and design professionals. In this complex cooperative enterprise, it is the comprehensive master plan, as Olmsted Jr. stated, that is key to creating "harmonious, beautiful and convenient residential communities."[2]

View of the Uplands subdivision in Victoria, BC, date unknown. Job #3276 – The Uplands (Victoria, BC, Canada).

Right: Portion of general plan of Riverside by Olmsted, Vaux & Co., Landscape Architects, 1869. Job #607 – Riverside (Riverside, IL).

GENERAL PLAN
OF
RIVERSIDE

OLMSTED, VAUX & CO. LANDSCAPE ARCHITECTS
1869.

Scale 400 feet to an inch.

Chicago Lithographing Co. Chicago.

Subdivisions and Suburban Communities

Job #	Job Name/Alternative Name	Job Location		Plans	Correspondence
		UNITED STATES			
03073	Birmingham Realty Company	Birmingham	AL	6 (1905-1907)	1905-1908
07837	Montgomery Subdivision/Board of Education/Baldwin Property	Montgomery	AL	9 (1927-1928)	1927-1929
09478	Park Hills/McDuffie Subdivision	Berkeley	CA	18 (1937-1939)	1937-1940
05658	Westgate Park Land Company/Mason-McDuffie/St. Francis Wood	Berkeley	CA	350 (1912-1917)	1913-1937
08036	Benmar Hills/Southern California Corporation	Burbank	CA	122 (1918-1924)	1923-1943
08205	Nutting, E.M./Laughlin Park Height	Hollywood	CA	5 (1927-1928)	1928
08201	Hobart Estate/Subdivision	Lake Tahoe	CA	7 (1926-1928)	1926-1928
08259	Rancho Los Alamitos Mesa/Bixby Mesa/Bryant Bixby Subdivision	Long Beach	CA	28 (1923-1936)	1929-1936
08001	Bear Lake Subdivision	Los Angeles	CA	0	1922
05219	Beverly-Arnaz Land Company	Los Angeles	CA	0	1939-1940
08084	Clark, Walter G./Meade Tract	Los Angeles	CA	9 (1924)	1926-1928; 1933
08000	Edwin Jones subdivision near Los Angeles	Los Angeles	CA	0	1922
08268	Hillside Gardens	Los Angeles	CA	1 (1933)	1933
08274	Imperial Western Tract/Leimert, W. H./Westmore Park Tract	Los Angeles	CA	7 (1937-1938)	1937-1938
05491	Los Angeles Investment Company	Los Angeles	CA	0	1911-1912
08265	McNulty, J. A.	Los Angeles	CA	3 (1932)	1933-1934
08002	Pacific Palisades/Pacific Palisades Association	Los Angeles	CA	104 (1922-1924)	1922-1929; 1973
08271	Monterey Terrace Homes Gardens	Monterey	CA	0	1933-1935
05945	Lake Shore Highlands/Wickham Havens/Sather Tract/Leimert, Walter H.	Oakland	CA	274 (1906-1922)	1913-1923
05950	Palos Verdes/Palos Verdes Syndicate	Palos Verdes	CA	385 (1909-1933)	1913-1948; 1962-1963
08045	Alta San Raphael Co.	Pasadena	CA	27 (1924-1926)	1924-1935
08066	Alta San Raphael Co./Mason, W.S.	Pasadena	CA	21 (1926)	1926-1927
08257	Pismo Beach Sales Co.	Pismo Beach	CA	14 (1926-1931)	1933-1935
05260	Lovdal Manor/Wood and Tatum Company	Sacramento	CA	1 (1911)	1911-1919
08050	Galbreath, George W./Shandin Hills	San Bernardino	CA	1 (1925)	1925-1927
01328	Town of Alessandro/Alesandro	San Bernardino	CA	7 (1892-1893)	1892-1896
05352	Marston, G. W./Martston, George W.	San Diego	CA	11 (1911-1913)	1910
06147	Moore, W. M. Subdivision	San Diego	CA	0	1915
08273	Sherman Oaks Subdivision	San Fernando Valley	CA	0	1936
06485	Monterey Boulevard/Westgate Park Company/Residential Development Co.	San Francisco	CA	5 (1916-1917)	1916-1917
06338	San Francisco Exposition Site Subdivision	San Francisco	CA	0	1916
05887	Arlington Heights	Santa Barbara	CA	0	1923
08269	Southern California Homes Gardens	Southgate	CA	0	1933-1934

Job #	Job Name/Alternative Name	Job Location		Plans	Correspondence
08080	West Rancho Aguajito/Subdivision for Duncan McDuffie	West Rancho Aguajito	CA	0	1926
08054	Broadmoor Heights/Dixon Ranch	Colorado Springs	CO	62 (1925-1929)	1925-1930
08053	Broadmoor Polo Club/Penrose, S./Polo Circle/Johnson Tract/	Colorado Springs	CO	22 (1925-1926)	1925-1927
08052	Penrose, Spencer/Portales, Count/ Broadmoor Estates	Colorado Springs	CO	60 (1925-1928)	1925-1969
01091	Lake Wauconda/Douglas County	Perry Park	CO	18 (1889-1891)	1888-1894
06222	Beacon Falls Rubber Shoe Company	Beacon Falls	CT	97 (1915-1917)	1915-1918
07074	Bassick Brothers/Bridgeport Housing Company/Bassick Property	Bridgeport	CT	25 (1916-1922)	1922-1923
09551	Edson Subdivision	Greenwich	CT	0	1938
09462	Rockefeller, Percy A.	Greenwich	CT	210 (1928; 1936-1941)	1936-1949
09463	Rockefeller, W. G.	Greenwich	CT	135 (1924-1949)	1936-1959
09660	Thompson, Raymond B.	Greenwich	CT	10 (1944-1945)	1943-1945
10366	Family Housing, U. S. Navy Submarine Base	Groton	CT	362 (1967; 1971-1972)	1971-1973
06615	Moorland Hill Subdivision	New Britain	CT	25 (1917-1927)	1916-1918; 1925-1927; 1936-1937
06566	Stanley Works - Andrews Subdivision/ Moorland Hill Subdiv./Stanley Works/ Andrews Subdivision	New Britain	CT	21 (1917-1921)	1917-1921
07838	Chester, M. E.	New Haven	CT	4 (1924-1929)	1927-1931
09242	Pine Orchard	Pine Orchard	CT	34 (1929-1931)	1930-1931
10034	Equipment Service Company, Inc	Somers	CT	13 (1927-1959)	1954-1959
07863	Stamford Development/Stamford Development Company	Stamford	CT	1 (1927)	1927-1928
06424	Gladdings, John R.	Thompson	CT	21 (1916-1917)	1916-1917; 1925
07949	Coe, Harry S. Subdivision/Coe, H.S.	Waterbury	CT	3 (1928-1929)	1928-1929; 1937; 1956
06818	Fairmount Subdivision/Chase Companies/ Fairmount	Waterbury	CT	3 (1919)	1920-1921
09065	Goss, E. W./Sherwood, Charles/Country Club Homes, Inc.	Waterbury	CT	53 (1929-1930)	1929-1938
07273	Heminway, H. H. Subdivision/Heminway, Merrit	Watertown	CT	8 (1958-1959)	1924; 1956-1959
06046	Heminway, M. & Sons Silk Company	Watertown	CT	3 (1914)	1914
09072	Watertown Realty Company	Watertown	CT	7 (1929)	1929
09460	Talcott Tract	West Hartford	CT	18 (1932-1937)	1929-1937
07006	Bradley Hills/Subdivision	Washington	DC	0	1921
01341	Chevy Chase Land Company	Washington	DC	7 (1891)	1891-1896
03086	Massachusetts Avenue Syndicate/Plumb, A. H.	Washington	DC	2 (1905)	1905-1906
06102	Homasassa Springs		FL	51 (1940-1942)	1929; 1939-1945
07285	Belleair Devlopment Co.	Belleair Heights	FL	0	1924
07353	Country Club Development Company	Daytona	FL	11 (1925-1928)	1924-1925
07574	Ganymede/Cowie, Gordon R.	Daytona	FL	41 (1925-1926)	1925-1929
07360	Ocean Dunes/C.M. Wilder	Daytona	FL	10 (1924-1925)	1924-1925
06807	Telfair Stockton and Company - Jacksonville Subdivision	Jacksonville	FL	0	1920

Job #	Job Name/Alternative Name	Job Location		Plans	Correspondence
06124	Lake Placid Land Company	Lake Placid	FL	0	1929-1930
07221	Development in Lakeland/Development at Lake Hollingsworth	Lakeland	FL	0	1923
06149	Lake Wales Land Company	Mountain Lake	FL	0	
06081	Mountain Lake Corporation/Lake Wales Land Co./Blanchard, D.	Mountain Lake	FL	791 (1910-1938)	1907; 1913-1966
06166	Mountain Lake Groves/Ekal Groves, Inc.	Mountain Lake	FL	7 (1932)	1932-1940
06020	Ruth, F. S. and Company	Mountain Lake	FL	0	
07210	Oldsmar Land and Development Company	Oldsmar	FL	0	1923
07472	Geneva Peninsula/Press Foundation/Press City/East Coast Finance Corporation/H.S. Kelsey	Orlando	FL	16 (1926)	1925-1942; 1951-1952
07563	Royal Palm Beach Company/Lindsley, Henry D./Clewiston	Palm Beach	FL	5 (1925)	1925-1926
07573	The Tropical/Florida Development Company	Poinciana	FL	0	1925
06781	Kelsey City/Palm Beach Harbor Land Company/East Coast Finance Corporation/Harry S. Kelsey	West Palm Beach	FL	47 (1919-1926)	1919-1920; 1925; 1928
06495	Fulton Bag and Cotton Mill Subdivision	Atlanta	GA	0	1917
00071	Kirkwood Land Company/Druid Hills	Atlanta	GA	43 (1892-1905)	1890-1908; 1931; 1975-1976
04054	Rivers Realty Company	Atlanta	GA	0	1910
06049	Subdivision near Atlanta Georgia/Moore, Wilmer L.	Atlanta	GA	0	1914
06301	DeRenne, W. J./Poplar Grove Subdiv.	Savannah	GA	4 (1897; 1913-1916)	1915-1916
06044	Gordon Estate Subdivision	Savannah	GA	0	1914
05874	O'Grady Subdivision	Sioux City	IA	0	1913
00607	Riverside	Riverside	IL	3 (1869)	1868-1882; 1931; 1964-1978
09486	Hudson, Hugh	Frankfort	KY	7 (1937)	1937
09838	Baquie, Gordon	Glenview	KY	34 (1947-1956	1949-1956
10038	Brown, George Garvin Subdivision	Harrods Creek	KY	9 (1956)	1956
05789	McReynolds and Radford	Hopkinsville	KY	0	1912
07020	Dumesnil & Rowland	Jefferson County	KY	3 (1922-1923)	1922
03054	Kentucky Title Company	Jefferson County	KY	1 (1905)	1905
04084	Jefferson Heights Land Company/McFerran, John B.	Jeffersontown	KY	8 (1910)	1910-1912
03005	Aylesford Land Company/Desha Breckenridge - Aylesford	Lexington	KY	2 (1904-1905)	1904-1906
03141	McDowell, Judge Henry C./Ashland/Breckinridge, Desha/subdivsion of estate "Ashland"	Lexington	KY	40 (1906-1917)	1906-1909; 1917
05956	Altscheler, Brent Subdivision/Altsheler, Brent	Louisville	KY	0	1914
03565	Audubon Park/Hunt, Bridgeford & Company	Louisville	KY	0	1908
09598	Clark Subdivision/Clarke Homestead	Louisville	KY	3 (1939-1940)	1940
07750	Consolidated Realty Company/Bernheim Subdivision/Hieatt, C.C.	Louisville	KY	3 (1927)	1926-1927

Job #	Job Name/Alternative Name	Job Location		Plans	Correspondence
07037	Consolidated Realty Company/Consolidated Realty/Deible Tract	Louisville	KY	2 (1925-1927)	1925
09734	Eline, A. J.	Louisville	KY	14 (1940; 1946)	1946-1947
03811	Fehr, Frank Subdivision/Fehr, Frank/Hillcrest/Braeview	Louisville	KY	21 (1905-1924)	1909-1912; 1924-1926
06882	Ford, Ben - Louisville Subdivision/Wakefield-Davis Realty Company/Bishop, Harry estate subdivision	Louisville	KY	0	1920-1921
08224	Henning, Julia D.	Louisville	KY	4 (1929)	1929
07449	Indian Hills Development Company	Louisville	KY	58 (1914-1926)	1925-1927; 1949-1953; 1961-1962
09511	Iroquois Gardens	Louisville	KY	11 (1937)	1937-1939
07746	Lee Callahan Subdivision	Louisville	KY	0	1926
05808	Meddis, S. J. Subdivision	Louisville	KY	0	1912
07892	Norbourne Estates/Ford, Ben O.	Louisville	KY	2 (1926-1927)	1927
07520	Perkins, Harry S./Lowry Watkins Company	Louisville	KY	2 (1926)	1925-1928
06490	Sackett, F. M. Subdivision/Otis & Bruce	Louisville	KY	0	1916-1919
09593	Speed, William S. Subdivision	Louisville	KY	29 (1939-1940)	1939-1940; 1945; 1954
03225	Starks, John P.	Louisville	KY	31 (1907-1939)	1906-1907; 1936-1939
07026	Wakefield-Davis Realty Company - Bishop Property	Louisville	KY	2 (1922)	1922
07192	Wakefield-Davis Realty Company/Louisville University	Louisville	KY	0	1923
07076	Wakefield-Davis Realty Company/Subdivision Land between Bonnycastle and Garlach Avenues	Louisville	KY	0	1922
07071	Wheeler Auction Corporation/Subdivision Arterburn Tract - Shelby Rd	Louisville	KY	3 (1922)	1922
07069	Wheeler Realty Company/Kaelin Tract/Kaelin Tract Subdivision/Bardston Road	Louisville	KY	14 (1922-1923)	1922-1923
07070	Wheeler Realty Company/subdivision Quarry Lot	Louisville	KY	0	1922-1923
10056	Harmony Land Company Subdivision	Prospect	KY	29 (1955-1957)	1953-1959
05385	Veech, James N. Subdivision/Indian Hills Subdivision/Jefferson County Subdivision	Saint Matthews	KY	9 (1914-1915)	1911-1915
09585	Wakefield Realty Company		LA	0	
10386	Bellows Farm Subdivision/Yankee Construction	Acton	MA	3 (1971-1972)	1972-1975
10423	Pine Hill Apartments/Yankee Construction	Acton	MA	2 (1971-1972)	1896; 1972
07016	Belmont Springs	Belmont	MA	0	
09384	Connolly, Gregory P. II Subdivision/Regency Park Connolly Subdivision	Beverly Farms	MA	13 (1935-1936)	1935-1939
	* See also Chestnut Hill	Boston	MA		
00942	Boston Building Association	Boston	MA	2 (1894)	1894
09898	Boston Housing/FHA (TC)	Boston	MA	89 (1951-1952)	1951-1952
05265	Forest Hills Cottages/Boston Dwelling House Company	Boston	MA	16 (1908-1912)	1911-1912
10283	One Eighty Beacon Apartments	Boston	MA	0	1968-1978

Job #	Job Name/Alternative Name	Job Location		Plans	Correspondence
09563	Roxbury Housing Project	Boston	MA	15 (1939-1940)	1937-1949
01138	West End Land Co.	Boston	MA	5 (1889-1890)	1886-1890
09889	Brockton Housing	Brockton	MA	30 (1950-1951; 1953)	1950-1954
09831	Brockton Housing	Brockton	MA	43 (1948-1949; 1957)	1948-1951
	* See also Chestnut Hill	Brookline	MA		
10068	Aspinwall Avenue Housing Project	Brookline	MA	0	1894; 1957
00622	Aspinwall Hill/Aspinwall, Thomas	Brookline	MA	30 (1880-1881)	1880-1886
10104	Brookline Housing	Brookline	MA	108 (1959-1962)	1958-1963
09823	Brookline Housing Authority	Brookline	MA	45 (1948-1950)	1948-1951
09822	Brookline Housing/Egmont St. Project	Brookline	MA	42 (1947-1950)	1948-1951
01321	Brookline Land Company/Chandler, Alfred D.	Brookline	MA	3 (1894)	1882; 1888; 1894-1895
01074	Chandler, A. D. et al.	Brookline	MA	3 (1894)	1887-1894
06323	Cliffside/White, Francis/Olmsted, J.C. Estate	Brookline	MA	599 (1914-1918; 1959)	1916-1917; 1959
09999	Gardner, G. Peabody	Brookline	MA	16 (1954-1955)	1947-1955; 1977-1979
01012	Goddard Land Co./Brookline Hill	Brookline	MA	74 (1884-1889)	1884-1894
05556	Heath Estates/Lyman Estate Subdiv.	Brookline	MA	98 (1945-1957)	1955-1959; 1978
07608	Hillfields/Boyd-Nichols-Morrison/Nichols, Morrison & Boyd/Hillfields Subdivision	Brookline	MA	119 (1926-1938)	1926-1938
01806	Livermore-Nickerson Estate/Nickerson-Livermore/Livermore - Wickerson Estate	Brookline	MA	9 (1895)	1892-1896
09702	Lowell Tract/Clark, Paul, and Thomas Chaflin	Brookline	MA	55 (1945-1946)	1945-1962
10023	Park Terrace Apartments	Brookline	MA	1 (1955)	1955
06057	Pierce, J. W./Goddard Estate	Brookline	MA	6 (1884-1914)	1914
10173	Regent Apartments	Brookline	MA	6 (1964)	1962-1964
01057	Reservoir Lane Lands	Brookline	MA	10 (1888-1889)	1901-1905
01145	Stokes, A. P./Philbrick Estate	Brookline	MA	30 (1956-1957)	1889; 1956-1960
03675	Stone, Galen L.	Brookline	MA	14 (1909-1910)	1909-1912; 1979
07310	Stone, Galen L. Subdivision	Brookline	MA	2 (1924)	1924-1925; 1931; 1978
09068	Wright, George H. Dr./Faulkner/Wright, George	Brookline	MA	1 (1929)	1929
12506	Brewster, William	Cambridge	MA	9 (1887)	1885
09876	Cambridge Housing	Cambridge	MA	223 (1950-1956)	1950-1957
09825	Cambridge Housing - Rindge Avenue Vets	Cambridge	MA	7 (1948-1951)	1948-1951
10377	Chauncy Street Apartments	Cambridge	MA	10 (1971)	1971
10581	Continental Gardens	Cambridge	MA	0	1976
07036	Dresser Estate Subdivision/Garden St. Trust/Morrison, Alvah	Cambridge	MA	28 (1922)	1922-1925
07797	Kirkland Trust Company	Cambridge	MA	1 (1927)	1927
07286	Morrisson, Alvah/Coolidge Hill/Gerry's Landing Association/Coolidge Hill Associates	Cambridge	MA	27 (1924-1931)	1897-1898; 1921-1931

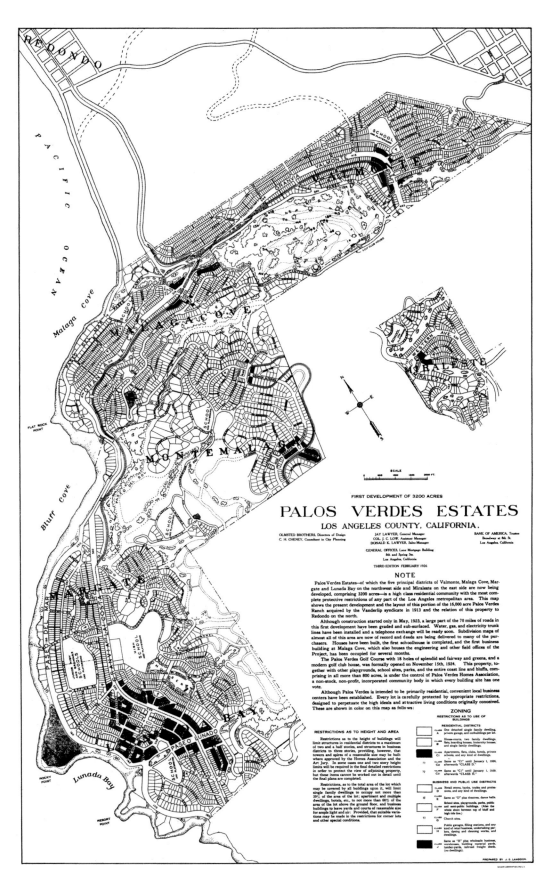

Plan of the first development of 3200 acres, Palos Verdes Estates, February 1926.
Job #5950 – Palos Verdes (Palos Verdes, CA).

Job #	Job Name/Alternative Name	Job Location		Plans	Correspondence
10396	Rindge I & Rindge II/Wasserman Development Corporation	Cambridge	MA	7 (1972)	
10382	Rindge III	Cambridge	MA	36 (1970-1973)	1972
12023	Shady Hill/Norton, Charles E.	Cambridge	MA	0	1866-1869
09803	Veterans Permanent Housing Sites	Cambridge	MA	33 (1947-1948)	1948
09713	Walcott, Charles F.	Cambridge	MA	19 (1944-1949)	1945-1951
07641	Eustis, A. H. & F. A./Scraggy Neck Company	Cataumet Harbor	MA	83 (1926-1930)	1926-1932; 1953
09374	Chestnut Hill Golf Club Subdivision	Chestnut Hill	MA	0	1935
07469	Oyster Harbor/Norris, F.W./Oyster Harbors	Cotuit	MA	18 (1925)	1925-1931
10371	Dalton Apartments	Dalton	MA	4 (1971)	1971
06227	Vanderpool, E. N. Mrs./Vanderpool, John H.	Dartmouth	MA	1 (1912)	1915
09639	Harper, R. H.- Subdivision/Watchuett Farm	East Longmeadow	MA	0	1941
06197	East Springfield Homes Building Company/ East Springfield Home Builders Company	East Springfield	MA	1 (1915)	1915
07602	Waquoit Land Trust/Jericho Development/ Beach, William E./Subdivision Waguoit Land Trust	Falmouth	MA	20 (1926)	1926-1932
10692	Chapel Hill Apartments	Framingham	MA	0	1978-1979
10378	Cherry Hill Housing	Gloucester	MA	14 (1958; 1968; 1971)	1971
09687	Downs, T. F. Subdivision	Hampden	MA	18 (1913; 1944-1949)	1944-1945
01051	Brewer, J. R./Planter's Hill/World's End	Hingham	MA	14 (1880-1886)	1886-1891; 1967-1970
09988	Redwood Acres	Hyannisport	MA	11 (1953-1954)	1953-1955
10463	Rolling Hills Subdivision/Wasserman Development Corporation	Lenox	MA	31 (1973-1974)	1973
10361	Heritage Gardens	Leominster	MA	3 (1970-1973)	1971-1973
10065	Perlstein Subdivision	Leominster	MA	2 (1951; 1957)	1957
09730	Bond, Raymond	Lexington	MA	13 (1946)	1946
09706	Higgins, E. W. Subdivision	Lexington	MA	23 (1945)	1940-1945
09479	Cooley Estate	Longmeadow	MA	2 (1937)	1937
06489	Hornblower - Atkins Subdivision/Juniper Hill/Hornblower, Henry/Greenough Juniper Hill Subdivision	Longmeadow	MA	121 (1916-1955)	1917; 1927-1963
07798	Munson Subdivision/Glen Arden/Glen Arden Subdivision	Longmeadow	MA	513 (1927-1948)	1927-1952
10154	Pearson Subdivision	Longmeadow	MA	4 (1954; 1962-1963)	1962-1963
01123	Linwood/Tapley Estate/Tapley, Philip P.	Lynn	MA	13 (1875-1889)	1889-1891; 1918
10567	Granada Highlands	Malden	MA	32 (1969-1976)	1976
00273	Lane, G. M./Dana, Richard H. Estate/Lane, Gardiner M.	Manchester	MA	63 (1902-1913)	1902-1916; 1922; 1947
01149	Marblehead Road/Crowninshield, B. W.	Marblehead	MA	4 (1890)	1882; 1890-1891
09459	Piney Points Estates	Marion	MA	9 (1924; 1936)	1936-1938
09841	Methuen Housing/Metheun Housing Project	Methuen	MA	2 (1949)	1949
09829	Milford Housing/Housing Projects	Milford	MA	52 (1948-1949)	1948-1951
09859	Millbury Housing	Millbury	MA	23 (1949-1954)	1949-1954
09635	Forbes Estate	Milton	MA	45 (1938-1941)	1939-1946

Job #	Job Name/Alternative Name	Job Location		Plans	Correspondence
12033	Needham Hundred	Needham	MA	0	1870; 1873
	* See also Chestnut Hill	Newton	MA		
07946	Annawan Realty Corporation	Newton	MA	3 (1928)	1928-1932
10492	Florence Street Town Houses	Newton	MA	24 (1973-1974)	1974
01365	Newton Boulevard Syn.	Newton	MA	21 (1893-1898)	1891-1899
01062	Newton Poor Farm	Newton	MA	3 (1890-1891)	1890-1897
06799	Tavern Land Company/Stevens, Nathaniel Subdivision	North Andover	MA	120 (1919-1922)	1920-1934; 1941
10015	Batchelder, George L., Jr. (Subdivision)/ Phillips, J. C./Moraine Farm	North Beverly	MA	31 (1948-1961)	1955-1958; 1963-1968
10184	Graves-Crane Development	Pittsfield	MA	20 (1959-1972)	1964-1972
09846	Faxon, Robert - Adams Street Tract	Quincy	MA	13 (1930-1945)	1936-1958
03361	Ellwanger & Barry	Rochester	MA	1 (1908)	1907-1913
10367	Rockland Place	Rockland	MA	39 (1969-1972)	1971-1974
10604	Scott's Glen Condominiums	Shirley	MA	0	1977
07088	Skinner, Joseph	South Hadley	MA	3 (1922)	1922
07427	Ames Heill Realty/Gordon Property Subdivision/Gordon Property - Ames Hill	Springfield	MA	7 (1925)	1925-1930
09191	Anderson, Richard B./Bradford, E. S./South Branch/Bradford Property	Springfield	MA	5 (1929-1930)	1930; 1945
02955	Atwater Estate/Atwater, George M., Estate/Lewis C. Hyde	Springfield	MA	5 (1904)	1866; 1904
12043	Bowles, Walker and Greenleaf	Springfield	MA	0	1872-1873
09039	Burbank, D. E. - Bliss Road Tract	Springfield	MA	87 (1929-1962)	1929; 1941-1964
09642	Christie, W. L./Hugh Property	Springfield	MA	6 (1930-1941)	1941-1945
07402	Colony Hills Extension	Springfield	MA	0	1925
06928	Colony Hills/Parsons Real Estate Dev.	Springfield	MA	178 (1921-1930)	1921-1930
09099	Homelands Indian Orchard Company/ Indian Orchard Company/Homelands	Springfield	MA	43 (1929-1930)	1929-1931; 1939; 1942
09650	Springfield Housing - FPHA	Springfield	MA	75 (1942-1943)	1943-1944
01053	Swampscott Land Trust	Swampscott	MA	16 (1884-1889)	1888-1901; 1925; 1928; 1968
09885	Taunton Housing (Federal)	Taunton	MA	44 (1951; 1953)	1949-1953
09855	Waltham Housing/Lexington St	Waltham	MA	42 (1950-1956)	1950-1951
09818	Waltham Housing/Prospect Hill Project	Waltham	MA	84 (1935-1949)	1948-1951
09877	Watertown Housing	Watertown	MA	150 (1934-1953)	1950-1959
09832	Watertown Housing	Watertown	MA	55 (1948-1951)	1949-1960
06840	Uplands, The	Wellesley Hills	MA	19 (1911-1928)	1920-1923; 1928
09746	Tatham Realty Assoc. Inc/Wyldwood Acres.	West Springfield	MA	0	1946-1947
07059	West Springfield Development Company	West Springfield	MA	4 (1912-1922)	1922
10278	Woodland Terrace Apartments	Westfield	MA	4 (1969)	1969
07657	Acoaxet Realty Company/Hawes, R. K./ Cockeast Acres Subdivision	Westport	MA	25 (1925-1926)	1926-1928
07033	Dowse, W. B. H. - Subdivision/Dowse, W. B. H.	Wianno	MA	7 (1916-1922)	1922-1926; 1949
09834	Winthrop Housing	Winthrop	MA	30 (1948-1949)	1948-1949

Job #	Job Name/Alternative Name	Job Location		Plans	Correspondence
09833	Winthrop Housing	Winthrop	MA	38 (1949)	1948-1950
09824	Woburn Housing	Woburn	MA	133 (1948-1949)	1948-1950
07758	Carpenter's Point	Baltimore	MD	2 (1926)	1926-1931
07576	Garrett, John W./Kernewood/Kernwood/ Subdivision on Cold Spring Lane	Baltimore	MD	18 (1922-1926)	1925-1926; 1944-1945
03551	Garrett, Robert	Baltimore	MD	3 (1908)	1908
06922	Gibson Island Development	Baltimore	MD	57 (1918; 1921-1924)	1920-1936; 1950
00068	Gordon, Douglas H./Normandie Heights/ Springdale	Baltimore	MD	6 (1902)	1902
03391	Guilford Park Company/Roland Pk/Abell Estate	Baltimore	MD	506 (1893; 1904-1916; 1942; 1950)	1907-1908
07766	Hahn Subdivision/Hahn, William A.	Baltimore	MD	13 (1894-1928)	1925-1930
07229	Homeland/Perine Tract/Perine Tract Subdivision/Bouton, Edward H.	Baltimore	MD	42 (1922-1927)	1923-1930; 1963-1965
09033	Idlewylde Cityco Realty Company	Baltimore	MD	7 (1926-1928)	1928-1929
02210	Roland Park/Bouton, E.H./Roland Park Company	Baltimore	MD	27 (1897-1914)	1897-1923; 1967-1971; 1978
01054	Sudbrook Land Co.	Baltimore	MD	18 (1889)	1887-1891; 1976
07593	Severnside/Chapman, Norvell P.	Boone	MD	1 (1925)	1925-1927
07550	Belgrade Lakes Project	Belgrade Lakes	ME	0	1925-1926
09465	Bok, Mrs./Lyndonwood/Curtis, Cyrus Estate/Zimbalist	Rockport	ME	21 (1936-1956)	1936-1956
03063	Cooksey Estate/Cooksey, Linda Dows/Hoe, Richard M.	Seal Harbor	ME	0	1905
09738	Young Orchard Company	Sorrento	ME	13 (1945-1947)	1946-1947; 1953; 1972-1973
09669	South Portland - Broadview Park/South Portland Project	South Portland	ME	18 (1943-1944)	1944
09670	South Portland - Longcreek Terrace	South Portland	ME	30 (1944)	1944
06196	Barton Hills Maintenance Corporation/ Barton Farm(s) Subdiv./Tower Farm/Boston Farm/Huron Farm Company	Ann Arbor	MI	92 (1916-1928)	1915-1928; 1975
09575	Bonisteel Field/Bonisteel, Roscoe O.	Ann Arbor	MI	2 (1928; 1938)	1937-1939
07152	Carr, L. D. et al. Subdivision/Ann Arbor Hills Company	Ann Arbor	MI	13 (1923-1924)	1922-1925
03622	Carr, L. D./Glendale (TC)/Glendale on the Parkway	Ann Arbor	MI	1 (1912)	1912-1916
03620	Felch Farm/Felch Farms/Huron Farms Company	Ann Arbor	MI	1 (1911-1912)	1911-1912
06491	Goulding and Buel/Geddes Avenue Syndicate	Ann Arbor	MI	0	1916-1917
07528	Huron Farms, "Blake Farm"/Huron Farms Company/South Side of River	Ann Arbor	MI	6 (1925-1927)	1925-1927
07529	Huron Farms, "Keedle Farm"/Wiedman/ Perkins/Cullinene Farm/Wiedman Culinene Perkins and Keedle Farm/North Side of River	Ann Arbor	MI	9 (1925-1926)	1925-1926
06909	John Sperry Subdivision	Ann Arbor	MI	0	1920-1921
07707	Speechley Farm/Tremmel, C.J. & Co.	Ann Arbor	MI	3 (1927)	1926-1927
06622	Stoner-Inglis Subdivision	Ann Arbor	MI	0	1917-1918

Job #	Job Name/Alternative Name	Job Location		Plans	Correspondence
03624	Woodmansee Tract/Huron Farm Company	Ann Arbor	MI	2 (1912-1913)	1913
01368	Log Cabin Farm Company/Palmer, T. W.	Detroit	MI	11 (1893-1895)	1893-1897
07823	Pleasant Lake Hills Corporation/Pleasant Lake Hills	Detroit	MI	1 (1927)	1927
10029	Homestyle Center Foundation Inc.	Grand Rapids	MI	14 (1955-1956)	1956-1957
06536	Grosse Point Twp. Imp. Co. Subdivision/ Grosse Pointe Township/Improvement Company	Grosse Point	MI	16 (1917)	1917-1918
03666	Sibley Subdivision/Huron River	Sibley	MI	0	1914
07330	Trenton Channel Plant/Detroit Edison Co./ Huron Farms Company/Land Across from Grosse Isle	Trenton	MI	28 (1924)	1924
03664	Geddes Power Plant/Edison Farm/Huron River/Detroit Edison Company	Ypsilanti	MI	22 (1905-1925)	1913; 1918; 1924-1925
03621	Milan Village	Ypsilanti	MI	2 (1911-1912)	1911-1913
05109	Dilworth/Latta, W. D.	Charlotte	NC	17 (1911-1913)	1911-1915
10031	Whalehead Club	Corolla	NC	172 (1949-1956)	1947; 1954-1971
07541	Jones, Southgate and Associates	Durham	NC	0	1925
01772	Tufts, J. W.	Pinehurst	NC	13 (1895)	1895-1896; 1973-1980
07086	Sawyer, James C.	Durham	NH	6 (1921-1923)	1922-1923
10479	Brickyard Mountain Condominiums	Laconia	NH	21 (1973-1974)	1973-1974
05839	McElwain, M. H. Company	Manchester	NH	0	1913
06585	Public Building Administration/Defense Housing Project	Manchester	NH	6 (1939-1941)	
12053	Lake Sunapee Resort	Sunapee	NH	0	1887; 1920-1921
03691	Subdivision at North Atlantic City/Atlantic Realty Contract Company	Atlantic City	NJ	0	1909
12063	Potter, Howard and Brown, Lewis B.	Elberon	NJ	0	1865-1868
07011	Board of Chosen Freeholders	Essex County	NJ	0	1922-1923
03753	Wright, Solomon Jr. Land Subdivision	Montclair	NJ	9 (1909-1911)	1909-1911; 1922; 1928
02226	Kahn & Wertheim	Morristown	NJ	7 (1898-1899)	1899
01179	Morristown Land Co.	Morristown	NJ	14 (1891-1892)	1891-1893
06903	White, Joseph J. - Whitesbog Development	New Lisbon	NJ	0	1920-1921
03340	Ocean City/Ocean City Land Scheme/ Ocean City Gardens	Ocean City	NJ	8 (1903-1907)	1907-1917
07182	Mali Estate	Plainfield	NJ	5 (1929)	1929; 1935
07897	Day, Joseph P.	Short Hills	NJ	10 (1928-1936)	1928-1929; 1936
12073	Pitcher, James R.	Short Hills	NJ	0	1890-1891
01170	Cadwalader Estate/Hill, Edmund C./ Cadwalader Heights	Trenton	NJ	18 (1890-1910)	1869; 1890-1892; 1905-1907; 1912
01185	Delaware River Improvement	Trenton	NJ	9 (1910-1911)	1911-1913
04080	Park Place Land Company	Trenton	NJ	0	1910
12093	Hyde Park Land Syndicate	Buffalo	NY	0	1888
00713	Parkside	Buffalo	NY	28 (N.D.)	1863-1893
01035	Rumsey, B. L. et al./Villa Land/Villa Park Land Company	Buffalo	NY	31 (1886-1887)	1870-1892

Granvia La Costa at Malaga Park, Palos Verdes Estates, date unknown. Job #5950 – Palos Verdes (Palos Verdes, CA).

Job #	Job Name/Alternative Name	Job Location		Plans	Correspondence
09594	Lindsay, Lady/Centre Island	Center Island	NY	20 (1939-1940)	1939-1940
07615	Harrimore National Real Estate Corporation/ Harmon National Real Estate Corporation	Chatham	NY	0	1926
12103	Chautauqua Point/Fair Point	Chautauqua	NY	0	1875-1876; 1878; 1880
07339	Turnbull Heights Inc./Turnball/Turnbull, B. E. & J. B./Turnbull Heights	Deerfield	NY	37 (1924-1928)	1924-1929
01290	Depew Land Company/Depew Improvement Company	Depew	NY	43 (1892-1894)	1892-1898; 1979
07251	Jackson Heights - #2/Jackson Heights Apartments - No. 2	Elmhurst	NY	0	1923; 1974-1975
07142	Jackson Heights Gardens/Queensboro Corporation/Jackson Heights Apartments - Elmhurst	Elmhurst	NY	41 (1922-1923)	1922-1923; 1974
07332	Fisher Island Club/Fisher Island Coporation	Fishers Island	NY	1140 (1882; 1911; 1924-1937)	1924-1977
06915	Flushing Country Club Land Company	Flushing	NY	1 (1921)	1921
07489	Cord-Meyer "Bayside"/Cord Mayer Development Company/Bayside	Forest Hills	NY	4 (1912; 1924)	1925

Job #	Job Name/Alternative Name	Job Location		Plans	Correspondence
07027	Cord-Meyer Development Company	Forest Hills	NY	31 (1922)	1922-1927
05102	Cord-Meyer Development Company	Forest Hills	NY	2 (1906-1911)	1911-1913
07467	Cord-Meyer Development Company/Arbor Close	Forest Hills	NY	11 (1924-1925)	1925
09144	Cord-Meyer Development Company/Forest Hill Apartments	Forest Hills	NY	2 (1929)	1929-1930
06617	Gardens Apartments Inc./Earle & Calhoun/ The Gardens Apartment	Forest Hills	NY	4 (1917)	1917-1919
03586	Sage Foundation - Forest Hills/Sage, Group II - XXXIII/Wilkes, N.R./Russell Sage Foundation	Forest Hills	NY	621 (1909-1939)	1908-1924
06842	Davis, Walter W./Avalon/Davis, W.W./ Avalon Subdivision	Great Neck	NY	5 (1874; 1920-1924)	1920-1924
06562	Great Neck Hills Subdivision/Wychwood, near RR stat./Davis, W.W.	Great Neck	NY	97 (1914-1924)	1917-1924; 1935
03804	Villa Park Association/McKnight Realty Company	Great Neck	NY	0	1909
12113	Unnamed Subdivision	Hastings	NY	0	1870-1891
12123	Field, Cyrus W., et al.	Irvington	NY	0	1871-1875
06871	Nicoll Park Subdivision	Islip	NY	8 (1920)	1920
05431	Sage Foundation Homes Company - Jamaica Property	Jamaica	NY	11 (1911)	1911
06575	Holt, Henry	Larchmont	NY	6 (1900-1918)	1917
06594	Kings & Westchester Land Company	Lewisboro	NY	1 (1912)	1917
06580	Cravath Subdivision/Walker & Gillette	Locust Valley	NY	77 (1916-1925)	1919-1922
06041	Matinecock Neighborhood Association	Locust Valley	NY	0	1914
03092	Barnum Island/Davis, L. Shannon	Long Island	NY	1 (1906)	1905-1906
05806	Kew Subdivision/Kew Station	Long Island	NY	0	1912-1913; 1922
03094	Shinnecock Hills/Shinnecock Hills and Peconic Bay Realty	Long Island	NY	10 (1893; 1906-1907)	1895; 1906-1910; 1924; 1939
07435	Munsey Subdivision/NY Museum of Art/Metropolitan Museum of Art/Munsey, Frank A. Estates/Joseph P. Day	Manhasset	NY	79 (1924-1927)	1926-1934
07817	Olwell, Lee E./Turkey Hollow	Millbrook	NY	5 (1927-1928)	1927-1930
12133	Montauk Summer Colony	Montauk	NY	0	1881; 1884
02635	Montauk, Long Island/Benson, Frank S./ Bensen, F.S.	Montauk Point	NY	42 (1897-1904)	1891-1898; 1904; 1961-1975
07278	Vanderlip, F. A./Rockefeller Subdiv.	Mount Pleasant	NY	2 (1924)	1924
07872	Whippoorwill Holding Corporation	New Castle	NY	359 (1928-1929)	1927-1936; 1942
05905	Brookside Park Company/Brookside Land Co. TC/Brookside Land Company/Procter Boulevard/Lynch,Willis & Titus	New Hartford	NY	54 (1908-1915)	1913-1922
07222	Jones, Hugh R. Co./Hoffman Tract/Oxford Heights/Hoffman Tract Subdivision	New Hartford	NY	27 (1924)	1923-1924
07195	Jones, Hugh R.- Cook Tract/Cook Tract/ Cook Property Subdivision/	New Hartford	NY	16 (1923-1924)	1923-1924
07560	Harmon, William Subdivision/Richmond Shores	New York City	NY	12 (1925-1926)	1925-1926

Job #	Job Name/Alternative Name	Job Location		Plans	Correspondence
01018	Olmsted, F. L. and others/Winsor Terrace/Windsor Terrace	New York City	NY	2 (1904)	1870-1875; 1884-1886
00506	Riverdale	New York City	NY	9 (1875-1877)	1894; 1899; 1975-1976
06115	Sheepshead Bay Realty/Sheepshead Bay Realties, Inc.	New York City	NY	3 (1915)	1915
09917	Metropolitan Corporation Subdivision	Northport	NY	8 (1951-1952)	1951-1953
09913	Steers Subdivision	Northport	NY	35 (1947-1952)	1951-1965
09078	Cove Neck Realty Company	Oyster Bay	NY	0	1929
09775	Dennis, John B. Subdivision/Dennis, John B.	Oyster Bay	NY	7 (1947)	1947
07547	Waterside Realty Corporation	Port Washington	NY	0	1925-1926
06591	Indian Head Farms Company Subdivision	Rye	NY	0	1917
09548	Law, Frances Mrs.	Rye	NY	1 (1938)	1938-1939
06259	Strater, Helme	Rye	NY	7 (1915-1916)	1915-1917
05177	Leonard & Minshull/Glenwood Estates	Saranac Lake	NY	16 (1911-1912)	1910-1913; 1923
07794	Hudon Shore Estates Inc./Hall, P.M./Subdivision	Scarborough	NY	0	1927
06423	Sleepy Hollow Country Club	Scarborough	NY	19 (1917)	1916-1921
07247	Vanderlip Subdivision/Scarborough Sub./Shepard/Vanderlip, Frank A./Eliot Shepard Tract	Scarborough	NY	129 (1907-1925)	1923-1925; 1940; 1948-1949
06444	Vanderlip, F. A./Wilson Prop. Subdiv.	Scarborough	NY	26 (1910-1919)	1917-1921; 1937
05816	Vanderlip, Frank A. Subdivision	Scarborough	NY	17 (1913-1916)	1913-1923
09007	Scarsdale Downs	Scarsdale	NY	11 (1928-1929)	1928
7211	Hutchins, C. H./Hutchins Estate	Shrewsbury	NY	5 (1923)	1923
06420	J. S. Clark Subdivision	Southampton	NY	0	1916
00076	Hazard, F. R. Subdivision/Sedgewick Farm	Syracuse	NY	6 (1891; 1893)	1893-1894; 1901
07437	Hills and Company	Syracuse	NY	0	1925
00075	Sedgwick Estate/Sedgewick Farm	Syracuse	NY	5 (1901)	1893; 1901
12143	Tarrytown Heights Land Co.	Tarrytown	NY	0	1870-1884
07473	Tuxedo Club Association	Tuxedo	NY	78 (1916-1929)	1925-1930
05781	Glass Farm Subdivision/Brookside Pk/Lynch and Willis	Utica	NY	6 (1912-1913)	1912-1917
07336	Hart & Best/Curran Farm/Harts Hill Associates/Curran Tract Subdivision	Utica	NY	20 (1924-1925)	1924-1926; 1937
07317	Harts Hill Associates/Hart, Merwin K./Hart's Hill Association	Utica	NY	4 (1908-1924)	1924
07294	Hugh R. Jones Company/Benton Property	Utica	NY	0	1924-1925
06966	Jones, Hugh R. Co./Hugh R. Jones Company/Osborn Tract	Utica	NY	6 (1921)	1921-1923
07387	Jones, Hugh R.- Ridgewood/Benton Property/Benton Tract/Jones, Hugh R. Company	Utica	NY	12 (1925-1931)	1924-1931
05833	Tilden Realty Corporation/Roberts, Harry W./Tilden Realty Company	Utica	NY	126 (1921-1931)	1922-1936; 1946
09040	Hicks Nursery Subdivision/Hicks Nurseries	Westbury	NY	41 (1909; 1929-1937)	1928-1937
07388	Whitney, H. P. Subdivision/Whitney, Harry Payne	Westbury	NY	4 (1899-1925)	1924; 1927
07878	Knollwood Manor, Inc./Subdivision	White Plains	NY	0	1927

Job #	Job Name/Alternative Name	Job Location		Plans	Correspondence
05832	Collins, W. H. Subdivision	Akron	OH	0	1913
05558	Rubicon Subdivision/Beavertown Subdivision/Patterson, J. C./Bevertown Rubicon Heights	Beavertown	OH	3 (1912)	1912; 1933
05805	Ambler Subdivision/Pomerene, Ambler & Pomerene	Canton	OH	0	1912-1913
05953	VanSweringen, O.P. & M.J. Subdivision/ Shaker Heights Subdivision	Cleveland	OH	6 (1916)	1913-1916
02274	Councilman/Pflum & Councilman/ Patterson, J. H./Hills and Dales	Dayton	OH	0	1907-1911
05853	Delco Dell/Delco Company	Dayton	OH	6 (1914)	1913-1917
05963	Dickey, Robert T. Mrs./Dickey, Robert R.	Dayton	OH	3 (1907-1914)	1914-1924
06703	Geo. H. Meade Subdivision	Dayton	OH	0	
03121	Hills & Dales/Patterson Pk/Patterson, J. H./Hills and Dales	Dayton	OH	84 (1906-1921)	1894; 1906-1924; 1958-1960
06846	Huffman, Horace M./Ridgeview Subdivision/Ridgeview	Dayton	OH	3 (1920)	1920
06690	Kettering, C. F. Subdivision/Kettering, C.F.	Dayton	OH	2 (1919)	1919
06180	Moraine Park Subdivision/Deeds, E. A.	Dayton	OH	61 (1915-1920)	1915-1922; 1927
05766	Moraine Station/Patterson, J.H.	Dayton	OH	4 (1912)	1912-1913
00280	National Cash Register/National Cash Register Co.	Dayton	OH	681 (1896-1956)	1896-1922; 1938-1960
00125	Oakwood/Houk, R. T./Oakwood Land Company	Dayton	OH	20 (1896-1912)	1901-1909; 1915-1919
06728	Patterson, J. H. - Apple Street Extension	Dayton	OH	0	
06726	Patterson, J. H. (Item 3 - OBLA PI Cards)	Dayton	OH	4 (1919-1922)	1919-1920
06725	Patterson, J. H. (Item 4 - OBLA PI Cards)	Dayton	OH	10 (1920-1921)	1919-1920
06725	Patterson, J. H./Hills & Dales Boulevard	Dayton	OH	9 (1919)	1919-1920
06727	Patterson, J. H. - Roads East of Hills and Dales	Dayton	OH	0	1919-1922
05258	Rubicon Road Land Subdivision/Rubicon Road Land	Dayton	OH	4 (1904-1911)	1910-1913
06720	Wade Tract/Patterson, J. H./Woodside/ Oakwood Village/Wade Tract Subdivision	Dayton	OH	10 (1919-1920)	1919-1921
05914	Gilpatrick, Ray Miss	Granville	OH	5 (1913)	1913
02942	King, H. W.	Mentor	OH	8 (1904)	1904-1905
06116	Schantz Park/Schantz, Adam	Oakwood	OH	14 (1913-1915)	1915-1916
06213	Ottawa Hills Tract/Close, E.H. Realty Company	Toledo	OH	13 (1916-1917; 1929)	1915-1917; 1929
10026	Beecher, Ward Subdivision	Youngstown	OH	1 (1956)	1945; 1955-1956
09995	Wick, J. L. Jr. Homesite Subdivision	Youngstown	OH	8 (1954-1955)	1954-1955
09817	Wicks Subdivision	Youngstown	OH	27 (1926-1958)	1921; 1948-1958
03417	Hazel Fern Farm/Ladd, W.M./Ladd, Charles E.	Portland	OR	10 (1906-1909)	1907-1909
05527	Irving Park Association	Portland	OR	2 (1910-1912)	1912
03740	Lewis & Wiley/Lewis and Wiley, Inc./ Westover Terrace	Portland	OR	2 (1911)	1909-1912
03413	Vista Avenue/Portland Hts Improv. Assoc./ Port Heights Improvement Club/Vista Avenue and Ford Street	Portland	OR	3 (1907-1908)	1907-1908

Job #	Job Name/Alternative Name	Job Location		Plans	Correspondence
03147	Lower Merion Realty Company/Roberts, T. W.	Cynwyd	PA	0	1906
05817	Lincoln Land Company	Grove City	PA	0	1913
05944	Lincoln Drive/St. Martins Dev./Woodward, George/Lincoln Drive/Houston Estate	Philadelphia	PA	8 (1913-1914)	1913-1915
12153	Murray Hill	Philadelphia	PA	0	1895-1896
05941	Saint Martin's Development/St. Martins Home/Woodward, Dr. George	Philadelphia	PA	22 (1906-1914)	1913-1914
09561	Woodward, George Dr./Group Home Development	Philadelphia	PA	4 (1931-1937)	1937-1939
03202	Woodward, George Dr./Slums	Philadelphia	PA	2 (1906)	1906-1907
06870	Hollidaysburg Development/Fording, Arthur O./Subdivision	Pittsburgh	PA	0	1920
06655	Neville Island - U. S. Housing Project	Pittsburgh	PA	0	1918
06350	Reading Subdivision/Meulenberg, Frederick H.	Reading	PA	0	1916
05970	Wyomissing Hills/Felix, George H.	Reading	PA	0	1914
06354	Sewickley Heights Estate/Tuxedo Land Company	Sewickley	PA	1 (1908)	1916
05338	Squaw Creek Property/Fording, A. O. & R. C. Hall	Squaw Creek	PA	0	1911
00204	Vandergrift/Apollo Iron & Steel Company	Vandergrift	PA	34 (1895-1897)	1895-1898; 1918
07876	McFadden, George H. Estate/Barclay Farm	Villa Nova	PA	3 (1927)	1927-1928
02995	Buch, C. A.	Wayne	PA	1 (1904)	1904
09453	Bok, Edward Mrs./Lyndon/Curtis Estate	Wyncote	PA	221 (1935-1940)	1936-1956
09307	Wyomissing Twin Group Dwellings	Wyomissing	PA	1 (1932)	1932
05333	Hoffman, William H. - Cottage Lot	Barrington	RI	5 (1911-1912)	1911-1914
06313	James, A. C. - "Artist's Lot"/King Glover Subdivision, Lot 43)/Sullivan, J.K.	Newport	RI	4 (1915-1916)	1915-1916
06315	James, A. C. - "Villa Lot"/King Glover Subdivision, Lot 37	Newport	RI	3 (1916)	
00681	King-Glover Lands/Bradley, C.S./King, G.G./Glover, John H.	Newport	RI	76 (1884-1885)	1883-1885; 1894
01070	Newport Land Trust	Newport	RI	48 (1882-1887)	1887-1892
02246	Rocky Farm	Newport	RI	2 (1886-1900)	1886; 1895
06314	Sullivan, J. K./King Glover Subdivision, Lot 43	Newport	RI	0	
03583	Read, C. O. Mrs./Hurt, Joel/Sweetwater Farm/	Pawtucket	RI	0	1908
01426	Eaton, S. B./Subdivision of Estate Oakdale	Providence	RI	10 (1893-1894)	1893-1894
06228	Freeman, John R. Subdivision	Providence	RI	25 (1913-1917)	1909-1917
10586	Mountaindale Housing	Smithfield	RI	0	1977
07589	Dwight, Charles S./Rhett, R.G./Rhett Associates/Wappoo Realty/Crescent Subdivision	Charleston	SC	23 (1919-1926)	1925-1930; 1959
09124	Folly Island	Charleston	SC	0	1925-1932
05837	Hampton Park Terrace	Charleston	SC	0	1913
06232	Yeamans Hall Development/E.W. Durant Subdivision	Charleston	SC	77 (1923-1936)	1914-1916; 1923-1936; 1947; 1966

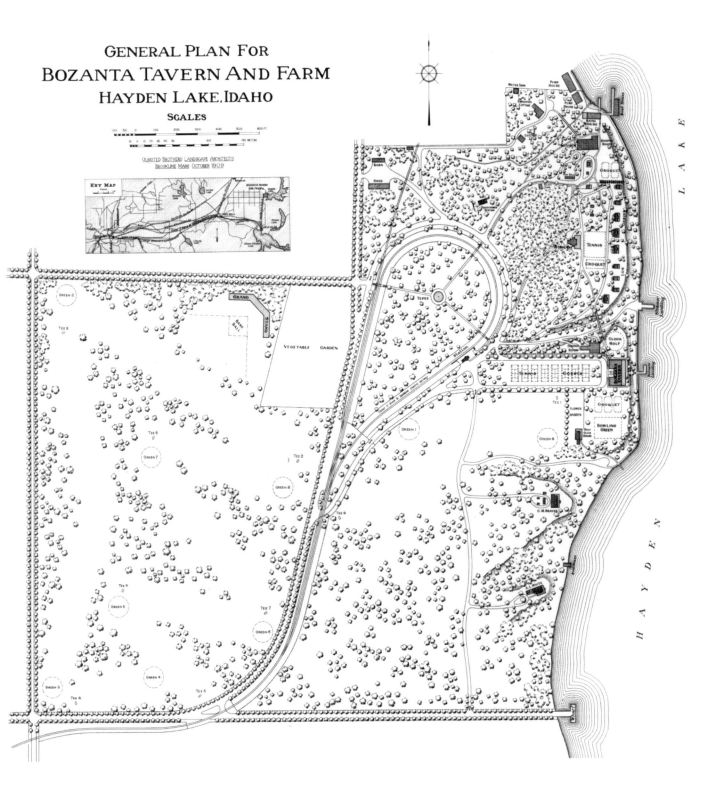

General plan for the Bozanta Tavern and Farm, Hayden Lake, ID, October 1909.
Job #3108 – Hayden Lake Improvement Company (Spokane, WA).

Job #	Job Name/Alternative Name	Job Location		Plans	Correspondence
05767	City Development Company/Edwin W. Robertson and Associates	Columbia	SC	6 (1913)	1912-1916
09761	Edwards, C. P. Jr./Ridgefield Farm	Kingsport	TN	39 (1939; 1945-1947)	1946-1948
09904	Green Acres Shopping Center	Kingsport	TN	35 (1951-1955)	1951-1957
09464	Puryear/Woodmont Estates/Puryear, G.A.	Nashville	TN	60 (1933-1937)	1936-1942; 1949
01173	Saint Cloud Hill	Nashville	TN	5 (1891)	1891-1902
07905	Wakefield-Davis Realty Company/Cherokee Park	Nashville	TN	2 (1927-1928)	1928; 1937
07327	Country Club Estates	Houston	TX	0	1924
10147	Miller Buildings Realty Subdivision	Richmond	VA	0	1962
01176	Sherwood Land Company	Richmond	VA	14 (1891-1893)	1890-1893
00100	Westhampton Park/Westhampton Park Railway Company	Richmond	VA	18 (1890-1902)	1901-1902
10110	Howe, C. Subdivision	Dorset	VT	13 (1941; 1960)	1895; 1960-1961
06199	Julia Farwell Subdivision	Wells River	VT	0	1915
03348	Golden Gardens/Cox, E. B.	Ballard	WA	0	1907-1908
06590	Puget Sound Steel Corporation Township	Elverado Township	WA	0	1917
03557	Northern Pacific Irrigation Company/Gould, David E.	Kennewick	WA	36 (1906-1910)	1908-1912
03876	Ainsworth, E. E./Blaine, E. F. (&)	Seattle	WA	3 (1910)	1909-1911
08243	Highlands, The	Seattle	WA	33 (1929-1930)	1929-1934
07399	Jefferson Park Tract/Frost, A.C./Jefferson Park Tract	Seattle	WA	11 (1913; 1925)	1925
03347	Licton Springs Park/Licton Mineral Springs Company/Denny Farm	Seattle	WA	5 (1907)	1907-1909; 1919-1920
07367	Magnolia Bluffs/Frost, A. C./Briar Cliff	Seattle	WA	4 (1924-1925)	1924-1932
03209	Mount Baker Park/Mount Baker Park Subdivision/Hunter Tract Improvement Company	Seattle	WA	3 (1907-1908)	1906-1910
08247	The Highlands Roadside Improvement Association	Seattle	WA	0	1930
07315	Uplands/Frost, A. C./Uplands Subdivision	Seattle	WA	92 (1924-1926)	1924-1943
03910	Belair Syndicate/White, Graves & Newberry	Spokane	WA	10 (1909-1914)	1909-1938
05341	Chalmer, W. J./Security Trust Company/Chalmers, W. J.	Spokane	WA	11 (1911-1914)	1911-1914; 1938-1939
03108	Hayden Lake Improvement Company	Spokane	WA	9 (1907-1909)	1906-1915; 1936
09667	Jones, Arthur D. Company/High Drive Prop. Subdivision	Spokane	WA	119 (1937-1956)	1937-1953
01142	Rockwood Home Sites	Spokane	WA	0	1915
03707	Rockwood Park Addition/Western Trust and Investment Company	Spokane	WA	5 (1909-1910)	1909-1912
03814	White & Graves Ranch/White, Aubrey L. & J. P. Graves	Spokane	WA	16 (1909-1911)	1909-1913; 1920
06454	Baker, John S.	Tacoma	WA	8 (1917-1918)	1916-1919
06466	Stoner, Inglis & Bishop/Geddes Avenue Syndicate Subdivision	Ann Arbor	WI	8 (1910-1917)	1916
02987	Harris, N. W./Harris & Swift/Leiter Place	Lake Geneva	WI	18 (1904-1915)	1904-1905

Job #	Job Name/Alternative Name	Job Location		Plans	Correspondence
03002	Swift, E. F./Harris, N. W./Swift, Edward F.	Lake Geneva	WI	15 (1904-1915)	1904-1907

CANADA

Job #	Job Name/Alternative Name	Job Location		Plans	Correspondence
03752	Doupe, J. Lonsdale/Sunalta	Calgary	AB	3 (1909-1910)	1909-1910
05092	Mount Royal, South	Calgary	AB	4 (1909-1910)	1910-1911
04055	Lonnquist-Mason Company	Lethbridge	AB	0	1910
09273	British Pacific Properties Ltd./Capilano Golf Club/Taylor, A.J.T.	Vancouver	BC	575 (1931-1937)	1931-1947
03276	Uplands, The/Oldfield, Kirby & Gardner	Victoria	BC	26 (1907-1913)	1907-1921
03704	Heubach, F. W./Tuxedo Park/Heibach, F. W. Ltd.	Winnipeg	MB	5 (1905-1909)	1909-1915
05064	Canadian Investors Ltd.	Halifax	NS	0	1910
09012	Maclean, Hugh C. Major	Toronto	ON	35 (1928-1929)	1928-1930
00440	Maxwell, Edward	Montreal	QC	0	1897-1900
05854	Mount Royal Heights/Hudson Bay Company	Prince Albert	SK	9 (1912-1914)	1913-1914

OTHER COUNTRIES

Job #	Job Name/Alternative Name	Job Location		Plans	Correspondence
07034	Bermuda Development Company/Bermuda Development Company Ltd.	Tuckers Town	BER	299 (1867; 1920-1938)	1921-1975
03606	Andorra Realty Company/Whitney Land Co.	Isle of Pines	CUB	121 (1909-1911)	1898; 1908-1921; 1945

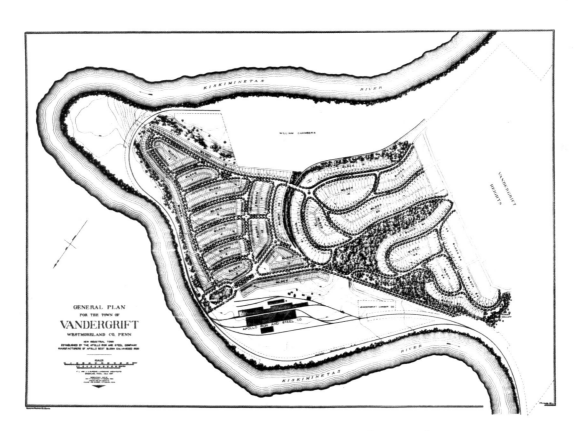

General plan for the town of Vandergrift, Pennsylvania, July 1897.
Job #204 – Vandergrift/Apollo Iron & Steel Co. (Vandergrift, PA).

Perspective sketch of Stanford University, date unknown. Job #1032 – Leland Stanford Jr. University (Stanford, CA).

Background: General plan for the College of New Jersey, 1893. Job #1169 – Princeton University/College of New Jersey (Princeton, NJ).

College and School Campuses

Francis R. Kowsky

The large number of entries in the category of school campuses, which encompasses locations in many places in the United States and Canada, testifies to the importance of educational clients to the success of the Olmsted firm. It also reflects the ever increasing importance that education came to occupy in American life after the Civil War. Frederick Law Olmsted was of a generation of social thinkers who gave credence to the notion that the physical environment of learning—buildings and grounds—played a significant role in the success of education. Olmsted had planned campuses for new universities, notably Cornell University and Stanford University; his successors carried on and expanded this sphere of landscape architecture. The names of many well-known colleges and universities, such as Wellesley College, Johns Hopkins University and Princeton University, highlight the list of commissions from institutions of higher education. Together with many private and public universities, the *Master List* includes public elementary schools and secondary schools, religious and private schools, private preparatory schools, normal schools, liberal arts colleges, women's colleges and agricultural colleges. The bulk of the projects in this category date from the first three decades of the twentieth century, the time during which John Charles Olmsted and Frederick Law Olmsted Jr. guided the firm.

As is the case in other thematic project categories, many of the school campus projects have a job number but this *Master List* shows no associated plans. This does not necessarily mean that the firm did not take on design work for these clients. For example, Gallaudet College (the present Gallaudet University) in Washington, D.C., was an important Olmsted project. Researchers are also advised to consult the thematic category Grounds of Residential Institutions, which includes some educational clients.

College and School Campuses

Job #	Job Name/Alternative Name	Job Location		Plans	Correspondence
		UNITED STATES			
03571	Alabama Polytechnic Institute	Auburn	AL	0	1908
07969	Auburn Polytechnic Institute	Auburn	AL	266 (1921-1930)	1928-1931
09724	Howard College	Birmingham	AL	78 (1931; 1947-1950)	1946-1950; 1973-1974
10032	Lyman Ward Military Academy	Camp Hill	AL	4 (1956)	1955
09816	Decatur Elementary School	Decatur	AL	11 (1948-1949)	1948-1949
09815	Decatur High School	Decatur	AL	24 (1948-1949; 1957)	1948-1957
09805	Florence Alabama High School	Florence	AL	22 (1948)	1939-1940; 1947-1948
07965	Florence Alabama State Normal School/State Teachers College	Florence	AL	193 (1928-1948)	1939-1948; 1957-1962
07966	Alabama Agricultural and Mechanical (A & M) College/Huntsville Negro Agricultural & Mechanical School	Huntsville	AL	2 (1928)	1928-1959
09862	Alabama Educational Foundation	Indian Springs	AL	226 (1939; 1949-1950)	1948-1952
07963	Jacksonville State Normal School/Jacksonville Normal School	Jacksonville	AL	7 (1929-1930; 1946)	1928-1934; 1944-1948; 1962
07964	Livingston Normal School	Livingston	AL	75 (1921; 1928-1930)	1928-1930; 1946-1949; 1956; 1962
09804	Judson College	Marion	AL	49 (1948-1951)	1948-1962
10120	Mobile Baptist College	Mobile	AL	75 (1953; 1959-1962)	1960-1962; 1969-1970
07968	Montevallo Women's College	Montevallo	AL	15 (1930-1948)	1928-1939; 1945
07971	Capitol Heights Jr. High School	Montgomery	AL	6 (1928-1929)	1928-1930; 1935-1936
03322	Huntington College/Methodist College of Alabama/Methodist Church of Alabama/College for Women/Huntingdon College	Montgomery	AL	41 (1908; 1923; 1946-1949)	1907-1909; 1945-1962
07857	Montgomery High School/Lanier, Sidney/Sidney Lanier High School	Montgomery	AL	27 (1927-1929)	1927-1929
07961	Montgomery State Normal School/Montgomery Negro Normal School	Montgomery	AL	22 (1929-1930)	1928-1935; 1980
07093	Alabama State Normal School	Troy	AL	0	1922
07962	Troy State Normal School/State Teachers College	Troy	AL	250 (1928-1959)	1928-1935; 1944-1950
07967	University of Alabama	Tuscaloosa	AL	299 (1945-1966)	1936-1970
07448	University of Arkansas	Booneville	AR	0	1925
08263	University of California		CA	4 (1897)	1925
08266	International House	Berkeley	CA	18 (1933-1934)	1933-1935
02047	University of California	Berkeley	CA	0	1890-1898; 1903-1904; 1911; 1949

Job #	Job Name/Alternative Name	Job Location		Plans	Correspondence
12014	University of California/California, College	Berkeley	CA	0	1865-1874
05488	Thacher School	Nordhoff	CA	0	1912
08035	Mills College	Oakland	CA	0	1923; 1945
08051	Malaga Cove School	Palos Verdes	CA	13 (1925-1926)	1925-1928; 1946
08238	Miraleste School	Palos Verdes	CA	3 (1928-1930)	1929-1933
08087	Redondo Union High School	Redondo Beach	CA	12 (1928-1933)	1927-1933
08250	Mount Tamalpais Boys School	San Rafael	CA	0	1927; 1930
08029	Santa Barbara High School	Santa Barbara	CA	7 (1921-1923)	1923-1924
01032	Stanford, Leland Jr. University/Leland Stanford Jr., University	Stanford	CA	256 (1883-1891; 1914; 1930-1931)	1881-1892; 1908; 1913-1915; 1931-1935; 1944; 1971-1978
05435	Union High School/Nordhoff Union H. S.	Ventura County	CA	4 (1910-1912)	1911-1912
03429	Colorado, University of/Colorado College	Boulder	CO	12 (1908; 1924)	1908; 1922-1925
03474	Colorado State University	Colorado Springs	CO	0	[1908?]
05599	Clayton, George W. College/Clayton College	Denver	CO	2 (1913)	1913
09036	Greenwich Country Day School	Greenwich	CT	2 (1929)	1928-1929
00601	Trinity College	Hartford	CT	20 (1873-1897)	1872-1898
05828	Litchfield High School/Litchfield Village Improvement	Litchfield	CT	0	1913; 1927-1929
01237	Naugatuck School	Naugatuck	CT	5 (1892-1894)	1891-1895; 1916
03059	Yale - Hillhouse Property/Yale University/Sachem's Wood	New Haven	CT	11 (1905)	1905-1912
00630	Yale Athletic Grounds	New Haven	CT	0	
12024	Yale University	New Haven	CT	0	1867; 1874
12084	Yale University Athletic Grounds	New Haven	CT	5 (1881)	1880-1881
03423	Yale University School of Fine Arts	New Haven	CT	0	1908
03470	Yale University/Yale Campus	New Haven	CT	38 (1905-1913)	1907-1914
05762	Connecticut College for Women	New London	CT	3 (1924)	1912-1913; 1924; 1931
02236	Westminster School	Simsbury	CT	7 (1900)	1900-1905
00235	Westminster School	Simsbury	CT	0	
03728	Connecticut Agricultural College	Storrs	CT	0	1896; 1909-1912
07276	Choate School	Wallingford	CT	0	1924
03554	Taft School	Watertown	CT	300 (1908-1932)	1909-1933; 1941
07937	Watertown High School	Watertown	CT	16 (1928-1929)	1927-1929; 1935
09361	Saint Joseph College	West Hartford	CT	212 (1934-1939)	1934-1942; 1972
07801	Saint Thomas Seminary	West Hartford	CT	130 (1920-1940)	1927-1940; 1945
07393	Westport Junior High School	Westport	CT	0	1924
01327	American University	Washington	DC	23 (1891-1896)	1891-1897
06487	Catholic University of America	Washington	DC	135 (1914-1933)	1895; 1916-1931; 1954
12034	Gallaudet College	Washington	DC	0	1866; 1872

Job #	Job Name/Alternative Name	Job Location		Plans	Correspondence
12044	Industrial Home School	Washington	DC	7 (N.D.)	1881-1882
07956	Saint Joseph's Seminary	Washington	DC	71 (1925-1958)	1928-1930; 1958
07458	Trinity College	Washington	DC	177 (1920-1935)	1925-1939; 1958
03346	Washington, George University	Washington	DC	3 (1949)	1907; 1931; 1946-1951
07023	University of Delaware	Newark	DE	0	1922
06649	Women's College of Delaware	Newark	DE	0	1918
07525	Florida University/University of Florida	Gainesville	FL	39 (1925-1927)	1925-1929
06169	Lake Wales School Grounds	Mountain Lake	FL	0	
07572	Florida State College for Women	Tallahassee	FL	0	1925-1928; 1947-1948; 1975
07612	Columbia Theological Seminary	Atlanta	GA	0	1926
06048	Oglethorpe University	Atlanta	GA	0	1913-1914
05505	Georgia Industrial School	North Georgia	GA	0	
03117	Iowa State College	Ames	IA	1 (1903-1906)	1902-1916; 1921-1923; 1979-1980
03644	Iowa College	Grinnell	IA	0	1904-1922
03032	Iowa, State University of	Iowa City	IA	3 (1902-1906)	1904-1906; 1970
02625	Cornell College	Mount Vernon	IA	15 (1903-1904)	1903-1904; 1916; 1923
03275	University of Idaho	Moscow	ID	8 (1906-1913)	1907-1920; 1977
03110	University of Illinois	Champaign	IL	6 (1906)	1903-1907; 1923
01999	Chicago Teachers College	Chicago	IL	7 (1903-1904)	1904-1906
00058	University of Chicago/Chicago University	Chicago	IL	43 (1891-1910)	1891-1921
03328	Bissell College of Photo Engraving	Effingham	IL	0	1907
03458	Northwestern University	Evanston	IL	5 (1907-1909)	1893-1894; 1908-1911
04014	Nazareth Academy	La Grange	IL	0	1910
04011	Rockford College	Rockford	IL	5 (1910)	1910
03031	Wheaton College	Wheaton	IL	2 (1905-1907)	1904-1911
09081	Indiana University/University of Indiana	Bloomington	IN	326 (1929-1936)	1896; 1930-1945; 1975
06801	Indiana Central University	Indianapolis	IN	25 (1920-1921)	1920-1922
09082	Indiana University Medical Center/University of Indiana	Indianapolis	IN	61 (1929-1936)	1929-1940
07405	Earlham College	Richmond	IN	1 (1927)	1925-1927; 1948
09043	Notre Dame, University of/University of Notre Dame	South Bend	IN	102 (1929-1932)	1929-1934
02393	Winona Agricultural and Industrial Institute	Winona Lake	IN	0	1904-1906
02391	Winona Assembly and Summer School Association/Winona	Winona Lake	IN	6 (1901-1907)	1904-1907
07743	Municipal University of Witchita	Wichita	KS	0	1926
06304	Anchorage Public School	Anchorage	KY	1 (1915)	
05050	Berea College	Berea	KY	43 (1910-1920; 1941)	1910-1928; 1961

Job #	Job Name/Alternative Name	Job Location		Plans	Correspondence
06631	Covington High School Grounds	Covington	KY	0	1918
07197	Centre College/Centre College of KY	Danville	KY	132 (1937-1948)	1923-1925; 1939-1948; 1955; 1975
03532	Kentucky State College of Agriculture and Mechanic Arts	Lexington	KY	0	1908
03007	Kentucky University	Lexington	KY	0	1904-1906
06361	Lexington High School/School Board (High School)	Lexington	KY	3 (1916-1917)	1916-1917
05263	University of Kentucky/Kentucky State University	Lexington	KY	16 (1916-1919)	1911; 1918-1919; 1949
09573	Baptist Training School/Woman's Missionary U.T. School	Louisville	KY	88 (1939-1953)	1939-1962
01286	Barret, Alex G. Jr. High School/Barrett	Louisville	KY	7 (1935)	1935
10098	Greater Louisville College of the Arts and Sciences	Louisville	KY	32 (1959-1960)	1946; 1956-1961
03950	Lincoln Institute/Lincoln Institute of Kentucky	Louisville	KY	10 (1910-1911)	1910-1911
05821	Louisville Parental School Property/ Louisville Parental Home and School Commission	Louisville	KY	0	1913
09997	Louisville Presbyterian Theological Seminary/Speed, Wm.	Louisville	KY	36 (1903; 1907; 1939; 1954-1956)	1954-1955
01288	Male High School	Louisville	KY	4 (1909-1910)	1909-1911
06974	Southern Baptist Theological Seminary	Louisville	KY	285 (1921-1970)	1921-1928; 1946-1974
04072	Southern Baptist Theological Seminary Grounds/Baptist Theological Seminary	Louisville	KY	4 (1911-1916)	1910-1915; 1924-1925
07084	University of Louisville	Louisville	KY	56 (1924-1931)	1922-1931; 1975
06958	Kentucky Female Orphan School	Midway	KY	35 (1921-1937)	1921-1927; 1936-1937
04077	Midway School Grounds	Midway	KY	5 (1910)	1910
07304	Morehead State Normal/Morehead Normal Schools	Morehead	KY	9 (1924)	1924
07263	Murray Normal School/Kentucky State Normal School	Murray	KY	6 (1924)	1923-1924
03498	Eastern Kentucky State Normal School	Richmond	KY	114 (1906-1959)	1908-1914; 1923-1927; 1934; 1957-1959
06771	Asbury College and Schools of Vocational Training	Wilmore	KY	0	1919
06888	Louisiana State University	Baton Rouge	LA	178 (1918; 1920-1923)	1920-1924; 1937
08230	Newcomb Memorial College/H. Sophie Newcomb Memorial	New Orleans	LA	16 (1931-1932)	1929-1932
06648	Newman, Isidore Manual Training School	New Orleans	LA	6 (1918)	1918
08227	Tulane University	New Orleans	LA	0	1929
00605	Amherst College	Amherst	MA	68 (1882-1925)	1870; 1876; 1883-1907; 1914-1917; 1924-1925; 1975-1976
02883	Amherst College Improvement	Amherst	MA	0	1904-1908; 1914; 1924

Job #	Job Name/Alternative Name	Job Location		Plans	Correspondence
03441	Massachusetts Agricultural College	Amherst	MA	1 (1866; 1911)	1866; 1908-1911
12054	Massachusetts Agricultural College/University of Massachusetts	Amherst	MA	0	1866-1867; 1870; 1876-1875
07785	Abbot Academy	Andover	MA	9 (1913-1939)	1927-1928; 1939-1940
06337	Andover High School	Andover	MA	0	1916
00176	Phillips Academy	Andover	MA	1331 (1891-1965)	1892-1965
10132	Jason-Russell House	Arlington	MA	4 (1961)	1961
	* See also Chestnut Hill, Roslindale and Roxbury	Boston	MA		
09856	Boston College High School	Boston	MA	204 (1923-1967)	1949-1959; 1966-1978
01413	Harvard University School of Business Administr./1413A/Harvard University Business School	Boston	MA	450 (1951-1953)	1924-1934; 1952-1964; 1978
09852	Archbishop Williams High School/South Shore Catholic Central High School	Braintree	MA	5 (1948-1949)	1949-1950
10081	Bridgewater State Teachers' College	Bridgewater	MA	6 (1958)	1958
10074	Cardinal Spellman Central High School	Brockton	MA	15 (1957-1958)	1958-1960
	*See also Chestnut Hill	Brookline	MA		
01312	Baker, Edith School	Brookline	MA	12 (1935-1942)	1940-1941
01305	Brookline High School	Brookline	MA	120 (1894-1895; 1921-1944)	1894-1896; 1938-1942; 1948
02937	Brookline School Museum Association	Brookline	MA	0	1904-1905
10137	John D. Runkle School	Brookline	MA	96 (1961-1964)	1962-1966
09197	Park School	Brookline	MA	2 (1884; 1930)	1930
10192	Town of Brookline - Park Department; Manual Training High School	Brookline	MA	1 (1965)	1965
09215	Brown & Nichols School/Browne and Nichols School	Cambridge	MA	1 (1930)	1895; 1930
01455	Cambridge English High School	Cambridge	MA	1 (1898)	1898
01456	Cambridge Latin School	Cambridge	MA	20 (1899)	1894-1899
01404	Dexter, Wirt Mrs./Harvard College Yard/Harvard University Fence and Yard	Cambridge	MA	3 (1927)	1894; 1901-1914; 1920-1928
05440	Episcopal Theological School	Cambridge	MA	4 (1911-1912)	1911-1912
01403	Harvard Aviary/Harvard University	Cambridge	MA	3 (1902-1903)	1903-1905
01414	Harvard College Traffic Problems/Harvard University Traffic Study/Street	Cambridge	MA	148 (1930-1940)	1926
01401	Harvard Medical School	Cambridge	MA	55 (1894-1913)	1900-1913; 1937
00308	Harvard Overseers/Harvard (Dignified Approach)/Harvard Riverside Associates/Harvard University	Cambridge	MA	38 (1894-1903)	1868; 1896-1907
01400	Harvard University	Cambridge	MA	146 (1893-1951)	1867-1868; 1895-1912; 1926-1934; 1941-1948
01417	Harvard University/Tercentennary	Cambridge	MA	0	
01412	Harvard University Boathouse	Cambridge	MA	0	
01416	Harvard University School of City Planning	Cambridge	MA	0	
01405	Harvard University, Emerson Hall	Cambridge	MA	0	1903-1905

Job #	Job Name/Alternative Name	Job Location		Plans	Correspondence
01406	Harvard University, Holmes and James Field/Holmes Field and Jarvis Field	Cambridge	MA	0	1895-1902
01407	Harvard University, Landscape Court/School of Landscape Architecture	Cambridge	MA	0	1899-1938; 1950-1951
01411	Harvard University, Laurence Scientific School	Cambridge	MA	0	1895-1900
01409	Harvard University, Salary of FL Olmsted and Special Expenses to Balance	Cambridge	MA	0	
01408	Harvard University, Visiting Committee of Overseers for Division of FIne Arts & Committee on Buildings and Grounds/Norton, Prof. C. E./School of Design Visiting Committee	Cambridge	MA	0	1940-1943
06154	M.I.T./MA Institute of Tec/Massachusetts Institute of Technology	Cambridge	MA	9 (1916-1917)	1915-1917; 1947-1948
02263	New Church Theological Church/New Church Theological School	Cambridge	MA	1 (1900)	1900
06884	Shady Hill School	Cambridge	MA	5 (1926)	1920-1921; 1926-1927
06684a	Shady Hill School	Cambridge	MA	0	1924
01466	Webster School	Cambridge	MA	2 (1897)	1897
03631	Boston College/Boston College Competition/Coolidge and Carson	Chestnut Hill	MA	14 (1908-1969)	1909; 1915; 1965-1969
10533	Pine Manor Junior College	Chestnut Hill	MA	0	1974
07667	Chicopee High School	Chicopee	MA	0	1926
00415	Middlesex School	Concord	MA	305 (1900-1930)	1899-1949
09109	Deerfield Academy	Deerfield	MA	168 (1925-1931)	1929-1933
07939	East Milton School/Collicot School	East Milton	MA	25 (1928-1930)	1928-1929
05674	Williston Seminary	Easthampton	MA	39 (1913-1914)	1912-1916
09369	Fitchburg High School	Fitchburg	MA	10 (1934)	1933-1935
10033	Marian High School	Framingham	MA	16 (1954-1957)	1956-1957
00031	Groton School	Groton	MA	71 (1884-1904)	1886-1899
06620	Lowthorpe School	Groton	MA	0	1917-1923; 1938; 1943-1945
10053	Haverhill Intermediate School	Haverhill	MA	2 (1957)	1957
01175	Smith College	Holyoke	MA	90 (1891-1909)	1891-1911; 1920; 1937; 1977
09931	Cranwell Prep School	Lenox	MA	21 (1952-1956)	1954-1956
09948	Lexington High School	Lexington	MA	96 (1951-1954)	1952-1954
10265	Littleton Middle School	Littleton	MA	0	1968
01379	Abraham Lincoln Playground	Lowell	MA	1 (1908)	
02386	Lowell Textile School	Lowell	MA	18 (1899-1902; 1952-1955)	1902; 1951-1956
10093	Mattapoisett Regional School	Mattapoisett	MA	26 (1958-1960)	1959-1960
07647	Tufts College	Medford	MA	19 (1926-1928)	1896; 1926-1928
09880	Mann, Horace School	Melrose	MA	29 (1944-1950)	1950
09123	Eliot Street School/Town of Milton	Milton	MA	4 (1927-1931)	1929-1931
07952	Milton Academy	Milton	MA	180 (1928-1965)	1928-1946; 1965-1978

Job #	Job Name/Alternative Name	Job Location		Plans	Correspondence
	* See also Chestnut Hill	Newton	MA		
09903	Claflin School	Newton	MA	5 (1951)	1951
03444	Smith Agricultural Institute	Northampton	MA	0	1896; 1908
05355	Northfield High School	Northfield	MA	0	1911
03754	Northfield Seminary	Northfield	MA	2 (1908-1910)	1909-1911
10092	Regional Catholic High School	Peabody	MA	11 (1958-1959)	1959-1961
01410	Harvard University Forest School/Harvard University/Bussey Institution	Petersham	MA	0	1895-1897; 1911-1924
03134	School House/Brooks, James W.	Petersham	MA	0	1907
05923	Hall, Miss School/Hall, Mira H.	Pittsfield	MA	24 (1913-1921)	1913-1918; 1923-1924
10138	Eastern Nazarene College	Quincy	MA	23 (1958-1962)	1961-1977
03329	Randolph, Mass. High School	Randolph	MA	0	1907
09956	Sacred Heart School	Roslindale	MA	46 (1952-1954)	1952-1954
01804	Roxbury Latin School	Roxbury	MA	264 (1890-1968)	1915-1932; 1947-1968; 1979
09973	Sharon High School	Sharon	MA	0	1954
03342	Buck School/Berkshire School for Boys	Sheffield	MA	0	1907; 1931
00256	Mount Holyoke College	South Hadley	MA	44 (1882-1922)	1896-1913; 1922; 1973-1980
00639	Saint Mark's School	Southborough	MA	4 (1894-1896)	1894-1895
06031	Southbridge High School	Southbridge	MA	0	1914
06355	Southbridge Primary School	Southbridge	MA	0	
06034	Southbridge Primary School	Southbridge	MA	0	1916
09318	Topsfield School	Topsfield	MA	3 (1932)	1932
09334	Notre Dame Academy	Tyngsboro	MA	16 (1928-1933)	1894; 1925; 1933
00250	Wellesley College	Wellesley	MA	56 (1901-1920)	1902-1922; 1973
00251	Whitin Observatory/Wellesley College	Wellesley	MA	1 (1900)	1900-1901
10197	Gordon College	Wenham	MA	16 (1955; 1962-1965)	1962-1969
09251	Cambridge School	Weston	MA	22 (1931-1932)	1930-1932; 1946; 1967
03495	Weston Center School Grounds	Weston	MA	7 (1906-1946)	1908-1911; 1946
09925	Weston Elementary School	Weston	MA	4 (1952)	1952
00318	Williams College	Williamstown	MA	668 (1902-1963)	1882; 1903-1912; 1941-1964; 1975
09844	Wilmington High School	Wilmington	MA	98 (1921; 1944; 1949-1950)	1949-1953
07795	Worcester Academy	Worcester	MA	0	1927
03083	Worcester Polytechnic Institute	Worcester	MA	31 (1899; 1906-1914)	1905-1915; 1978
00182	Naval Academy/Annapolis, Maryland	Annapolis	MD	0	1895
05991	Baltimore Technical High School	Baltimore	MD	0	1914
01320	Bryn Mawr School	Baltimore	MD	8 (1892-1913)	1891-1892; 1913
07816	Homeland Friends School	Baltimore	MD	8 (1925-1927)	1927

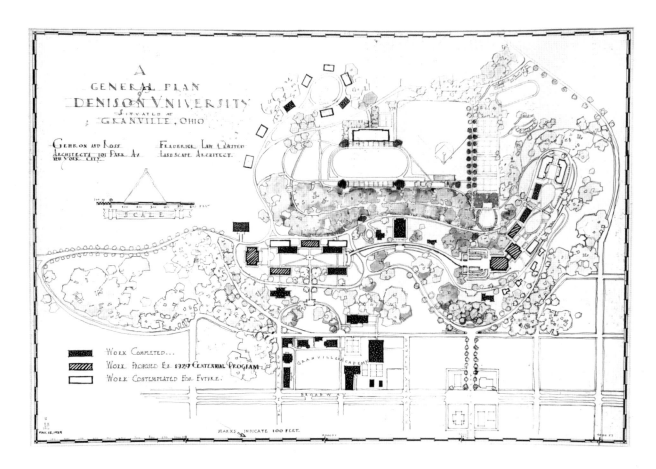

General plan of Denison University, May 15, 1929. Job #6373 – Dennison University (Granville, OH).

Perspective drawing of Louisiana State University, October 1921. Job #6888 – Louisiana State University (Baton Rouge, LA).

Job #	Job Name/Alternative Name	Job Location		Plans	Correspondence
02376	Johns Hopkins University	Baltimore	MD	279 (1906-1917)	1876; 1902-1919
07468	Saint Mary's Seminary	Baltimore	MD	65 (1924-1931)	1925-1933
07871	Maryland University/University of Maryland	College Park	MD	30 (1927-1939)	1927; 1930; 1939-1940; 1972
02265	Jacob Tome Institute	Port Deposit	MD	1 (1900)	1899-1900
00441	Jacob Tome Institute/The Tome School	Port Deposit	MD	0	1900
10099	Saint Mary's Seminary Junior College	Saint Mary's City	MD	31 (1949-1960)	1957-1960; 1969
09990	Towson State Teacher College	Towson	MD	77 (1950-1963)	1954-1969
03758	Western Maryland College	Westminster	MD	2 (1911-1912)	1909-1926
09092	Bowdoin College	Brunswick	ME	1 (1929)	1929
07918	Hinckley School/Goodwill Home Association/Goodwill School	Hinckley	ME	14 (1926-1928)	1928; 1965
03692	Bates College	Lewiston	ME	0	1909-1913
12064	Maine Agricultural College/University of Maine	Orono	ME	0	1866-1867
03090	University of Maine	Orono	ME	260 (1867; 1921-1950)	1866; 1872; 1905-1914; 1924-1977
12074	South Berwick, Maine Academy	South Berwick	ME	0	1894
09101	Colby College	Waterville	ME	110 (1932-1955)	1929-1930; 1950-1963
06920	Maine School for the Feeble-minded	West Pownal	ME	3 (1916-1921)	1921
05975	Michigan University/University of Michigan	Ann Arbor	MI	28 (1910-1920)	1907-1922
07986	Sacred Heart Academy	Detroit	MI	4 (1928-1929)	1929
05881	Michigan Agricultural College/Michigan State Agricultural College	East Lansing	MI	18 (1913-1922)	1913-1923; 1955
02621	Kalamazoo, State Normal School at	Kalamazoo	MI	9 (1894; 1904-1905)	1903-1908; 1977
03616	Saline Village/Saline Village High School Grounds	Saline VIllage	MI	14 (1908-1912)	1912
03625	Michigan State Normal/Huron River Improvement/MI State Normal School	Ypsilanti	MI	12 (1905-1915)	1913-1915
03392	University of Minnesota	Minneapolis	MN	0	1896; 1907-1914; 1941-1945
01729	Washington University	Saint Louis	MO	12 (1894-1899)	1895-1899; 1976-1979
10115	Alcorn Agricultural and Mechanical College	Alcorn	MS	48 (1950-1962)	1960-1961; 1970
10179	Blue Mountain College	Blue Mountain	MS	2 (1966)	1964-1967
10124	Delta State Teachers College	Cleveland	MS	22 (1950-1962)	1960-1962
10127	Mississippi College	Clinton	MS	207 (1959-1977)	1961-1980
09939	Mississippi State College for Women	Columbus	MS	140 (1952-1975)	1952-1980
09920	Mississippi Southern College/University of Southern Mississippi	Hattiesburg	MS	137 (1949-1974)	1951-1961; 1971-1976
10114	Mississippi Vocational College	Itta Bena	MS	19 (1950-1962)	1960-1963
10174	Jackson Academy	Jackson	MS	8 (1964-1965)	1964-1969
09897	Jackson City Schools	Jackson	MS	7 (1936-1951)	1950-1952
09868	Jackson State College	Jackson	MS	68 (1930-1963)	1949-1964
10106	Millsaps College	Jackson	MS	13 (1946-1960)	1959-1960

Job #	Job Name/Alternative Name	Job Location		Plans	Correspondence
10679	Mississippi College Law School	Jackson	MS	0	
09843	University of Mississippi Medical School and Medical Center	Jackson	MS	343 (1947-1970)	1950-1969
07479	Negro Village Industrial School	Laurel	MS	0	1925
09791	University of Mississippi	Oxford	MS	1879 (1939-1977)	1947-1980
10144	University of Mississippi Golf Course	Oxford	MS	42 (1954-1965)	1962-1967; 1979
09989	Mississippi State College	Starkville	MS	913 (1948-1978)	1954-1980
10089	University of Mississippi	Stone County	MS	31 (1958-1960)	1958-1960
10170	Yazoo City High School	Yazoo City	MS	3 (1950; 1957)	1963-1964
02233	Asheville Industrial School	Asheville	NC	0	
07411	Duke University/Blue Devils	Durham	NC	852 (1925-1965)	1925-1934; 1945-1946; 1959-1975
02962	North Carolina College of Agriculture & Liberal Arts	Raleigh	NC	0	1899-1904; 1976
05382	North Carolina School for Feeble Minded	Washington	NC	2 (1911)	1911
09543	Bethlehem School	Bethlehem	NH	0	1938-1939
00119	Saint Paul's School	Concord	NH	88 (1895-1922)	1898-1908; 1921-1923
09921	University of New Hampshire	Durham	NH	6 (1951)	1951
03118	Phillips Exeter Academy	Exeter	NH	347 (1904-1932)	1906-1908; 1923-1934; 1949-1952
01385	Dartmouth College	Hanover	NH	70 (1893; 1926-1929; 1954-1959)	1893-1899; 1922-1928; 1954-1961
10084	Dartmouth College Housing	Hanover	NH	6 (1957-1958)	1958-1959
09148	Portsmouth High School/Prescott, Mary E. and Josie F.	Portsmouth	NH	0	1929-1930
09136	Russell Sage College	Troy	NH	138 (1926-1930)	1929-1940
10085	Dartmouth College Married Students Housing	West Lebanon	NH	3 (1958)	1958-1959
07768	Newman School	Lakewood	NJ	9 (1925-1927)	1927-1929
00052	Lawrenceville School	Lawrenceville	NJ	139 (1883-1901)	1883-1964
01383	Drew Theological Seminary	Madison	NJ	1 (1893)	1893
07613	Bonnie Brae Farm/Osborn, H.V.	Millington	NJ	4 (1926-1930)	1926-1932
01362	Princeton Theological Seminary	Princeton	NJ	7 (1880; 1893)	1892-1893
01169	Princeton University/College of New Jersey	Princeton	NJ	25 (1890-1893; 1904-1907)	1890-1895; 1907
09489	Summit Junior High School	Summit	NJ	34 (1937-1939)	1935-1956
04093	Wells College	Aurora	NY	11 (1910-1911)	1910-1912; 1925-1926
06693	University of Buffalo	Buffalo	NY	0	1919
06711	Chautauqua Institution	Chautauqua	NY	0	1919
12094	Elmira School	[Elmira?]	NY	0	1873-1874; 1878
09758	Triple Cities College/Syracuse University, subsidiary of	Endicott	NY	2 (1939; 1945)	1946-1947
07991	Forest Hills School/Our Lady Queen of Martyrs School	Forest Hills	NY	23 (1926-1929)	1928-1931
00679	Madison University	Hamilton	NY	1 (1883)	1883; 1891

Job #	Job Name/Alternative Name	Job Location		Plans	Correspondence
03203	Bennett School (New)/Halcyon Hall	Irvington	NY	1 (1907)	1904-1907
02630	Bennett School/Fairlawn, Dunham Dr./ Miss May Bennett	Irvington	NY	22 (1900-1905)	1903-1905; 1913
06461	Irvington School/Public School Grounds	Irvington-on-Hudson	NY	4 (1916-1917)	1916-1917
12104	Cornell University	Ithaca	NY	0	1867; 1874; 1879
05055	Cornell University/Cornell University Agricultural College	Ithaca	NY	2 (1913-1915)	1867-1879; 1910
00242	Columbia University	New York City	NY	17 (1905-1906)	1888-1898; 1904-1906
05529	New York University/University of the City of New York	New York City	NY	37 (1895-1918)	1912-1923
03605	Rockefeller Institute/Dunham, Edward T.	New York City	NY	2 (1909)	1909
09873	Saint John Fisher College	Pittsford	NY	46 (1948-1950)	1950
01439	Vassar College	Poughkeepsie	NY	72 (1878; 1926-1927; 1929-1932)	1868; 1896; 1905-1909; 1921-1939; 1968-1970
07588	Rochester University/University of Rochester	Rochester	NY	309 (1925-1930)	1925-1942; 1952-1953
07328	Roslyn High School	Roslyn	NY	16 (1924-1925)	1924-1925
01143	Rexleigh School	Salem	NY	2 (1890)	1890-1891
06427	Scarborough School/Vanderlip, F.A.	Scarborough	NY	22 (1916-1927)	1916-1923; 1931-1935
01771	Union College	Schenectady	NY	3 (1895)	1895-1896
07770	Syracuse University - School of Forestry	Syracuse	NY	0	1927
03954	Syracuse University Campus	Syracuse	NY	374 (1910-1963)	1871; 1910-1912; 1943-1964
02278	Hackley School	Tarrytown	NY	2 (1901-1902)	1901-1902
09177	Willard, Emma School	Troy	NY	27 (1930)	1929-1931
09149	Tuxedo Club School/Tuxedo High School	Tuxedo	NY	3 (1930)	1929-1931
09759	Utica College/Syracuse University	Utica	NY	35 (1923-1957)	1946-1958
07585	Summer School for Women Workers	West Park	NY	0	1925-1926
00322	U. S. Military Academy/West Point	West Point	NY	355 (1904-1906)	1890-1891; 1902-1915; 1931; 1944
01243	Saint Joseph Seminary	Yonkers	NY	8 (1893-1894)	1891-1896
03066	Hebrew Union College/Bernheim, I. W.	Cincinnati	OH	8 (1905-1906)	1905-1907
07985	Saint Gregory's Seminary	Cincinnati	OH	59 (1928-1929)	1928-1929
06306	High School/Packard, F. L.	Cleveland	OH	0	1915
03084	Ohio State University	Columbus	OH	45 (1905-1911)	1905-1917; 1925
06680	Air Academy/Deeds	Dayton	OH	0	1919
05253	Bonebrake Seminary/Bonebrake Theological Seminary	Dayton	OH	11 (1913-1922)	1911-1922; 1935
09638	Dayton Art Institute	Dayton	OH	1 (1941)	1941; 1978
06383	Dayton High School	Dayton	OH	0	1916
06721	Moraine Park Primary School/Moraine Park School/Deeds, E.A.	Dayton	OH	3 (1919-1920)	1919-1921
06688	Moraine Park School	Dayton	OH	8 (1919-1920)	1919-1923
05814	Oakwood School/Oakwood Village	Dayton	OH	5 (1913-1916)	1913-1917

Job #	Job Name/Alternative Name	Job Location		Plans	Correspondence
06997	University of Dayton	Dayton	OH	0	1921-1922
05336	Ohio Wesleyan University	Delaware	OH	0	1911
06373	Denison University	Granville	OH	384 (1916-1929)	1916-1931; 1937-1938
02928	Oberlin College	Oberlin	OH	39 (1913-1914)	1900-1914
05486	Miami University	Oxford	OH	2 (1912)	1911-1912
06299	Western College	Oxford	OH	27 (1916-1929)	1915-1922
09879	Youngstown College	Youngstown	OH	25 (1950)	1950-1951
03699	Oregon Agriculture College/Oregon Agricultural College	Corvallis	OR	3 (1909)	1909-1914
03383	University of Oregon	Eugene	OR	0	1907
03411	McMinnville College	McMinnville	OR	3 (1904-1908)	1907-1910
03595	Pacific University	Portland	OR	0	1908-1909
05340	Reed College	Portland	OR	0	1911
07774	Pennsylvania School of Horticulture for Women	Ambler	PA	4 (1924-1927)	1927
01435	Bryn Mawr College	Bryn Mawr	PA	57 (1895-1927)	1891-1899; 1905-1934; 1975-1980
07284	Shipley School/Howland & Brownell, Misses	Bryn Mawr	PA	2 (1924)	1924; 1932-1934
03536	Lafayette College	Easton	PA	49 (1909-1963)	1908-1924; 1963-1975
03327	Greenville Public School Grounds	Greenville	PA	0	1907
09192	Grove City College	Grove City	PA	685 (1929-1956)	1929-1963
07434	Haverford College	Haverford	PA	43 (1925-1932)	1925; 1931-1932
07432	Mercersburg Academy/Calvin Coolidge, Jr., Memorial	Mercersburg	PA	23 (1923-1925)	1925
01340	Academy of New Church	Moreland	PA	7 (1892-1893)	1893; 1899
03116	Westminster College	New Wilmington	PA	11 (1906-1907)	1906-1912
10587	Eastern Nazarene College	Newtown	PA	3 (1976-1977)	1976-1977
07526	Friends Central School	Overbrook	PA	8 (1896; 1925-1926)	1925-1928; 1953
05824	College of Physicians	Philadelphia	PA	6 (1913)	1913
06346	Girard College	Philadelphia	PA	0	1916
05481	Pennsylvania, University of	Philadelphia	PA	3 (1912)	1912-1913
09785	Pennsylvania College for Women	Pittsburgh	PA	35 (1940; 1947)	1947-1948
09836	University of Pittsburgh	Pittsburgh	PA	15 (1948-1949)	1949-1952
00043	Hill School	Pottstown	PA	5 (1895-1900)	1900-1906
03410	Shannon School for Girls	Schuylkill County	PA	4 (1907-1908)	1907-1908
05575	Swarthmore College	Swarthmore	PA	100 (1913-1930)	1912-1935; 1940-1942; 1975
07198	Wyomissing High School	Wyomissing	PA	26 (1923-1924)	1923-1924
05504	Puerto Rico Agricultural College/Porto Rico Agricultural College	Mayagüez	PR	0	1912-1914
03553	Saint Andrews School/St. Andrews Industrial School	Barrington	RI	4 (1909-1925)	1908-1913; 1925
01392	Rhode Island Agricultural College/Rhode Island College of Agriculture and Mechanic Arts/Rhode Island State College	Kingston	RI	11 (1894-1897)	1894-1899; 1973-1975

Job #	Job Name/Alternative Name	Job Location		Plans	Correspondence
00302	Saint George School/St. George's School	Newport	RI	10 (1904-1906)	1902-1909; 1913; 1923
07147	Pawtucket High School	Pawtucket	RI	9 (1924)	1922-1925
06518	Pawtucket Schools	Pawtucket	RI	0	1917-1919
02231	Brown Library	Providence	RI	0	1899-1900
00225	Brown University	Providence	RI	14 (1900-1906)	1900-1906; 1975
05101	Brown, Moses School/Moses Brown School	Providence	RI	9 (1911-1926)	1911-1926
07445	Providence College of Education	Providence	RI	0	1925-1928
09716	Rhode Island School of Design	Providence	RI	0	1945-1946
09379	Wakefield Grammar School	Wakefield	RI	13 (1935)	1935
09882	Furman University	Greenville	SC	5 (1940-1950)	1950-1951
06072	Dakota Wesleyan University	Mitchell	SD	1 (1914)	1914
00430	University of Tennessee	Knoxville	TN	0	1891
09249	Fisk University	Nashville	TN	59 (1929-1933)	1930-1934; 1955
05335	Peabody College	Nashville	TN	0	1911-1913
09720	University of the South	Sewanee	TN	170 (1916-1922; 1942-1951)	1945-1956; 1970
08057	University of Texas	Austin	TX	0	1925
06396	Hampton Normal & Agricultural Institute	Hampton	VA	1 (1917)	1916-1917
05947	Virginia Military Institute & Washington and Lee University	Lexington	VA	0	1913
06914	Washington & Lee University	Lexington	VA	3 (1923)	1921-1923
07159	Mary Baldwin College	Staunton	VA	0	1923
06253	Handley Industrial School/Handley Board of Trustees/Buildings for Industrial School	Winchester	VA	3 (1916)	1915-1916; 1923
10000	Fair Haven High School	Fair Haven	VT	0	1955-1956
05760	Middlebury College	Middlebury	VT	0	1912; 1941
05498	Farwell, Julia H./Julia A. Farwell School for Girls	Wells River	VT	1 (1915)	1912-1914
00346	Washington State University Grounds/ State University of Washington	Seattle	WA	13 (1902-1915)	1903; 1915-1916; 1961
05389	Otis Orchards School/School House Otis Orchards	Spokane	WA	1 (1911)	1911
05939	Whitworth College	Tacoma	WA	0	1913-1914
03201	Whitman College	Walla Walla	WA	0	1906
03079	Yerkes Observatory/University of Chicago	Lake Geneva	WI	8 (1904-1906)	1905-1907; 1914
07261	Davis and Elkins College	Elkins	WV	0	
06332	Parkersburg High School	Parkersburg	WV	0	1916-1917

CANADA

Job #	Job Name/Alternative Name	Job Location		Plans	Correspondence
05902	University of British Columbia	Vancouver	BC	0	1913
05063	Manitoba Agricultural College	Winnipeg	MB	0	1910

Job #	Job Name/Alternative Name	Job Location		Plans	Correspondence
03911	Manitoba University/University of Manitoba	Winnipeg	MB	30 (1906-1911)	1909-1914
05836	Manitoba University/University of Manitoba/St. Vital Stat	Winnipeg	MB	5 (1913)	1913-1914
06753	Mount Allison University	Sackville	NB	1 (1914)	1919
05068	Dalhousie College	Halifax	NS	0	1910
03428	Acadia University	Wolfeville	NS	0	1908
00236	University of Toronto	Toronto	ON	0	
03703	University of Saskatchewan	Regina	SK	0	1909

OTHER COUNTRIES

Job #	Job Name/Alternative Name	Job Location		Plans	Correspondence
09217	Bermuda Biological Station for Research Inc./International Marine Biological Institute		BER	8 (1930)	1930-1932
05097	University of Liverpool/School of Architecture	Liverpool	ENG	0	1909-1911

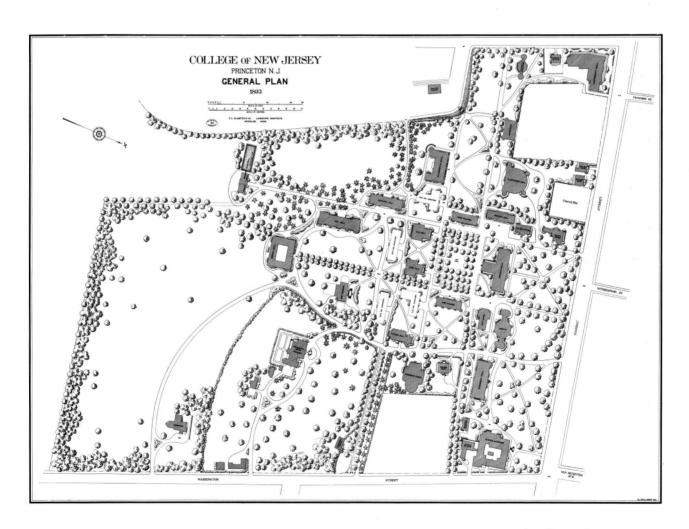

General plan for the College of New Jersey, 1893. Job #1169 – Princeton University/College of New Jersey (Princeton, NJ).

View of the old McLean Asylum grounds, formerly the Barwell Estate, date unknown. Job #98 – McLean Asylum (Belmont, MA).

Background: Detail of revised preliminary plan for the Washington State Hospital grounds, June 14, 1911. Job #3678 – Washington State Hospital Grounds (Sedro-Woolley, WA).

Grounds of Residential Institutions

Francis R. Kowsky

This thematic category includes a wide variety of building types, some of which might not be readily identified with residential institutions. The types of structures for which landscape plans were considered or prepared include public mental institutions (e.g., the New York State Insane Asylum at Poughkeepsie), hospitals of various types (e.g., the Contagious Disease Hospital in Holyoke, Massachusetts), homes for the elderly (e.g. the Keep Home in Watertown, New York), tuberculosis sanatoriums (e.g., the Dayton Tuberculosis Hospital in Dayton, Ohio), military housing (e.g., South Portland Housing in South Portland, Maine), orphan asylums (e.g., the Polish Orphanage in New Britain, Connecticut) and religious institutions (e.g., the Blessed Gabriel Monastery in Brighton, Massachusetts).

Residential institution projects range in date from the years of Olmsted's partnership with Calvert Vaux (1865-1872) to the later years of the Olmsted firm in the 1970s. Some undertakings, such as the New York State Asylum at Poughkeepsie, were done in collaboration with Vaux. After Frederick Law Olmsted ceased active practice in 1895, the firm's residential institution projects were guided by John Charles Olmsted, Charles Eliot and Frederick Law Olmsted Jr. The residential institutions for which Frederick Law Olmsted and the successor firm provided landscape plans, most of which date from the twentieth century, were designed by a variety of architects, some well-known and some not so well known.

The *Master List* indicates that many residential institution projects have a job number but no associated plans, but this does not necessarily mean that the firm did not undertake design work for these clients. For example, the campus of the Columbia Institution for the Deaf (the present Gallaudet University) in Washington, D.C., was laid out by Olmsted and Vaux in the 1860s.[1] Likewise, Olmsted's association with the Bloomingdale Asylum in New

York City played a significant role in his thinking about therapeutic landscapes. The categories Subdivisions and Suburban Communities and Grounds of Public Buildings also contain a few similar residential institution projects such as the United States War Department housing, which appears in the latter category.

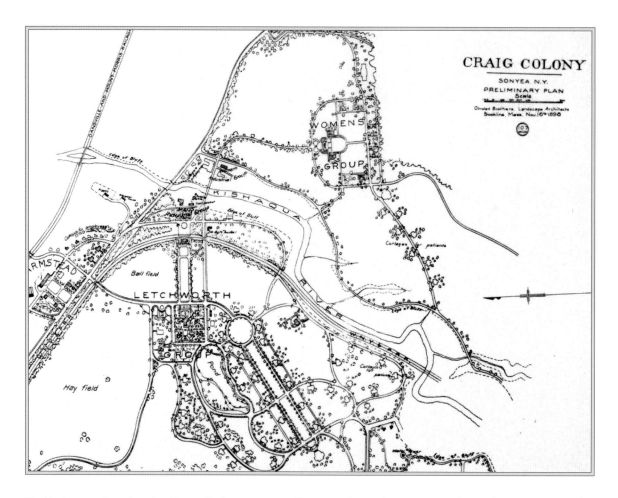

Preliminary plan for the Craig Colony, originally a residential institution for epileptics, November 16, 1898. Job #190 – Craig Colony (Sonyea, NY).

Grounds of Residential Institutions

Job #	Job Name/Alternative Name	Job Location		Plans	Correspondence

UNITED STATES

Job #	Job Name/Alternative Name	Job Location		Plans	Correspondence
09755	Birmingham Medical Center	Birmingham	AL	158 (1942; 1946-1949)	1947-1951
08011	Long Beach Hospital	Long Beach	CA	6 (1922-1923)	1923-1924
08270	Good Hope Clinic Garden/Bryant, E. A. Dr./Bryant, Susanna Bixby Mrs.	Los Angeles	CA	6 (1933-1934)	1933-1934
12015	Hartford Insane Asylum/Hartford Retreat for the Insane	Hartford	CT	1 (N.D.)	1860-1887
03493	Saint Joseph Convent/formerly Hamilton Heights	Hartford	CT	4 (1902-1908)	1908
06705	Home for Delinquent Girls	Lyme	CT	0	
01429	Curtis Home	Meriden	CT	3 (1894-1897; 1903)	1894-1898; 1903-1904; 1910
09372	Mother House & Novitiate/Polish Orphanage	New Britain	CT	7 (1920; 1934-1935)	1935
09640	Saint Raphael Hospital	New Haven	CT	32 (1940-1945)	1941-1945
07318	Newington Home for Crippled Children	Newington	CT	1 (1924)	1924
06060	Hungerford, Charlotte Hospital/Torrington Hospital	Torrington	CT	37 (1911-1931)	1914-1915; 1927-1933; 1941
06849	Waterbury Hospital	Waterbury	CT	3 (1919-1920)	1920; 1927
09373	Convent of Mary Immaculate/Sisters of St. Joseph Corporation	West Hartford	CT	74 (1927; 1934-1936; 1940-1942)	1935-1942
07555	Elks Home	Willimantic	CT	1 (1925)	1925
00290	Columbia Institution for the Deaf and Dumb/Gallaudet University	Washington	DC	0	1977
02825	Government Hospital for the Insane	Washington	DC	2 (1901)	1900-1901
00330	Soldiers' Home/Washington Veterans' Home	Washington	DC	0	1907
06995	Home for Feeble Minded	Gainesville	FL	0	1921
06100	Lake Wales Hospital	Mountain Lake	FL	5 (1930)	1930-1931
06660	Polk County Rest Home/Sanitorium Rest Home	Polk County	FL	0	1918
09610	Camp Blanding	Stark	FL	145 (1940-1941)	1940-1941
03802	Peachtree Heights Sanatorium	Atlanta	GA	0	1909
09393	Ormsby Village/Louisville and Jefferson County Children's Home	Anchorage	KY	0	1935
09837	Mercer General Hospital	Harrodsburg	KY	17 (1947; 1949)	1949
00089	Hospital Grounds	Louisville	KY	3 (1894)	
03043	House of the Good Samaritan	Louisville	KY	0	1905
07262	Kentucky Baptist Hospital	Louisville	KY	10 (1923-1924)	1923-1924
03426	Louisville Tuberculosis Hospital	Louisville	KY	44 (1924; 1930-1931)	1908-1912; 1930-1933
00434	Masonic Home	Louisville	KY	0	1902

Job #	Job Name/Alternative Name	Job Location		Plans	Correspondence
07874	Masonic Widows & Orphans Home	Louisville	KY	24 (1926-1927)	1927-1928
09839	Methodist Hospital	Louisville	KY	13 (1949-1952)	1947-1952
07793	Abington Memorial Hospital	Abington	MA	11 (1924-1927)	1927-1929
05570	Alpha Delta Phi Society Grounds/Amherst College	Amherst	MA	0	1912
10014	Fort Devens	Ayer	MA	365 (1955-1956)	1955-1956
00098	McLean Asylum/McLean Hospital	Belmont	MA	1 (1923)	1872-1975; 1965
	* See also Brighton, Dorchester, Jamaica Plain, Roxbury and South Boston	Boston	MA		
07471	Boston Dispensary	Boston	MA	9 (1925-1926)	1925-1928
06051	Children's Hospital	Boston	MA	0	1914
02941	Hospital for Chronic Disease/Municipal Hospital for Chronic Diseases	Boston	MA	0	1904
09523	Massachusetts Eye and Ear Infirmary	Boston	MA	0	1938
10595	Sherill House, Inc.	Boston	MA	26 (1968; 1977)	1977
05105	Blessed Gabriel Monastery	Brighton	MA	12 (1908-1914)	1911-1915
10003	Crittenton-Hastings House	Brighton	MA	0	1955
09525	Brooks Hospital	Brookline	MA	7 (1938)	1938
02383	Corey Hill Hospital	Brookline	MA	7 (1902-1903)	1902-1907; 1917
10061	Housing for Aged Project	Brookline	MA	28 (1957-1959)	1955-1959
01342	Women's Free Hospital/Free Hospital for Women	Brookline	MA	12 (1892-1893)	1893-1897; 1978
09021	Cambridge Hospital	Cambridge	MA	5 (1928)	1928-1931
02952	Holy Ghost Hospital	Cambridge	MA	10 (1900-1911)	1899-1911
09619	New Towne Court	Cambridge	MA	130 (1936-1960)	1940-1960
05388	Soldiers Home	Chelsea	MA	7 (1912-1916)	1912; 1916
10060	Emerson Hospital	Concord	MA	18 (1957-1959)	1957-1959; 1969
09869	Carney Hospital	Dorchester	MA	189 (1949-1971)	1950-1955; 1962-1971
09386	Lathrop Free Home for Incurable Cancer/Lathrop, Rose Hawthorne Home	Fall River	MA	7 (1932; 1935)	1935
10218	Mental Health Center	Fitchburg	MA	17 (1962-1967)	1967
06061	Danvers State Hospital	Hawthorne	MA	0	1914; 1931
02369	Holyoke Contagious Disease Hospital	Holyoke	MA	7 (1909-1910)	1909-1915
10418	Amory Street Housing	Jamaica Plain	MA	33 (1970-1972)	1972-1974
09915	Nazareth	Jamaica Plain	MA	192 (1933; 1951-1957)	1951-1957
01719	Malden Hospital	Malden	MA	5 (1916-1924)	1906-1907; 1916; 1924-1926
10380	Congregational Retirement Homes II, Inc.	Melrose	MA	1 (1971)	1971
10435	Family Housing - U. S. Army Laboratories	Natick	MA	88 (1956; 1970-1973)	1972-1979
10696	Regency Manor	Newton	MA	0	1979
09335	Notre Dame Rest Home/Notre Dame Property	North Leominster	MA	0	1933
10211	Norwood Hospital	Norwood	MA	5 (1960; 1966)	1966

Job #	Job Name/Alternative Name	Job Location		Plans	Correspondence
09391	Clara Barton Homestead Camp	Oxford	MA	30 (1928; 1935-1938)	1935
09181	Children's Hospital	Roxbury	MA	86 (1930-1956)	1955-1963
02245	Rutland Sanatorium	Rutland	MA	2 (1900-1907)	1900; 1907
10090	Somerville Housing for the Elderly	Somerville	MA	2 (1959)	1959
09636	South Boston Housing	South Boston	MA	166 (1941)	1941-1945
09895	U. S. Navy Housing	South Weymouth	MA	99 (1941-1952)	1950-1952
09184	Springfield Hospital	Springfield	MA	127 (1925-1932)	1930-1933; 1949
00637	Springfield Y. M. C. A./International Y. M. C. A. College	Springfield	MA	23 (1894-1927)	1867; 1894; 1926-1928; 1944; 1959
09857	Wesson Memorial Hospital	Springfield	MA	16 (1939; 1949-1950)	1949-1954
09652	Camp Miles Standish	Taunton	MA	0	1943
06324	Westboro State Asylum/Westboro Asylum for the Insane	Westboro	MA	0	1915
09892	Delta Phi Fraternity	Williamstown	MA	1 (1955)	1949-1951
10421	City Hospital Intern Housing	Worcester	MA	0	1972
00611	Johns Hopkins Hospital	Baltimore	MD	3 (N.D.)	1869-1879
09010	Augusta State Hospital	Augusta	ME	0	1928
10231	Camden Community Hospital	Camden	ME	10 (1958; 1967)	1967-1968
09648	Brighton Avenue/Portland Housing Project	Portland	ME	120 (1942-1944)	1942-1943
09647	South Portland Housing - Red Bank	South Portland	ME	358 (1942-1944)	1938-1945
09781	Methodist Home for Aged	Charlotte	NC	13 (1944-1950)	1947-1955
09497	Littleton Hospital	Littleton	NH	0	1937-1938
07032	Irvington General Hospital/Irvington Hospital	Irvington	NJ	12 (1932)	1922-1923
07394	Ward Home for Aged & Respect. Bachelors & Widowers/Marcus Ward Home/Winchester Gardens	Maplewood	NJ	125 (1924-1931)	1924-1932; 1960
06231	All Souls Hospital	Morristown	NJ	0	1915
09932	Morristown Memorial Hospital	Morristown	NJ	7 (1950-1952)	1952
09028	Saint Peter's Hospital	New Brunswick	NJ	45 (1926-1929)	1928-1929
09180	Paterson Old Ladies Home/Old Ladies Home Memorial/Hobart, Garret	Paterson	NJ	3 (1930)	1930
07287	Bergen County Hospital/Spalding, G. R.	Ridgewood	NJ	5 (1924)	1924
09158	Sea Cliff Country Home for Convalescent Babies	Sea Cliff	NJ	28 (1929-1931)	1929-1932
12025	Unnamed Sanitarium	Adirondacks	NY	0	1887
12035	Buffalo State Asylum for the Insane/New York State Asylum	Buffalo	NY	0	1876-1877
00612	New York State Asylum	Buffalo	NY	25 (1872)	1892-1894
06711	Chautauqua Institution	Chautauqua	NY	0	1919
09922	Andrus, John E. Home	Hastings-on-Hudson	NY	61 (1948-1952)	1951-1952
12085	Bloomingdale Asylum	New York City	NY	0	1866; 1868
09641	Carmelite Convent	New York City	NY	0	1941

Job #	Job Name/Alternative Name	Job Location		Plans	Correspondence
09338	Staten Island Farm Colony/New York City Colony	New York City	NY	0	1933
12055	Orleans County Poorhouse	Orleans County	NY	0	1878
12065	New York State Insane Asylum	Poughkeepsie	NY	0	1867-1869
03397	Letchworth/Eastern New York State Custodial Asylum	Rockland County	NY	14 (1907-1937)	1907-1908; 1920; 1933-1939
00602	U. S. Hotel	Saratoga	NY	1 (1874)	1874-1888; 1976
00190	Craig Colony	Sonyea	NY	23 (1895-1900)	1894-1899
05067	Saint Elizabeth's Hospital	Utica	NY	0	1910
05921	Saint John's Orphan Asylum	Utica	NY	0	1913-1914
05528	Keep Home/Henry Keep Home	Watertown	NY	2 (1912)	1912-1913
01323	Bloomingdale Asylum/Ames, William H.	White Plains	NY	28 (1893)	1892-1895; 1905
01160	Leake and Watts Orphan Asylum	White Plains	NY	116 (1890-1892)	1889-1893
05553	Dayton Tuberculosis Hospital/Dayton District Tuberculosis Hospital	Dayton	OH	4 (1912-1913)	1912
02282	Deaconess Hospital	Dayton	OH	0	
05811	Miami Valley Hospital	Dayton	OH	10 (1912-1953)	1941-1942; 1953-1955
06962	Stillwater Sanatorium	Dayton	OH	12 (1921-1922)	1921-1923
05825	Lima State Hospital/Ohio State Hospital	Lima	OH	25 (1907; 1913-1915)	1913-1917
05962	Ohio State Penitentiary	London	OH	4 (1916-1917)	1914-1918
03093	Ohio State Sanatorium	Mount Vernon	OH	42 (1906-1911)	1906-1912
07146	Masonic Home	Springfield	OH	0	1922-1923
04094	Masonic Home	Elizabethtown	PA	0	1910
07149	Hamot Hospital	Erie	PA	0	1922-1924
07658	Jeanes Hospital	Fox Chase	PA	3 (1925-1926)	1926
05992	Lehigh Coal and Navigation Company Hospital	Lansford	PA	0	1914
06468	Pennsylvania State Institute for the Feeble Minded	Polk	PA	15 (1909-1918)	1916-1919
06469	Pennsylvania State Institute for the Feeble Minded/of Western PA/Beaux Arts Salon Competition	Polk	PA	0	1916-1917
07579	Reading Hospital & Art Museum	Reading	PA	112 (1925-1930)	1925-1934
05274	White Haven Sanatorium	White Haven	PA	14 (1906-1933)	1911-1913; 1933
01039	Newport Hospital	Newport	RI	41 (1886-1895)	1886-1888; 1894-1900; 1921; 1956
02262	Newport Hospital Lands/Rocky Farm	Newport	RI	0	1886-1900
09579	L'Hospice St. Antoine	North Smithfield	RI	15 (1939)	1939
00336	Butler Hospital	Providence	RI	17 (1895; 1903; 1911-1912)	1903-1904; 1910-1912
07373	Homeopathic Hospital of Rhode Island	Providence	RI	1 (1922)	1895; 1924
01898	Rhode Island Hospital	Providence	RI	6 (1896-1897)	1896-1898
12075	Sacred Heart Convent	Providence	RI	0	1881
05257	Charleston Orphan Home	Charleston	SC	0	1911
05332	South Carolina State Insane Hospital	Columbia	SC	0	1911

Job #	Job Name/Alternative Name	Job Location		Plans	Correspondence
05938	Galveston Orphan's Home	Galveston	TX	0	1913
05442	Elk's Home (H. L. Ottenheimer Arc.)	Bedford	VA	0	1911
02388	Brattleboro Hospital	Brattleboro	VT	2 (1902)	1902
03132	Vermont Sanatorium/Proctor, Redfield	Pittsford	VT	12 (1906-1908)	1906-1907
03727	Washington State Reformatory	Monroe	WA	0	1909
03390	Washington Veterans Home/Soldiers' Home	Port Orchard	WA	2 (1907-1908)	1907-1908
03912	Antituberculosis League/Anti-Tuberculosis League of Seattle/Fort Lawton	Seattle	WA	0	1909
03914	Kings County Consumptive Hospital	Seattle	WA	0	
03678	Washington State Hospital Grounds/Northern Hospital for Insane	Sedro-Woolley	WA	12 (1911-1919)	1910-1919
09627	American Legion Home/American Legion House	Sheboygan	WI	3 (1940-1941)	1941-1942
	CANADA				
01777	Royal Victoria Hospital	Montreal	QC	5 (1895-1912)	1895-1897; 1911-1912
05946	Nadeau Workingmen's Homes	Quebec City	QC	0	1913

Government Hospital for the Insane, December 1900. Job #2825 – Government Hospital for the Insane (Washington, DC).

Washington State Capitol grounds, April 1932. Job #5350 – Washington State Capitol (Olympia, WA).

Background: Detail of general plan for the Washington State Capitol, May 1928. Job #5350 – Washington State Capitol (Olympia, WA).

Grounds of Public Buildings

Arleyn A. Levee

The Olmsted firm's landscape work for public buildings spans about 100 years. The nineteenth century planning for public buildings by Frederick Law Olmsted was characterized by its curvilinear grace, stately proportions and fitting enhancement for the structure to be served. In the City Beautiful period, the firm designed grounds of public buildings with more axial formality, to serve as decorative anchors for the municipalities. Later, in the 1920s and 1930s, civic enrichments were often memorial projects (such as the Newton City Hall and War Memorial in Newton, Massachusetts, or the Robbins Memorial Town Hall in Arlington, Massachusetts). Regardless of style, the Olmsted firm maintained a notable design aesthetic, which gave dignity of setting to projects large and small. The work for public buildings from the Olmsted Associates era (1962-1979) was less extensive, consisting of consultations on earlier projects with some new library work (such as the West End Branch Library in Boston, Massachusetts, and the Rice Library in Kittery, Maine).

The practice of the Olmsted firm included about 150 listings for the grounds of public buildings of all types, of which approximately 100 generated at least one plan. The largest group in this category is the group of libraries (about 34 listings), followed by projects for municipal buildings such as city and town halls (15 listings), civic centers (11 listings), court houses (3 listings) and utilitarian structures such as incinerators (3 listings). Museums and various art-related institutes account for another twelve listings, many of which were projects that generated a considerable amount of work over several decades, such as the Metropolitan Museum of Art in New York and the Cleveland Art Museum.

However, the most prominent sub-type within this thematic category is the work done for capitol buildings (11 listings), the oldest and most notable being the iconic design for the United States Capitol begun by Frederick Law Olmsted in 1874, a project that actively continued to the first decade of the twentieth century. Also beginning in the 1870s, the firm planned the New York State Capitol, a design collaboration of Frederick Law Olmsted and architects H. H. Richardson and Leopold Eidlitz; as well as Bushnell Park abutting the Connecticut State House in Hartford. The successor firm of Olmsted Brothers continued to work on state capitols, its most prominent commissions being those for the grounds of the Washington Capitol at Olympia, the Kentucky Capitol at Frankfort and the Alabama Capitol at Montgomery. Smaller projects included more limited work for the Utah Capitol in Salt Lake City, the Maine Capitol in Augusta, the North Carolina Capitol at Raleigh and the Pennsylvania Capitol at Harrisburg, as well as other states where the firm was consulted about capitol work.

There are various miscellaneous but important public building projects included in this thematic category, such as planning for the White House in Washington, D.C., or for the Maine Governor's Mansion in Augusta; and for military establishments such as the Armory in Ansonia, Connecticut, the Schuylkill Arsenal in Philadelphia, Pennsylvania, or the Jeffersonville Depot in Jeffersonville, Indiana, where Frederick Law Olmsted again worked with Montgomery Meigs, who had directed some of the United States Capitol construction. The emergency wartime planning that engaged much of the time of Frederick Law Olmsted Jr. during 1917-1918, and in which many of the firm's apprentices were involved, was for the United States War Department to plan military cantonments and bases for the armed forces rapidly deployed as the United States entered World War I.

There are several caveats that should be understood in the consideration of entries in this and other thematic categories. For example, there are numerous cross-overs in the references for projects such as the White House. While this project seems to indicate only three plans, all from 1903, many other plans and documents were prepared in the 1930s as a component of the extensive multiple-project planning for the Fine Arts Commission in Washington, D.C., labeled for "the Executive Mansion," and found in the category Miscellaneous Projects. Additionally, some of the public building work came about as an element in more extensive and varied planning within a community, sometimes sponsored by a particular patron, such as Mary Curtis Bok for the Rockport Library Park in Rockport, Maine, and Camden-Rockport Information Bureau in Camden, Maine. Therefore, the researcher must consider creative linkages when exploring these various categories and look for references for any project under other project listings in a location or under a sponsor.

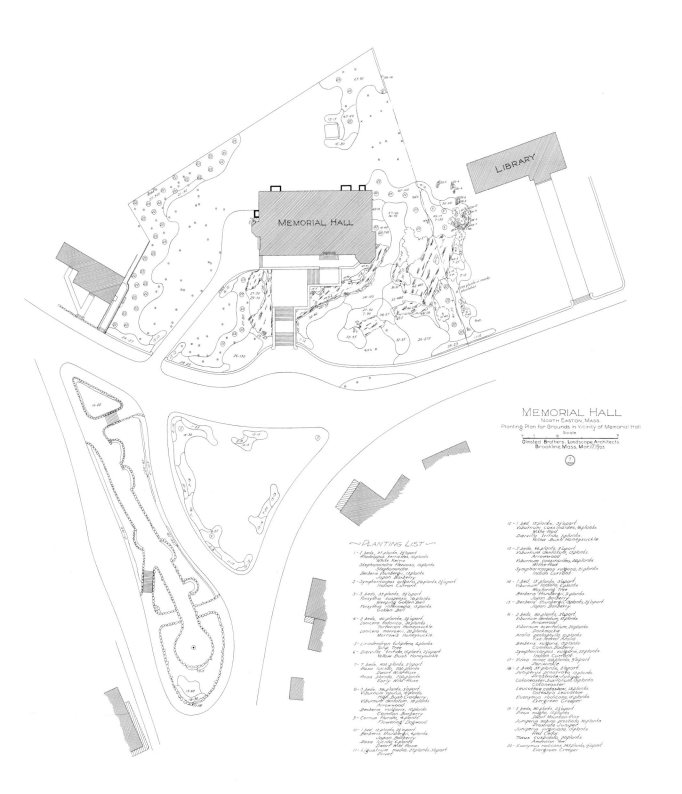

Planting plan for the grounds of Memorial Hall, March 1903. Job #649 – Memorial Hall (North Easton, MA).

Memorial Hall, November 1902. Job #649 – Memorial Hall (North Easton, MA).

Grounds of Public Buildings

Job #	Job Name/Alternative Name	Job Location		Plans	Correspondence
03036	Municipal Museums			0	1904-1905

UNITED STATES

Job #	Job Name/Alternative Name	Job Location		Plans	Correspondence
07960	Alabama State Capitol	Montgomery	AL	155 (1928-1946)	1889; 1927-1948; 1953
07973	Montgomery County Board of Education Administration Building/County Board of Education/Administration Buildings	Montgomery	AL	7 (1929-1930)	1929-1931
08076	Burbank Civic Center	Burbank	CA	2 (1926)	1926-1928
08049	Jacks, Margaret/Old Pacific Building	Monterey	CA	32 (1924-1927)	1924-1931
06600	Oakland Municipal Building/Oakland Municipal Auditorium	Oakland	CA	2 (1913-1917)	1917
08237	Palos Verdes Library	Palos Verdes	CA	9 (1913-1933)	1929-1933
08206	Riverside Municipal Auditorium and Soldiers Memorial	Riverside	CA	0	1928
08030	Santa Barbara City Hall Garden	Santa Barbara	CA	5 (1923-1924)	1924
05489	Ventura County Building	Ventura	CA	0	1911-1912
05581	Denver Civic Center	Denver	CO	17 (1912-1914)	1908-1916
06898	Ansonia Armory	Ansonia	CT	64 (1920-1921)	1920-1921
01171	Blackstone Library	Branford	CT	5 (1890-1891)	1890-1893
00613	State House/Bushnell Park/Connecticut State House	Hartford	CT	75 (1878)	1870-1895
00314	Curtis Memorial Library	Meriden	CT	0	1903-1904
01399	Naugatuck Library	Naugatuck	CT	5 (1894)	1894
01137	Williams Institute	New London	CT	5 (1890)	1890-1891
02820	Capitol Grounds/U. S. Capitol Grounds	Washington	DC	216 (1876-1889; 1894; 1903-1904)	1873-1907; 1915; 1921-1981
02831	Department of Agriculture Building	Washington	DC	0	
09300	Georgetown Incinerator	Washington	DC	8 (1930-1931)	1931-1932
02834	National Museum/National Museum Building	Washington	DC	2 (1905)	1904-1907
09299	O Street Incinerator	Washington	DC	8 (1930-1931)	1931-1932
05358	Pan American Building	Washington	DC	0	1911
02842	Standards, Bureau of/U. S. Bureau of Standards	Washington	DC	5 (1907-1908)	1907-1911
02833	The Plaza/Union Station	Washington	DC	0	1904-1907
02826	U. S. Fish Commission	Washington	DC	16 (1880-1882)	1881-1882
06570	U. S. War Department, Cantonment Division/U. S. Department of Labor/U. S. Housing Corporation	Washington	DC	218 (1917-1918)	1917-1924
02827	White House	Washington	DC	3 (1903)	
03636	Iowa State Capitol	Ames	IA	0	1909; 1914-1915
05430	Coeur d'Alene Civic Center	Coeur d'Alene	ID	0	1911

Job #	Job Name/Alternative Name	Job Location		Plans	Correspondence
02921	Art Institute	Chicago	IL	0	1904-1965
01298	Chicago Art Institute	Chicago	IL	5 (1894-1895)	1894-1897; 1907
06883	Landon, H. McK./Landon, Hugh McKennan/Oldfields/Indianapolis Museum of Art	Indianapolis	IN	52 (1920-1927)	1920-1934; 1967-1981
00603	Jeffersonville Depot/U. S. Army	Jeffersonville	IN	2 (N.D.)	1873-1878
03449	Kentucky State Capitol/State Capitol Building	Frankfort	KY	33 (1908-1910)	1905-1912
03006	Kentucky Agricultural Experiment Station	Lexington	KY	3 (1904-1905)	1904-1906
01289	Louisville Free Public Library	Louisville	KY	15 (1904-1935)	1902-1915; 1923-1924; 1935
10482	Monument Office Building	Acton	MA	2 (1973)	
10214	Municipal Office Building	Andover	MA	23 (1943; 1962-1966)	1965-1966
02252	Robbins Memorial Town Hall	Arlington	MA	127 (1938-1941)	1938-1947; 1964-1966
	* See also Roxbury	Boston	MA		
00945	Boston Custom House	Boston	MA	7 (N.D.)	1903-1905
00939	Boston Public Library, Copley Square	Boston	MA	6 (1890-1892)	1898-1899
10196	Copley Square Competition	Boston	MA	12 (1891; 1935; 1940; 1965)	1965
10238	West End Branch Library	Boston	MA	13 (1966-1967)	1967-1968
12056	Brookline Hills RR Station	Brookline	MA	0	1884
01302	Brookline Public Library	Brookline	MA	11 (1903-1904)	1896; 1904-1907
12046	Longwood Station	Brookline	MA	0	1890-1891
01313	Municipal Incinerator	Brookline	MA	2 (1951-1952)	1952
09337	Cambridge Community Center	Cambridge	MA	3 (1933)	1933
01457	Cambridge Public Library	Cambridge	MA	4 (1897)	1894-1899
00234	Cambridge Station/Fitchburg Railroad	Cambridge	MA	2 (1899)	1899
01453	City Hall - Cambridge	Cambridge	MA	1 (1896)	1896-1897
10389	Canton Public Library	Canton	MA	0	
09145	Crane Library	Dalton	MA	14 (1929-1930)	1929-1930; 1973
07115	Dalton Community House	Dalton	MA	23 (1922-1924)	1923-1928
01802	Parlin Library	Everett	MA	2 (1895)	1895-1898
07439	Lanesboro Public Library	Lanesboro	MA	1 (1925)	1925
01371	Lowell City Hall	Lowell	MA	4 (1893; 1911)	1894-1897; 1910-1911
01163	Lynn Library/Lynn Public Library	Lynn	MA	6 (1897-1902)	1897-1902
01700	Malden Civic Centre/Prescott, F. M.	Malden	MA	0	1921
00292	Malden Library	Malden	MA	5 (1885)	1884-1885
10052	Methuen Municipal Building	Methuen	MA	77 (1955-1958)	1957-1960
02900	Milton Central Station - Improvements	Milton	MA	0	
06006	New Bedford Free Public Library	New Bedford	MA	1 (1914)	1914
10255	Jackson Homestead	Newton	MA	0	1968-1975
01064	Newton City Hall/War Memorial	Newton	MA	165 (1931-1932)	1931-1938; 1956
01063	Newton Technical High School/Civic Center	Newton	MA	4 (1907-1909)	1893; 1907-1916

Job #	Job Name/Alternative Name	Job Location		Plans	Correspondence
00462	North Cambridge Station Grounds, Fitchburg Division/Boston & ME Railroad	North Cambridge	MA	0	1899-1901
00649	Memorial Hall//North Easton Memorial Hall/Ames Memorial	North Easton	MA	7 (1881-1903)	1881-1887; 1902-1903; 1977
05171	Plymouth Federal Building/Brewster Memorial	Plymouth	MA	14 (1913-1916)	1910-1916
00624	Crane Library/Thomas Crane Public Library	Quincy	MA	22 (1881-1913)	1881-1882; 1891; 1913-1918; 1923; 1977
09928	Branch Library	Roxbury	MA	5 (1952-1953)	1952-1953
10028	Essex Institute	Salem	MA	4 (1956)	1955-1957
00210	Hemenway Museum	Salem	MA	3 (1888)	1888-1890; 1906
06033	Southbridge Municipal Offices	Southbridge	MA	0	
06032	Southbridge Police Station	Southbridge	MA	0	
10733	Senior Citizens' Center	Sturbridge	MA	0	
01727	Bristol County Court House	Taunton	MA	5 (1894)	1894-1897
10222	Waltham Field Station	Waltham	MA	0	1967
06672	Watertown Arsenal	Watertown	MA	30 (1919)	1919; 1974-1976
06058	Baltzell, W. H. Dr./Baltzell, William Hewson/Elm Bank	Wellesley	MA	18 (1914-1926)	1914-1916; 1926-1927; 1934; 1938
12096	Reservoir Station	Wellesley	MA	0	1887
09086	West Springfield Y. M. C. A.	West Springfield	MA	0	1929
03385	Town Hall	Whitman	MA	0	1907
03898	Worcester City Hall Grounds	Worcester	MA	7 (1916; 1942)	1942-1943
03896	Worcester Free Public Library	Worcester	MA	0	1916
00083	Mount Vernon		MD	0	
07724	Baltimore Art Museum	Baltimore	MD	10 (1926-1927)	1926-1929
06342	Baltimore Art Museum/Aldrich, S.	Baltimore	MD	5 (1916)	1916-1917; 1923
07019	Old Fellows of Maryland	Baltimore	MD	0	1922
06838	Maine Governor's Mansion/Executive Mansion	Augusta	ME	31 (1920; 1923)	1920-1929
06839	Maine State Capitol Grounds/State Capitol Building	Augusta	ME	4 (1921; 1923)	1921-1923
09827	Camden-Rockport Information Bureau	Camden	ME	15 (1949-1952)	1948-1952
10552	Rice Public Library	Kittery	ME	6 (1975-1976)	1975-1976
09326	Rockport Library Park/Bok, Edward	Rockport	ME	26 (1932-1933; 1937)	1932-1937
06929	Ypsilanti Armory	Ypsilanti	MI	0	1921
10215	Saint Louis Gateway Mall Competition	Saint Louis	MO	5 (1966)	1966-1967
00431	Montana State Capitol	Helena	MT	0	1901
07886	North Carolina State Capitol	Raleigh	NC	14 (1928)	1927-1935; 1942-1946
09541	Franconia Town Hall	Franconia	NH	1 (1938)	1938-1939
07702	New London Public Library	New London	NH	3 (1926-1927)	1926-1928
10035	Society for Preservation of New England Antiquites	Portsmouth	NH	0	1956

Job #	Job Name/Alternative Name	Job Location		Plans	Correspondence
07893	East Orange City Hall	East Orange	NJ	15 (1927-1929)	1927-1930
07490	Glen Ridge Library Grounds	Glen Ridge	NJ	10 (1925-1927)	1925-1927; 1941; 1951
06673	Montclair Plaza/Upper Station/Station Plaza/Near Upper Montclair	Montclair	NJ	2 (1918-1919)	1919
07444	Newark Museum Grounds	Newark	NJ	0	1925-1929
09315	Summit Public Library/Summit Womens Club	Summit	NJ	0	1932
04098	Zoos (in general)/Zoological Gardens		NY	8 (1898-1910)	
00608	New York State Capitol	Albany	NY	35 (1875-1878; 1897-1898)	1864; 1877-1899
12106	Buffalo City Hall	Buffalo	NY	2 (N.D.)	1876; 1892
00730	Buffalo Civic Center	Buffalo	NY	28 (1919)	1919-1920
09617	Nassau County Court House	Garden City	NY	10 (1940-1941)	1940-1941
06663	Geneva New York Chamber of Commerce	Geneva	NY	1 (1919)	1919; 1935
09718	East Norwich Library	Long Island	NY	8 (1942-1948)	1945-1948
03057	Brooklyn Central Library/Brooklyn Central Library and Plaza	New York City	NY	2 (1912)	1905; 1911
00540	Court House Location: City Hall Park	New York City	NY	0	1876-1877; 1910
12116	Jerome Park	New York City	NY	0	1880; 1898
10027	Metropolitan Museum of Art Parking Area	New York City	NY	212 (1897; 1934-1935; 1944; 1946-1948; 1950-1960)	1955-1963
00541	Town Hall, The/Frederick Law Olmsted Memorial	New York City	NY	0	1922
02947	Ogdensburg Public Library	Ogdensburg	NY	0	1904
01118	Rochester Civic Commission/Rochester Civic Center	Rochester	NY	13 (195-1910)	1908-1912; 1924; 1929; 1977
12136	Congress Spring Hotel	Saratoga	NY	0	1864; 1876
03187	Utica City Hall	Utica	NY	8 (1926-1927)	1926-1927
03184	Utica Civic Center	Utica	NY	5 (1910)	1910-1915
00439	Roswell P. Flower Memorial Library	Watertown	NY	0	1902
05661	Cleveland Art Museum/Wade Pk/Ambler Pk/Cleveland Museum of Art	Cleveland	OH	252 (1912-1929)	1912-1917; 1925-1948; 1956; 1971
05660	Cleveland Group Plan/Cleveland, Ohio	Cleveland	OH	85 (1905-1931)	1921-1932
06573	Ohio Governors House	Columbus	OH	5 (1919-1920)	1917-1920
03282	Dayton Civic Center	Dayton	OH	6 (1910)	1910-1914; 1924; 1935; 1947
06639	Sabine Avenue Fire Station Grounds/Salem Avenue Fire Station Grounds	Dayton	OH	0	1918
06810	East Oakwood Community Club	East Oakwood	OH	11 (1920-1921)	1920; 1926
05822	Elyria Ohio Public Comfort Station	Elyria	OH	0	1913
07906	Tracy, Newton A.	Naumee	OH	1 (1928)	1928
07610	Henry Stambaugh Memorial Auditorium	Youngstown	OH	0	1926
09277	Pennsylvania State Capitol/Harrisburg Group Plan	Harrisburg	PA	7 (1930-1931)	1929-1933

Newton City Hall and War Memorial Grounds shortly after construction, September 1933. Job #1064 – Newton City Hall (Newton, MA).

Job #	Job Name/Alternative Name	Job Location		Plans	Correspondence
05940	Allen Lane Station	Philadelphia	PA	0	
12126	Schuylkill Arsenal/Schuyllkill Arsenal	Philadelphia	PA	4 (1875)	1875-1877
01349	Scranton Library	Scranton	PA	2 (1893)	1893-1894
05802	Barrington Rhode Island Town Hall/Town Hall Grounds	Barrington	RI	0	1912
01829	Art Association of Newport	Newport	RI	0	1920-1922
06891	Newport Art Association	Newport	RI	4 (1920)	
07138	Redwood Library	Newport	RI	0	1922
02950	Providence Public Library	Providence	RI	0	
05357	Utah State Capitol	Salt Lake City	UT	14 (1894-1912)	1911-1914
07457	Restoration of Monticello, Thomas Jefferson Memorial Fund/Thomas Jefferson Memorial Foundation		VA	0	1925-1927
10131	Richmond Civic Center	Richmond	VA	19 (1960-1961)	1961
01020	Billings Library/University of Vermont	Burlington	VT	4 (1884-1885)	1885
07639	Burlington City Hall	Burlington	VT	0	1926
01031	Webb, William Seward/Shelburne Farms	Burlington	VT	37 (1886-1889)	1886-1891; 1979
09091	West Rutland Library	West Rutland	VT	2 (1929)	1929
05350	Washington State Capitol	Olympia	WA	196 (1908-1934)	1911-1912; 1927-1934
03212	Seattle Public Library	Seattle	WA	4 (1906)	1906-1907

Biltmore estate grounds, date unknown. Job #170 – George W. Vanderbilt/Biltmore (Asheville, NC).

Background: Detail of guide map of Biltmore estate, 1896. Job #170 – George W. Vanderbilt/ Biltmore (Asheville, NC).

Private Estates and Homesteads

Arleyn A. Levee

The design of residential grounds constituted the largest category of projects for the Olmsted firm over the entirety of its practice, with more than 3,000 listings, of which about 2,000 generated at least one plan. Although parks and park systems were initially the major area of endeavor for Frederick Law Olmsted and his partners, domestic design increasingly became an important component of the practice as transportation improvements extended suburban enclaves beyond city boundaries. From the last decade of the nineteenth century through the first three decades of the twentieth century, commissions for private home grounds steadily increased so that, for the 1910-1930 decades alone, they numbered more than 1,000 projects.

For Frederick Law Olmsted, the concern was to create tasteful domestic settings, artistically coherent, appropriate in scale and unblemished by extravagant materialistic displays. He sought to enhance natural site features to create a series of separate spaces, giving the home its distinctive character, much as he did in his own domestic landscape at Fairsted in Brookline, Massachusetts, making the two acres seem more expansive. These same design criteria influenced planning for larger estate properties, though for these he often included a greater utilitarian purpose, such as forestry (J. C. Phillips/Moraine Farm in North Beverly, Massachusetts), scientific farming (W. S. Webb/Shelburne Farms in Shelburne, Vermont, which is listed in Burlington, Vermont) or horticultural education with forestry at a uniquely monumental scale of thousands of acres (G. W. Vanderbilt/Biltmore in Asheville, North Carolina).

While essentially retaining these criteria in their residential work, the Olmsted Brothers firm was frequently called upon to include more decorative and formal elements—pergolas, pools, tea houses, etc. —in their estate practice, which flourished in the post World War I years. The client list reads like the *Who's Who* of American society, national civic and business leaders as well as prominent individuals from cities across the country. The nexus of grand estates on Long Island for many of these wealthy clients (e.g., Otto Kahn in Cold Spring Harbor, New York; William R. Coe's Planting Fields in Oyster Bay, New York; and J. E. Aldred in Glen Cove, New York) reflected similar work, some begun by the earlier firm, for clients in Newport, Rhode Island, (e.g., estates for Ogden Goelet, Arthur Curtiss James and John Nicholas Brown, as well as F. W. Vanderbilt's Rough Point). The firm designed domestic landscapes for multiple generations within families (e.g., Anson P. Stokes in Newport, Rhode Island, and I. N. Phelps Stokes in Greenwich, Connecticut). The firm designed grounds for clients' city homes and for their country places (e.g., Misses Norton in Louisville, Kentucky, and Hendersonville, North Carolina).

The firm's extensive planning for residential subdivisions and resort communities across the country led to numerous private commissions within these enclaves. In Seattle, work for The Highlands/Seattle Golf & Country Club generated eleven other residential commissions within this gated community; for the Palos Verdes Syndicate in California the firm worked on nineteen individual projects; for Yeamans Hall in Charleston, South Carolina, on another seven homes while for the Mountain Lake Corporation in Mountain Lake (Lake Wales), Florida, the client roster grew to more than eighty individual listings.

As the economy changed, the Olmsted Brothers firm was called back by several of these substantial clients to plan for subdividing what had once been grand estates. In particular, the original work done in the first decade of the twentieth century for the reconstructed Tudor mansion for I. N. Phelps Stokes in Greenwich, Connecticut, became a multiplot high-end residential community, Khakum Woods. This subdivision, begun in the 1920s, was carefully crafted to retain the original landscape character. Likewise, Fernwood, the original Brookline, Massachusetts, estate for Alfred Douglas, was divided into smaller units. In both of these examples the documents for both the single property and the subdivision are found under the same job number.

However, the Olmsted firm also designed residential grounds on small lots for worker housing within Subdivisions and Suburban Communities, as in the multiple projects for National Cash Register in Dayton, Ohio, or for the Beacon Falls Rubber Shoe Company in Beacon Falls, Connecticut, among other such commercial projects. This residential work is incorporated within the documents under the job number for the larger project. Therefore, as extensive as this thematic category is, there is still more related research to be done to extract the full range of the Olmsted firm's domestic work from the archival records.

Private Estates and Homesteads

Job #	Job Name/Alternative Name	Job Location		Plans	Correspondence
03351	Brown, James			0	
00610	Dana, Charles Anderson			5 (1876)	1874-1878; 1891
03711	Foster, J. F.			0	
12027	Hubbard, Charles T.			0	1884
12057	Lee, C.			0	1880
12087	Pitcairn, Mrs. G.S.			0	1893-1894
07674	Ruth, F. S.			0	1926-1927
07382	Sewall, for client			0	
06140	Tayler, Albert D.			0	
00458	Woods, L. G.			0	1901

UNITED STATES

Job #	Job Name/Alternative Name	Job Location		Plans	Correspondence
03075	Fulenwider, A. L.	Birmingham	AL	6 (1902; 1905)	1905-1908
09786	Pittman, J. D.	Birmingham	AL	1 (1947)	1947
07509	Erving, Hampton/Ewing, Hampton D./Country Estate 640 Acres	Mobile	AL	0	1925
03576	Baldwin, A. M.	Montgomery	AL	0	1908
03569	Ball, Fred S.	Montgomery	AL	0	1908
03573	Jones, Henry C.	Montgomery	AL	0	1908
03574	Thorington, Jack	Montgomery	AL	0	1908-1909
03567	Willcox, James S.	Montgomery	AL	0	1908
03572	Wilson, Albert F.	Montgomery	AL	0	1908
06109	Yates, Mrs. E.A.	Shade Mountain	AL	3 (1930)	1930
05906	Barton, E. M. et al.	Walker County	AL	0	1913
08246	Marshall, F. E./Marshall, E. Frank	Phoenix	AZ	5 (1926-1930)	1930
08233	Allison, D. C.	Bel Air	CA	9 (1929-1930)	1929-1932
08021	Lowe, Mrs. Edward Jr.	Berkeley	CA	11 (1923)	1923
05883	McDuffie, Duncan	Berkeley	CA	78 (1912-1934)	1913-1939; 1950
06212	McDuffie, Sophie B.	Berkeley	CA	16 (1915)	1915
08026	Swift, Henry Jr.	Berkeley	CA	4 (N.D.)	1923-1924
06087	Tompkins, P. T.	Berkeley	CA	2 (1915)	1915
08222	O'Melveny, Harry W.	Beverly Hills	CA	29 (1928-1938)	1929; 1938
07085	McDuffie, Duncan	Carmel	CA	10 (1922)	1922; 1934
08220	Smith, Dr. Ralph	Claremont	CA	8 (1928)	1928-1930
08038	Hayter, R./Hayter, Richard	Hollywood	CA	0	1923
07048	Mead, William	Hollywood	CA	0	1922-1928
10609	Keyes, James	Laguna Beach	CA	0	
08201	Hobart Estate/Subdivision	Lake Tahoe	CA	7 (1926-1928)	1926-1928
08085	Bixby, Frederick Mrs.	Long Beach	CA	19 (1923-1934)	1927-1934
08082	Bryant, Mrs. Ernest Albert	Long Beach	CA	2 (1935)	1926; 1933

Job #	Job Name/Alternative Name	Job Location		Plans	Correspondence
08223	Hart, Mrs. Alden L.	Long Beach	CA	8 (1929)	1929-1930
08253	Jergins, A. T.	Long Beach	CA	0	1930
08239	Rancho Santa Ana Botanic Gardens	Long Beach	CA	55 (1928-1939)	1927-1952
08042	Campbell, Ella/Campbell, Ella D.	Los Angeles	CA	5 (1924)	1923-1924
08262	O'Melveny, H. W.	Los Angeles	CA	9 (1932)	1932-1933
08041	Schipkowsky, Rudolph	Los Angeles	CA	5 (1924)	1924
08244	Edwards, L. T.	Los Cerritos	CA	2 (1930)	1930-1931
05351	Sharon, Frederick W.	Menlo Park	CA	0	1912
08079	McDuffie, William	Montecito	CA	52 (1927-1928)	1928-1929
08056	Nelson, William P.	Montecito	CA	0	1925
08020	Jacks, Lee Miss/Rancho Aguajito	Monterey	CA	89 (1923-1932)	1923-1936; 1945
08095	Jacks, Margaret/Castro Adobe	Monterey	CA	7 (1927)	1927
08069	Bowles, P. E./McDuffie, Duncan/Bowles Property	Oakland	CA	6 (1912; 1916; 1926)	1926
03684	Olmsted, F. L. House	Palo Alto	CA	0	
08058	Barrett,W. R./Barratt, Whitford R.	Palos Verdes	CA	2 (1925)	1925-1926
08060	Benedict, H. E.	Palos Verdes	CA	9 (1926; 1929)	1926-1930
08071	Bloch, J. L. Dr.	Palos Verdes	CA	18 (1926-1927)	1926-1928
08044	Cameron, A.E.	Palos Verdes	CA	18 (1924)	1924-1926
08062	Gard, E.W.	Palos Verdes	CA	7 (1927)	1927
08089	Haggarty, J.J.	Palos Verdes	CA	12 (1927-1928)	1927-1931
08061	Harden, E.W.	Palos Verdes	CA	21 (1925-1929)	1925-1933
08210	Lane, Mr. and Mrs. Fulton	Palos Verdes	CA	4 (1928)	1928
08229	Levinson, E.D.	Palos Verdes	CA	11 (1929)	1929
08046	Olmsted, F. L.	Palos Verdes	CA	42 (1925-1938)	1924-1940; 1945; 1951
08252	Phillips, J. Norman	Palos Verdes	CA	2 (1930)	1930
08226	Raleigh, W.W.	Palos Verdes	CA	3 (1929)	1929-1930
08251	Samuels, Mrs. Homer	Palos Verdes	CA	9 (1930)	1930-1933
08070	Schreiber, Mrs. Oliver	Palos Verdes	CA	0	1927
08225	Schwedtman, F. Charles	Palos Verdes	CA	6 (1930-1931)	1930-1933
08219	Stein, Dr. Otto J.	Palos Verdes	CA	6 (1928)	1928-1929
08096	Sutherland, W. M.	Palos Verdes	CA	0	1927-1929
08023	Vanderlip/Filiorum Corporation/Villetta Narcisca/Vanderlip, F.A.	Palos Verdes	CA	42 (1924-1931)	1923-1931
08088	Woods, Paul M./Keith, Mrs. Margaret	Palos Verdes	CA	8 (1924-1929)	1927-1936
05487	Cravens, John S.	Pasadena	CA	23 (1912-1915)	1912-1915
05994	Harris, N. W./Chancellor, Dr./Oak Knoll	Pasadena	CA	4 (1911-1914)	1914
08039	Warren, T. W.	Pasadena	CA	0	1923
08264	Orrick, W. H.	Pebble Beach	CA	9 (1923-1933)	1932-1935
06356	Pittsburg/Davison, Henry P./Hegemann, Werner/McDuffie, Duncan	Pittsburg	CA	0	1916
08086	Buchanan, James E.	Redondo Beach	CA	13 (1927; 1929)	1927-1930
08027	Webster, E. E.	Redondo Beach	CA	0	1923

Job #	Job Name/Alternative Name	Job Location		Plans	Correspondence
08098	Dibbler, B. H.	Ross	CA	14 (1928-1932)	1927-1932
08249	Livermore, Norman B.	Ross	CA	26 (1930-1932)	1930-1932
08005	Patterson, R.L. (Subdivision)	San Carlos	CA	0	1922-1923
12097	Howard, George P.	San Francisco	CA	0	1885
05886	Merritt, Dr. Ema	San Francisco	CA	0	1913
12107	Mills, Darius Ogden	San Francisco	CA	0	
03683	Olmsted, F. L. - Gill House	San Francisco	CA	0	1945
08272	Bryant, Susannah Bixby	San Marino	CA	17 (1936)	1935-1937
08248	Chamberlain, Selah Mrs.	San Mateo	CA	65 (1931)	1930-1931
08258	Hammond, Mrs. L. C.	San Mateo	CA	0	1930-1931
08024	Robbins, Mrs.	San Pedro	CA	0	1923
05830	Cowles, W. H./W. M. S. Cowles	Santa Barbara	CA	53 (1913-1918)	1913-1928
02046	Goodhue, Bertram	Santa Barbara	CA	0	
08081	Parkford, E. A.	Santa Barbara	CA	17 (1916; 1926-1927)	1926-1930
08325	Pio Pico Mansion/California State Parks	Whittier	CA	0	
03475	Gilbert, Dr. O. M.	Boulder	CO	0	1908
03473	McHarg, J. A.	Boulder	CO	0	1908
08007	Cusack, [Thomas?]	Cascade	CO	0	1923
07160	Burns, A. Martin	Colorado Springs	CO	0	1923
03607	Depew, Mrs. Grace Goodyear/Broadmoor	Colorado Springs	CO	0	1909
03362	Palmer, Gen. William J./Glen Eyrie	Colorado Springs	CO	4 (1906)	1907
06453	Penrose, Spencer	Colorado Springs	CO	57 (1916-1928)	1916-1928; 1937
07268	Stewart, Philip B.	Colorado Springs	CO	6 (1924)	1923-1928
09527	Archbald, Mrs. Olive H.	Arlington	CT	0	1937-1938
07329	Gibbons, Mr. John H.	Avon	CT	0	1924
06371	Lewis, Tracy S.	Beacon Falls	CT	2 (1916)	1916-1919
07813	Bryant, W. G.	Bridgeport	CT	9 (1927)	1927-1928
07884	Bryant, Waldo C./Black Rock	Bridgeport	CT	4 (1927)	1927-1930
07885	McNeil, W. C./Black Rock/McNeil, K.W.	Bridgeport	CT	0	1927-1928
09267	Ingraham, E.	Bristol	CT	3 (1931)	1931
01360	Scoville, Robert	Chapinville	CT	19 (1893-1896)	1893-1896
03452	Cromwell Hall	Cromwell	CT	11 (1905-1908)	1908
02998	Dunham, Edward K.	Cromwell	CT	1 (1904)	1904-1906
01890	Crimmins, J. D./Crimmins, John D.	Darien	CT	0	1891-1897
10627	Sharon, Mr. & Mrs. William A.	Essex	CT	0	1978-1979
06395	Jennings, Annie B.	Fairfield	CT	0	1916
07789	Noyes, Henry F. Mrs.	Fairfield	CT	11 (1927-1928)	1926-1928
07733	Spelman, H. B.	Fairfield	CT	7 (1926-1927)	1926-1928
01026	Sturgis, F.	Fairfield	CT	17 (1884-1885)	1883-1886; 1893
09118	Baldwin, Roger S.	Greenwich	CT	71 (1930-1931)	1929-1933; 1939
09500	Beckjord, Walter B./Percy A. Rockefeller Estate	Greenwich	CT	5 (1937)	1937

Job #	Job Name/Alternative Name	Job Location		Plans	Correspondence
10045	Brown, R.R.	Greenwich	CT	16 (1951-1957)	1956-1957
09578	Chapman, John D. Mrs./Chapman, John D./Round Island	Greenwich	CT	20 (1939)	1939
07717	Davison, G. W.	Greenwich	CT	0	1926-1928
06345	Edwards, Duncan	Greenwich	CT	0	1916
06392	Fisher, Harry J./Sabine Farm	Greenwich	CT	3 (1916-1917)	1916-1917; 1946-1956
09208	Howe, George H./Storm, George H.	Greenwich	CT	0	1930-1931
09117	Kinney, Gilbert	Greenwich	CT	7 (1929-1930)	1929
07880	Lillibridge, Ray D.	Greenwich	CT	9 (1929-1930)	1927-1930; 1937
07827	McDonnell, Hubert	Greenwich	CT	6 (1927-1929)	1928-1931
06434	Redfield, Tyler L./The Orchards	Greenwich	CT	7 (1910-1917)	1916-1917
09493	Rockefeller, Avery	Greenwich	CT	4 (1937-1948)	1937-1948
09193	Rogerson, James C./Stokes/Khakum Wood	Greenwich	CT	79 (1930-1931)	1929-1938
07678	Rowe, H. W./Rowe, Henry	Greenwich	CT	5 (1926)	1926-1927
07652	Smith, Alfred G./Khakum Wood Subdivision	Greenwich	CT	12 (1926-1929)	1926-1932
09176	Stevens, R. P./Howard, V. Noel/Khakum Wood	Greenwich	CT	64 (1928-1931)	1927-1932; 1938-1939; 1944-1945
09284	Stevens, Ray P./Khakum Wood	Greenwich	CT	55 (1931-1932)	1931-1932
07696	Stokes, I. N. P./Indian Point/Stokes, I.N. Phelps	Greenwich	CT	7 (1926)	1926-1928
02924	Stokes, I. N. Phelps/Khakum Wood	Greenwich	CT	920 (1903-1979)	1903-1980
09268	Thomson, Graham C./Stokes/Khakum Wood	Greenwich	CT	30 (1930-1931)	1929-1931
06300	Topping, Henry J.	Greenwich	CT	85 (1915-1917)	1915-1917
06269	Tubby, W. B.	Greenwich	CT	0	1915-1916
07075	Walworth, C. W.	Greenwich	CT	22 (1923)	1922-1924
06666	Walworth, C. W. Mrs./Walworth, Charles W.	Greenwich	CT	5 (1919)	1919
09471	Yandell, Lunsford P.	Greenwich	CT	3 (1936-1937)	1936-1939; 1951
09309	Goodwin, F. Spencer	Hartford	CT	0	1932-1933
02043	Goodwin, J. J.	Hartford	CT	4 (1897)	1893-1898
07272	Goodwin, Walter L.	Hartford	CT	54 (1923-1925)	1924-1925
06079	Hart, John B.	Hartford	CT	7 (1914-1915)	1914-1915
06500	Karper, Louis J.	Hartford	CT	0	1917
05250	Kohn, George E.	Hartford	CT	0	1911
00041	Olmsted, A.H	Hartford	CT	4 (1890-1891)	1882-1902
07864	Porter, John	Hartford	CT	32 (1927-1928)	1927-1928
09227	Putnam, W. H.	Hartford	CT	9 (1930-1931)	1930-1932
06800	Putnam, William H.	Hartford	CT	0	1920
06568	Seaverns, Charles F.T.	Hartford	CT	14 (1917-1919)	1917-1920; 1972
03400	Talcott, George S.	Hartford	CT	4 (1907-1908)	1907-1908; 1922
09087	Twitchell, H. D.	Hartford	CT	0	1929
07073	Kennedy, Sinclair	Haviland Hollow	CT	0	1922

Job #	Job Name/Alternative Name	Job Location		Plans	Correspondence
07844	Camp, Arthur G.	Litchfield	CT	0	1927
07369	Liggett, Richard H.	Litchfield	CT	73 (1925-1929)	1924-1930; 1939
07334	Richards, George	Litchfield	CT	11 (1923-1929)	1924-1929
07312	Swayze, R. C./Swayze, Robert C.	Litchfield	CT	11 (1925-1935)	1917-1918; 1924-1927
09049	Swayze-Chase House/Swayze, Robert C./Old Chase House	Litchfield	CT	2 (1929)	1929; 1934-1942
00301	Curtis, George M.	Meriden	CT	2 (1903)	1903-1905
09978	Eggleston, A. F.	Meriden	CT	0	1954
07675	Sperry, Mark L. J.	Middlebury	CT	0	1926
07293	Swenson, A. C. Dr.	Middlebury	CT	26 (1924-1929)	1924-1929
01343	Whittemore, J. H.	Middlebury	CT	13 (1893-1895)	1893-1896
00023	DeZeng, Richard L.	Middletown	CT	4 (1897-1902)	1896-1901
00035	Wadsworth, C. S./Long Lane	Middletown	CT	22 (1901; 1921)	1900-1922
06173	Corbin, Philip	New Britain	CT	0	1915
07325	Moore, E. A.	New Britain	CT	1 (1924)	1924-1925
03393	Lapham, Lewis H. Mrs./Lapham, Lewis H./Waveny	New Canaan	CT	282 (1902-1938)	1907-1917; 1935-1940
07831	Taggart, Alice Miss	New Canaan	CT	0	1927-1928
07725	Taggart, Rush	New Canaan	CT	58 (1925-1930)	1926-1936
09690	Zimbalist, Efrem Mrs.	New Hartford	CT	99 (1905; 1937; 1945-1947; 1952-1955)	1945-1957
02631	Bennett, T. G. Mrs./Bennett, Thomas G.	New Haven	CT	12 (1902)	1902
05344	Bingham, Hiram Prof.	New Haven	CT	9 (1910-1911)	1911-1912
02382	Fisher, Irving	New Haven	CT	2 (1902)	1902
00050	Kingsbury, T. J. Jr./Kingsbury, Frederick J.	New Haven	CT	1 (1902)	1888-1903
00417	Guthrie, Charles S.	New London	CT	19 (1901-1903)	1900-1904
07453	Lee, George B. Mrs./Lee, George B.	New London	CT	6 (1925-1926)	1925
01397	Olmsted, A. H.	New London	CT	8 (1894-1895)	1894-1895
07258	Rogers, E. E./Rogers, Ernest E.	New London	CT	5 (1923)	1923-1924
09172	Spaulding, Elmer H.	New London	CT	3 (1929-1930)	1929-1930
12117	Williams, C. A.	New London	CT	0	N.D.
09367	Fosdick, Raymond B.	Newtown	CT	5 (1934)	1934-1935
03274	Bond, Stephen N./Black Point	Niantic	CT	4 (1907)	1907-1908
01728	Bridgman, H. H./Bridgeman, H. H.	Norfolk	CT	5 (1894-1896)	1894-1896
09220	Childs, Starling W. Mrs./Childs, S. W.	Norfolk	CT	10 (1930)	1930
03715	Walcott, F. C.	Norfolk	CT	0	1909
12517	Mathews, Charles D.	Norwalk	CT	0	1876
09482	Streeter, Mrs. Milford B. Jr.	Norwalk	CT	2 (1937)	1935-1937
10543	Gorrissen, Mr. & Mrs. Willy E.	Norwich	CT	2 (1975)	1975
10706	Quirin, Mr. & Mrs. Edward J.	Old Lyme	CT	0	1979
05573	Cottrell, Edgar H.	Pawcatuck	CT	4 (1912)	1912-1913
01209	Clark, R. M./Clark, Mary V. (Mrs. R. M.)	Pomfret	CT	22 (1890-1892)	1890-1904
09480	Mallory, H. B./Mallory, Harry B.	Ridgebury	CT	31 (1929-1937)	1937-1938

Job #	Job Name/Alternative Name	Job Location		Plans	Correspondence
09330	Ballard, Edward L.	Ridgefield	CT	0	1932
00024	Maynard, Effingham Mrs./Maynard Walter E.	Ridgefield	CT	38 (1902)	1901-1903
06113	Lewis, F. E. 2nd	Saugatuck	CT	22 (1910-1916)	1914-1916
03138	Schlaet, Arnold	Saugatuck	CT	16 (1906-1914)	1906-1914
09753	Bingham, Harry Payne	Sharon	CT	15 (1942-1946)	1946
09045	Hatch, Harold A.	Sharon	CT	168 (1927-1950)	1929-1934; 1945-1950
00350	Dodge, A. M./Dodge, Arthur M.	Simsbury	CT	5 (1895-1903)	1903
00332	Wood, C. B. Mrs.	Simsbury	CT	29 (1903)	1903-1904; 1913
00196	Cheney, Anne W.	South Manchester	CT	23 (1893-1903)	1894-1904
09132	Altschul, Frank	Stamford	CT	26 (1927-1930)	1929-1934
06662	Bartram, J. Percy	Stamford	CT	0	1918-1919
09127	Rickey, Hunter/Richey, S. Hunter	Stamford	CT	0	1929-1930
10728	Gibson, Dr. & Mrs. J. Merill Jr.	Stonington	CT	0	1979
10683	Holt, Mr. & Mrs. L. Emmett	Stonington	CT	0	1979
07917	Hendee, George M.	Suffield	CT	11 (1928-1929)	1928-1929

Perspective sketch of shelter for the Kennedy estate, August 1930. Job #9199 – Joseph P. Kennedy (Hyannisport, MA).

Job #	Job Name/Alternative Name	Job Location		Plans	Correspondence
09376	Bryant, T. W. Mrs.	Torrington	CT	29 (1935-1936)	1935-1936
03730	Migeon, Elizabeth/Migeon Place	Torrington	CT	26 (1909-1919)	1909-1917; 1937-1938
06657	Torrington-Trinity Rectory/Trinity Church Rectory	Torrington	CT	15 (1917-1920)	1918-1920
09501	Vincent, Mrs. Clive B.	Torrington	CT	0	1937-1938
09120	Bronson, Richardson	Waterbury	CT	7 (1929)	1929-1930
06940	Brown, Charles H. Dr.	Waterbury	CT	2 (1921)	1921
06843	Dye, John S./Dye, J.S./Wade, Henry L.	Waterbury	CT	3 (1920)	1920
06823	Goss, Edward Otis	Waterbury	CT	0	1920
07561	Swenson, A. C. Dr.	Waterbury	CT	5 (1924-1926)	1925-1927
06552	White, William H.	Waterbury	CT	0	1917
09071	English, Edwin H.	Watertown	CT	1 (1929)	1929-1933
07476	Heminway Homestead/Heminway, Harry H.	Watertown	CT	9 (1925)	1925-1926
07716	Heminway, Bartow L.	Watertown	CT	72 (1926-1946)	1926-1933; 1941-1946
07271	Heminway, H. H./Heminway, Harry H.	Watertown	CT	1 (1924)	1924
07274	Heminway, Merritt	Watertown	CT	25 (1924-1928)	1924-1928
09070	Lilley, Theodore	Watertown	CT	0	1929-1931
06194	Merriman, H. Morton	Watertown	CT	4 (1912-1915)	1915
07845	Stranahan, R. A.	Westport	CT	75 (1927-1928)	1927-1928
10425	Harvey, Mr. & Mrs. Cyrus Jr.	Woodstock	CT	2 (1973)	1972-1973
00676	Anderson, N.L.	Washington	DC	4 (1883)	
06790	Ansberry, Timothy T.	Washington	DC	10 (1920)	1920-1921; 1927
03643	Arms, John Taylor	Washington	DC	3 (1909)	1909-1910
05178	Aspinwall, C. A.	Washington	DC	0	1911
03648	Cross, Whitman	Washington	DC	0	
07714	Erwin, H. P.	Washington	DC	31 (1922-1927)	1926-1927
07308	Gaillard, D. P.	Washington	DC	11 (1927)	1924-1937
07022	Ihlder, John	Washington	DC	4 (1922)	1922
02914	Johnston, Mrs. Frances B.	Washington	DC	0	1904-1909
01242	Leiter, L. Z.	Washington	DC	6 (1893-1894)	1892-1900
03358	Lothrop, A. M.	Washington	DC	1 (1909)	1907-1910
00297	Newlands, Francis G.	Washington	DC	11 (1902)	1891; 1902-1903
05518	Parmlee, James	Washington	DC	0	
07054	Russell, Canon/Russell, J. Townsend	Washington	DC	0	1922-1923
02956	Smith, Hamilton Mrs.	Washington	DC	4 (1904)	1904
00296	Townsend, R. H. Mrs./Townsend, R.H.	Washington	DC	9 (1900-1902)	1900-1902
06574	Vanderbilt, George W. Mrs.	Washington	DC	12 (1917)	1917
02966	Wells, Isabella Miss	Washington	DC	9 (1904)	1904-1905
00623	Windon, William	Washington	DC	10 (1881)	1881
03578	Robinson, C. W.	Claymont	DE	0	1908
12127	Field, William M.	Wilmington	DE	0	1889-1890

Job #	Job Name/Alternative Name	Job Location		Plans	Correspondence
06768	DuPont, H. F./Country Club	Winterthur	DE	47 (1919-1921)	1919
06559	Evans, Rush E.		FL	0	1917
07519	Hurd, R. L./Florida Land Development		FL	0	1925
09470	Hobart, G. A.	Belleair	FL	30 (1931-1937)	1936-1941
07306	Boca Grande Land Company/Peterkin, C. R.	Boca Grande	FL	29 (1913-1925)	1924-1925
07119	Ricker, V. C.	Clearwater	FL	20 (1923)	1923
06811	Shotwell, E. C.	Enterprise	FL	32 (1920-1921)	1920; 1926
07559	Venable, George V./Subdivision	Gainesville	FL	0	1925
07622	Hypoluxo Island/Demarest, J. M.	Hypoluxo Island	FL	12 (1925-1927)	1926-1927
06158	Ferguson, Alfred/Indian River Islands Corporation	Indian River	FL	5 (1931)	1915; 1931
07077	Cummer, A. G. Mrs./Cummer, Arthur G.	Jacksonville	FL	9 (1922)	1922
06165	Cummer, W. E.	Jacksonville	FL	24 (1931)	1931-1933; 1948
09324	O'Hara, Edna L.	[Melvin?]	FL	0	1928-1934
06984	Abbott, William L.	Mountain Lake	FL	13 (1916; 1920-1921)	1921-1923
06016	Abbott, William L.	Mountain Lake	FL	11 (1928-1929)	1928-1929
07609	Alvord, Charles H.	Mountain Lake	FL	10 (1926-1931)	1926-1931
06530	Ard, Dr. F. C./Mt. Lake Corporation	Mountain Lake	FL	0	1918; 1922
07082	Ard/Mt. Lake	Mountain Lake	FL	0	1922
06509	Babcock, George L./Babcock, George L. (Henry O.)	Mountain Lake	FL	7 (1920-1922)	1918-1922
07080	Babson, R. W./Babson, Roger W.	Mountain Lake	FL	9 (1922)	1922
06028	Ballantine, Percy	Mountain Lake	FL	3 (1930)	1929-1933
06104	Barrows, Ira	Mountain Lake	FL	4 (1930)	1930
07783	Barrows, Ira - Lot 2, Block 32	Mountain Lake	FL	514 (1927-1948)	
07165	Bedford, E. T.	Mountain Lake	FL	0	1923
06025	Bibb, William S./Bibb, William G.	Mountain Lake	FL	6 (1929)	1929-1930
07362	Billstein, A. M.	Mountain Lake	FL	14 (1924-1929)	1924-1926
06630	Blanchard, Denman	Mountain Lake	FL	33 (1918)	1918
06936	Bok, Edward W.	Mountain Lake	FL	15 (1921-1923)	1921-1926; 1941
06023	Buck, C. A.	Mountain Lake	FL	22 (1929-1932)	1927-1939; 1969-1970
07428	Bush, Irving T.	Mountain Lake	FL	64 (1925-1926)	1925-1928
06017	Bush, S. P.	Mountain Lake	FL	5 (1928-1930)	1928
06826	Cassell, W. B.	Mountain Lake	FL	3 (1920)	1920
07248	Chapin, Alfred H.	Mountain Lake	FL	135 (1923-1930)	1923-1934; 1943-1946
06828	Chase, Charles E.	Mountain Lake	FL	0	1920
07921	Clarke, E. F.	Mountain Lake	FL	0	
06134	Coakley, C. G. Dr./Oakley, Cornelius G.	Mountain Lake	FL	5 (1931)	1931
07669	Cox, R. W.	Mountain Lake	FL	7 (1926-1931)	1926-1931
07438	Crane, H. M./Crane, Henry M.	Mountain Lake	FL	8 (1925-1929)	1925-1932
07459	Curtis Brothers	Mountain Lake	FL	0	
07779	Curtis, F. Kingsbury	Mountain Lake	FL	29 (1923-1927)	1927; 1932

Job #	Job Name/Alternative Name	Job Location		Plans	Correspondence
07157	Curtis, F. Kingsbury	Mountain Lake	FL	0	1923-1931
06925	DeGraff, James W.	Mountain Lake	FL	18 (1922-1925)	1921-1926
06844	Dillon, Herbert L./Gordon, C. W./Hamill, J.L./Dillon, Herbert	Mountain Lake	FL	0	1920-1940
07052	Dohme, A. R. L. Dr.	Mountain Lake	FL	24 (1922-1931)	1922; 1927-1931; 1936
07635	Douglas, J. H.	Mountain Lake	FL	1 (1926)	
07042	Douglas, James H./Miller, Daniel	Mountain Lake	FL	20 (1922-1925)	1922
07365	Douglas, James H./Ruth, F.S./Old Dudley House	Mountain Lake	FL	9 (1924-1930)	1924-1927
07079	Edgarton, C. F.	Mountain Lake	FL	22 (1922-1923)	1922-1923
06139	Ellsworth, H. E.	Mountain Lake	FL	6 (1930-1931)	1931-1932
06015	Ensign, Joseph R.	Mountain Lake	FL	13 (1928-1930)	1928-1932
06981	Ensign, Joseph R.	Mountain Lake	FL	6 (1921-1930)	1921
07780	Ferguson, Helen G.	Mountain Lake	FL	13 (1929)	1927-1932
07621	Field, R. E.	Mountain Lake	FL	0	1926-1927
06029	Fulford, George T.	Mountain Lake	FL	2 (1930)	1930-1933; 1960
06850	Gilmor, Robert	Mountain Lake	FL	0	1920
06024	Glass, Alexander Mrs.	Mountain Lake	FL	2 (1929)	
07436	Goss, John H.	Mountain Lake	FL	21 (1924-1927)	1925-1928
07118	Gribbel, John	Mountain Lake	FL	1 (1923)	1923
06414	Gribbel, John/Heckscher, August	Mountain Lake	FL	246 (1916-1926)	1916-1919; 1925-1926
07922	Gunther, F. L.	Mountain Lake	FL	5 (1928)	1928-1929
07684	Hamill, James L./Lake Wales	Mountain Lake	FL	0	1926-1934
07898	Hanson, Willis T.	Mountain Lake	FL	12 (1928-1930)	1928-1929
07483	Heckscher, August	Mountain Lake	FL	15 (1924-1926)	1925-1926
07361	Hemphill, Clifford R.	Mountain Lake	FL	15 (1924-1926)	1924
06136	Hill, J. F. Mrs.	Mountain Lake	FL	3 (1931)	
06825	Holt, Julia Miss/Maddox, W.S./Holt, Julia W.	Mountain Lake	FL	0	1920-1929
06827	Hubert, Conrad	Mountain Lake	FL	11 (1920)	1920-1925
07081	Jacquelin, H. T./Jacquelin, H. T. B.	Mountain Lake	FL	14 (1922)	1922
06783	Jennings, Oliver G./Cook	Mountain Lake	FL	16 (1916-1927)	1919-1920; 1926-1927
06018	Johnson, H. M./Johnson, Harry M.	Mountain Lake	FL	2 (1928)	1928
06504	Kingsbury, F. J./Bull, F. Kingsbury/Kingsbury, Frederick J.	Mountain Lake	FL	74 (1917-1923)	1917; 1923
06845	Kingsbury, H. D./Kingsbury, Herbert D.	Mountain Lake	FL	2 (1922)	1922
06105	Kolb, Sarah E./Emma V.	Mountain Lake	FL	0	1930
07514	LaFrentz, F. W.	Mountain Lake	FL	2 (1926; 1930)	1926-1932
06829	Laughlin, George M./Gale, Philip/Gale, Philip B.	Mountain Lake	FL	22 (1927-1930)	1920; 1927-1931
06021	Lillibridge, Roy D./Lillibridge, Ray D.	Mountain Lake	FL	2 (N.D.)	1929
07788	Lykes, Howell/Ballast Point	Mountain Lake	FL	0	1927
06816	Macomber, George E./Gannet, Guy P./Archibald, F.A.,	Mountain Lake	FL	5 (1920)	1920

Job #	Job Name/Alternative Name	Job Location		Plans	Correspondence
07430	Mann - Hamill/Mann, Isaac T./Hamill, James L.	Mountain Lake	FL	0	1925-1926; 1964
07614	Mann, I. T./Mann, Isaac T.	Mountain Lake	FL	11 (1924-1927)	1926-1930
06137	Marsh, H. W.	Mountain Lake	FL	0	1931
07164	Marshall, Howard W.	Mountain Lake	FL	0	
06457	Martin, A. B./Mountain Lake Corporation	Mountain Lake	FL	0	1916-1917
07928	Martin, W. H./Martin, Walter H.	Mountain Lake	FL	0	1928-1929; 1937
06122	Mason, James H.	Mountain Lake	FL	0	1930
06019	Maxwell, Howard W.	Mountain Lake	FL	7 (1929)	1929
07697	McCarter, Thomas N.	Mountain Lake	FL	5 (1926-1930)	1926-1930
06106	McTierney, Thomas H./McInnerney, Thomas H.	Mountain Lake	FL	0	1930
07364	Miller, Daniel B./Douglas, James H./Miller, Daniel B./Riker, Charles L.	Mountain Lake	FL	20 (1922-1925)	1924-1930; 1937
07424	Miller, George P.	Mountain Lake	FL	37 (1925)	1925
07778	Mitchell, S. Z./Ruth, F. S./Mitchell, Sidney Z.	Mountain Lake	FL	19 (1926-1939)	1927-1940
06027	Montgomery, R. H. Mrs.	Mountain Lake	FL	1 (1929)	1929
07919	Munroe, Jay	Mountain Lake	FL	0	
06103	Nichols, W. H. Jr.	Mountain Lake	FL	13 (1930)	1930-1931; 1960
07619	Noyes, Jansen	Mountain Lake	FL	0	1926-1927
06460	Olmsted, F. L.	Mountain Lake	FL	0	
06026	Paine, Nathan	Mountain Lake	FL	9 (1930)	1929-1930
07772	Parks, A. A./Tobey, Allen	Mountain Lake	FL	2 (1928)	1927-1928
06832	Parks, Arthur A.	Mountain Lake	FL	39 (1920-1925)	1920-1924
07117	Pierce, Winslow	Mountain Lake	FL	0	1923
06539	Reynolds, R. J.	Mountain Lake	FL	6 (1917)	1917-1918
07929	Rice, E. W.	Mountain Lake	FL	0	1928-1929
07370	Ruth, F. S.	Mountain Lake	FL	13 (1924)	1924
06022	Ruth, F. S.	Mountain Lake	FL	0	1929
06830	Ruth, F. S./Mitchell, S.Z./Ruth, Frederick S.	Mountain Lake	FL	13 (1926-1939)	1926
06138	Sanford, Mrs. C. G./Sanford, C.G.	Mountain Lake	FL	2 (1931)	1931
07930	Scofield, W. B.	Mountain Lake	FL	0	
07920	Starkey, W. P.	Mountain Lake	FL	8 (1928-1929)	1928-1929; 1940
07363	Starrett, Paul	Mountain Lake	FL	5 (1924-1927)	1924-1927
07620	Starrett, Paul/Ruth, F. S.	Mountain Lake	FL	0	1926
07781	Tobey, Allen	Mountain Lake	FL	27 (1927-1928)	1927-1932
07830	True, Frank O./True, Frank D.	Mountain Lake	FL	0	1927
06733	Wallace, Sumner Mrs./Wallace, Sumner/Curtiss, V.H.	Mountain Lake	FL	46 (1919-1920)	1919-1920
06982	Warner, W. H. - new tract/Van Sweringen	Mountain Lake	FL	4 (1921-1922)	1921-1926; 1962
06551	Warner, W. H. - old job	Mountain Lake	FL	43 (1917-1918)	1917-1926
07912	Webb, Thomas D.	Mountain Lake	FL	6 (1928-1929)	1928

Job #	Job Name/Alternative Name	Job Location		Plans	Correspondence
07626	Webb, Thomas D.	Mountain Lake	FL	0	1926-1927
06831	West, Charles A.	Mountain Lake	FL	3 (N.D.)	1920
06809	Wheeler, Harlan B./Emory, A.C.	Mountain Lake	FL	15 (1920)	1920; 1926
07484	Williams, Thomas	Mountain Lake	FL	15 (1925-1926)	1925-1930
07429	Zimmerman, John E.	Mountain Lake	FL	10 (1924-1929)	1925-1927
05493	Rand, Samuel	Orlando	FL	0	1936-1945
07618	Curtis, Kenneth/Curtis Park	Polk County	FL	0	1926
07592	Sullivan, W. R.	Polk County	FL	0	1925
07167	Curtis, F. Kingsbury	Sarasota	FL	0	1923
07518	Wooley, Fred F./Oyster Bay	Sarasota	FL	15 (1926)	1925-1932; 1951
06341	Palmer, Mrs. Potter	Sarasota Bay	FL	0	1916
07849	Gillett, D. C.	Tampa	FL	1 (1927)	1927-1932
07911	Lykes Homesite	Tampa	FL	2 (1928)	1928
06135	Hill, Dr. L. C.	Vero Beach	FL	0	
06133	Hill, Dr. T. C.	Vero Beach	FL	2 (1931)	
07193	Bacheller, Irving	Winter Park	FL	0	1923
06685	Rogers, W. A.	Winter Park	FL	4 (1918-1919)	1919-1921
09488	Glenn, Thomas K.	Atlanta	GA	4 (1926-1929)	1937
00306	Hurt, Joel	Atlanta	GA	5 (1896-1903)	1903-1904; 1976
03801	Kontz, Ernest C.	Atlanta	GA	0	1909
02975	Maddox, Dr. Robert F./Old Dominion Guano Co.	Atlanta	GA	0	1904
07148	Mitchell, Walter G.	Atlanta	GA	4 (1923)	1922-1926
06946	Richardson, Hugh	Atlanta	GA	0	1921
06863	Baird, J. M.	Columbus	GA	0	1920
06797	Bradley, W. C./Miller, B. S.	Columbus	GA	99 (1911-1928)	1920-1934
07616	Jenkins, Mrs. W. E.	Columbus	GA	0	1926
07666	Scarborough, Claude	Columbus	GA	8 (1925-1926)	1926
06866	Swift, E. W.	Columbus	GA	5 (1920)	1920
07486	Turner, D. Abbot	Columbus	GA	27 (1925-1926)	1925-1927
06219	Client of P. E. Dennis	Macon	GA	0	1915
02884	McDonald, M. G.	Rome	GA	0	1904
07120	Clarke, D. C./Subdivision	Des Moines	IA	0	1923
03535	Kenton, Judge W. S./Kenyon, W. S.	Fort Dodge	IA	0	1908
08043	Anderson, C. C.	Boise	ID	28 (1924-1927)	1924-1930
09539	Rust, Adlai	Bloomington	IL	16 (1938-1939)	1938-1942
00249	Bissell, J. H.	Chicago	IL	0	1892-1898
06867	Doering, O. C.	Chicago	IL	0	1920
03998	Garvey, Paul D./Harvey, Paul D.	Chicago	IL	0	1910
05093	Gross, S. E.	Chicago	IL	1 (1907; 1911)	1910-1911
06378	Leopold, Alfred E./Western Mining Company, Town Site	Chicago	IL	0	1916
00683	Wyman, A. Phelps	Chicago	IL	0	1897

Job #	Job Name/Alternative Name	Job Location		Plans	Correspondence
01382	Fullerton, C. W.	Highland Park	IL	5 (1893-1894)	1894-1895
07302	Moseley, Carleton	Highland Park	IL	40 (1922-1925)	1924-1925
00029	Barton, E. M.	Hinsdale	IL	138 (1902-1903)	1897-1911
06187	Baldwin, A. Rosecrans	Lake Forest	IL	0	1915-1916
03476	Brewster, Walter S./Brewster, Walter L.	Lake Forest	IL	2 (1906-1908)	1908-1909
01231	Cobb, Henry Ives/Rockdale Farm	Lake Forest	IL	4 (1892)	1892-1894
03555	Coonley, Prentiss	Lake Forest	IL	13 (1906-1911)	1908-1917
01893	Farwell, J. V. and F. C.	Lake Forest	IL	3 (1895)	1895-1896
02991	Hamill, E. A./Hamill, Ernest A.	Lake Forest	IL	43 (1904-1908)	1904-1918
00199	Jones, D.B./Jones, David B.	Lake Forest	IL	8 (1892-1896)	1893-1895; 1900
05930	Leatherbee, R. W.	Lake Forest	IL	0	
05106	Leatherbee, R. W./Leatherbee, Robert W.	Lake Forest	IL	13 (1911-1915)	1911-1915; 1933
03356	Lord, James Fuller	Lake Forest	IL	0	1907
00200	McCormick, Cyrus H.	Lake Forest	IL	11 (1895)	1893-1895; 1932
05343	Poole, Ralph H.	Lake Forest	IL	18 (1911-1914)	1911-1915
03951	Rumsey, N. A.	Lake Forest	IL	0	1910
00354	Wrenn, J. H.	Lake Forest	IL	6 (1903-1904)	1903-1905
06758	Morton, Joy	Lisle	IL	0	
09577	Morgan, Jack	Austin	IN	19 (1938-1939)	1938-1939
03438	Williams, Henry M.	Fort Wayne	IN	0	1908
06883	Landon, H. McK./Landon, Hugh McKennan/Oldfields/Indianapolis Museum of Art	Indianapolis	IN	52 (1920-1927)	1920-1934; 1967-1981
05276	Levey, Mrs. L. H.	Indianapolis	IN	0	1911; 1917
07269	Wathen, O. H./Utica Pike	Jeffersonville	IN	0	1923-1934
01803	Norton, G. W.	New Albany	IN	3 (1895-1896)	1895-1896
06805	Bockhoff, William F.	Richmond	IN	0	1920
05231	Hammon, Alonzo J.	South Bend	IN	0	1914
00648	Anderson, J. A.		KS	4 (1882)	
01233	Plumb, Preston B.	Emporia	KS	9 (1883)	
00167	Bernheim, I. W.	Anchorage	KY	16 (1900)	1900-1902; 1914; 1977-1980
03068	Bernheim, I. W./Homewood	Anchorage	KY	14 (1905-1906)	1900-1907
06225	Marshall, Mrs. John	Anchorage	KY	0	1915-1916
00289	Robinson, C. B./Robinson, C. Bonnycastle/Bartlett, J.H.	Anchorage	KY	4 (1897-1903)	1894; 1902-1904; 1919
06774	Shallcross Farm	Anchorage	KY	0	1919
06003	Kennedy, F. R.	Benham	KY	0	1914
03039	Strater, Henry	Florida Heights	KY	20 (1905-1908)	1905-1908
06598	Taylor, E. H./Taylor, E.H., Jr.	Frankfort	KY	7 (1917-1918)	1917-1919
06114	Cantrill, Mary Cecil	Georgetown	KY	0	1911-1915
06709	Allen, W. B.	Glenview	KY	6 (1913-1920)	1919-1920
05065	Ballard, Charles T.	Glenview	KY	5 (1911)	1910-1911
07833	Ballard, G. Breaux	Glenview	KY	14 (1927-1928)	1927-1928

Rockefeller estate at Pocantico Hills, April 1928. Job #243 John D. Rockefeller (Pocantico Hills/Tarrytown, NY).

Job #	Job Name/Alternative Name	Job Location		Plans	Correspondence
07631	Hickman, Mrs. Baylor	Glenview	KY	0	1926-1951
07068	Rodes, Clifford Mrs./Rodes, Clifford	Glenview	KY	4 (1922)	1922
09559	Crutchfield, J. S.	Goshen	KY	0	1938
09766	Bingham, Robert W. Mrs.	Harrods Creek	KY	9 (1928-1957)	1946-1947
10071	Brown, Robinson Jr. (part of R. W. Bingham Property)	Harrods Creek	KY	34 (1958)	1954-1958
09797	Brown, W. L. Lyons	Harrods Creek	KY	31 (1948)	1947-1948
10008	Frazier, Amelia Brown, Mrs.	Harrods Creek	KY	47 (1953-1960)	1955-1962
10139	Widmer, Dr. Nelson D.	Lebanon	KY	0	1960-1961
09485	Dabney, William C.	Lee County	KY	34 (1937)	1936-1938
03404	Breckenridge, D./Breckinridge, Desha	Lexington	KY	0	1907-1911; 1919
03408	Cox, Leonard	Lexington	KY	7 (1907)	1907-1909
05880	Fishback, W. P.	Lexington	KY	0	1913
03409	Graves, George/Graves, George K.	Lexington	KY	4 (1907)	1907-1908
05770	Haggin, J. B./Widener	Lexington	KY	0	1912-1913
03405	Justice, Paul/Justice, Paul M.	Lexington	KY	0	1907-1908
07685	McDowell (Ashland)/Ashland Subdivision	Lexington	KY	1 (1926)	1925-1926
03443	McLintock, John	Lexington	KY	0	1907

Job #	Job Name/Alternative Name	Job Location		Plans	Correspondence
07744	Walton, H. Burclette/Walton, H. Burdette	Lexington	KY	0	1926
07729	Widener, Joseph E.	Lexington	KY	10 (1926)	1926; 1934
03069	Belknap, W. R./Belknap, William K./Lincliff	Longview	KY	14 (1905-1906)	1905-1911
09484	Allen, Lafton Judge	Louisville	KY	46 (1937-1938)	1937-1939
00288	Atherton, P. L./Atherton, C. P./Ardeen	Louisville	KY	5 (1902-1904)	1902-1904; 1974
00455	Atherton, P. S.	Louisville	KY	0	1902
10209	Ayre, Robert	Louisville	KY	0	1953; 1959
03033	Barker, Maxwell S.	Louisville	KY	9 (1905-1906)	1904-1906
03088	Barr, J. W./Barr, John W.	Louisville	KY	1 (1905)	1905-1910; 1916
06403	Barr, John W. Jr./Sackett	Louisville	KY	6 (1916)	1916
06418	Belknap, W. R. Mrs./City Lot/Belknap, Juliet R./Belknap, Mr. W.R.	Louisville	KY	5 (1916-1926)	1916-1926
06226	Belknap, W. R. Mrs./New Place/Belknap, Juliet R.	Louisville	KY	10 (1910-1916)	1915-1916
09553	Bickel, George R.	Louisville	KY	35 (1938-1939)	1938-1943
09574	Blakely, Charles S. Gen./Blakeley, Charles S.	Louisville	KY	9 (1934-1940)	1938-1940
03004	Bonnycastle, Everett Mrs./Bonnycastle, Harriet Everett/Bonnycastle	Louisville	KY	17 (1904-1907)	1904-1909
06229	Brainard, Lemon	Louisville	KY	0	1915
09735	Brown, George Garvin	Louisville	KY	131 (1945-1963)	1947; 1956; 1963
06887	Bulleit, V. J.	Louisville	KY	9 (1920-1921)	1920-1921
03128	Burd, M. W.	Louisville	KY	0	
03056	Burford, H. M.	Louisville	KY	0	1904-1908
00246	Caperton, John H.	Louisville	KY	3 (1902)	1902; 1917
03539	Carrier, R. M.	Louisville	KY	0	1908-1909
02275	Castleman, John B./Castlewood	Louisville	KY	0	1905-1907
07053	Clancy, J. M.	Louisville	KY	1 (1922)	1922; 1930
07298	Clark, Walter S.	Louisville	KY	22 (1924-1954)	1924-1954
07745	Collis, John	Louisville	KY	33 (1926-1928)	1926-1928; 1936-1937
06362	Collis, John/Cox, Attila/Collis, Mrs. John V.	Louisville	KY	81 (1914-1924)	1916-1917; 1922-1939
09472	Courtenay, Erskine H./Heuser, Henry	Louisville	KY	15 (1936-1950)	1936-1938; 1950
02986	Cowan, Albert	Louisville	KY	0	
02979	Cowan, Andrew	Louisville	KY	36 (1904-1939)	1897; 1904-1922
02973	Cowan, Gilbert	Louisville	KY	0	1904-1906
06557	Cox, Attilla	Louisville	KY	5 (1916-1918)	
03442	Davies, W. W./Estate in Cherokee Park	Louisville	KY	0	1908
07544	Duncan, Stuart E./Duncan, D. E.	Louisville	KY	0	1925-1931
07629	Durrett, R. L. 2nd	Louisville	KY	0	1926
10229	Dwyer, Mr. and Mrs. James J.	Louisville	KY	4 (1953)	
03076	Fehr, Frank Home/Hillcrest	Louisville	KY	11 (1905-1911)	1905-1911
09590	Fitzhugh, Henry	Louisville	KY	13 (1939-1941)	1939-1941

Job #	Job Name/Alternative Name	Job Location		Plans	Correspondence
07166	Ford, Ben O.	Louisville	KY	5 (1923)	1923
09985	Frank, W. G.	Louisville	KY	37 (1953-1956)	1954-1956
09675	Giles, W. Glover	Louisville	KY	2 (1944)	1944-1946
01247	Green, John E.	Louisville	KY	8 (1892-1894)	1891-1895
07705	Haldeman, Mrs. Bruce	Louisville	KY	0	1926
07044	Hall, Vincent	Louisville	KY	0	1922
07517	Helm, Bruce	Louisville	KY	12 (1923-1925)	1925-1928
06234	Hert, A. T.	Louisville	KY	0	1915-1916
07264	Hieatt, C. C./Goose Creek	Louisville	KY	0	1923-1925
02622	Hilliard, Byron	Louisville	KY	7 (1900-1904)	1902-1904; 1911
02277	Hite, Allen R./Estate in Alta Vista subdivision	Louisville	KY	4 (1901)	1901-1902
03805	Hite, W. W. Mrs./Hite, W. W.	Louisville	KY	4 (1909)	1909
03293	Hughes, E. L./Estate in Alta Vista subdivision	Louisville	KY	1 (1907)	1907
03272	Humphrey, Judge Alexander P.	Louisville	KY	0	1901-1902; 1907
07805	Jacobsen, J.	Louisville	KY	0	1927-1928
07711	Jacobson, J.	Louisville	KY	0	1926
09977	Johnson, M. M.	Louisville	KY	7 (1954)	1954
07510	Kendall, Harry	Louisville	KY	25 (1924-1926)	1925-1926
06143	Knott, Richard W./Thorn Hill	Louisville	KY	0	1914-1915
07776	Lemon, Brainard	Louisville	KY	15 (1939)	1927-1928
06394	Look, David M.	Louisville	KY	0	1916
03748	Marvin, J. B. Dr./Blakemore Wheeler Miller Wihry & Brooks/Landward House	Louisville	KY	4 (1909)	1909-1910; 1969-1975
02064	McFerran, J. B./McFerran, John B./Alta Vista	Louisville	KY	9 (1898-1912)	1893-1916; 1923
06295	McKellar, R. L.	Louisville	KY	0	1915-1916
07769	Mengel, C. R./Four lots in Castlewood Subdivision	Louisville	KY	3 (1926)	1927-1929
07713	Mengel, C. R./Hawthorn Highlands/Mengel, Clarence R.	Louisville	KY	3 (1926)	1926-1927
07693	Mengel, Clarence R.	Louisville	KY	0	1926
02063	Norton, G. W. Mrs./Norton, George W./Norton, Lucie and Mattie	Louisville	KY	106 (1898-1947)	1895-1906; 1926-1931; 1947
03030	Norton, Misses/Caldwell, Mrs. W. B./Norton, Mattie & Lucie, Caldwell/George Norton	Louisville	KY	104 (1904-1927)	1898-1899; 1904-1947
09487	Ogden, Squire R.	Louisville	KY	26 (1936-1939)	1936-1939
07377	Otis & Bruce/Sackett Subdivision/Fairfield/Cherokee Gardens	Louisville	KY	122 (1916-1926)	1924-1927; 1937
09507	Overbacker, Gilmore/Querbacker, Gilmore	Louisville	KY	201 (1937-1939)	1937-1940; 1947-1948
09225	Porter, H. Boone	Louisville	KY	0	1930; 1946
09564	Reynolds, C. K./Cowan, Andrew	Louisville	KY	1 (1938)	1938-1940
09750	Rodes, Clifton	Louisville	KY	9 (1946)	1946

Job #	Job Name/Alternative Name	Job Location		Plans	Correspondence
04092	Sackett, F. M.	Louisville	KY	35 (1910-1924)	1910-1928; 1938
09599	Scheirich, Henry J. Jr.	Louisville	KY	37 (1939-1941)	1940-1941; 1946
05456	Seelbach, Louis	Louisville	KY	13 (1912)	1912-1913
05447	Seelbach, Louis	Louisville	KY	0	1911
07218	Semonin, Paul	Louisville	KY	0	1924; 1927
06294	Speed, W. S./Speed, William S.	Louisville	KY	3 (1916)	1915-1919; 1947
05819	Strater, Charles Helme	Louisville	KY	6 (1912-1913)	1913-1914
02951	Strater, W.E./Watson, A.M./Strater, William E./Fitzhugh, Henry	Louisville	KY	32 (1904-1964)	1904-1905; 1935-1937; 1955-1970
09819	Strickler, Mrs. Frank P.	Louisville	KY	0	1948-1949
07012	Taylor, Marion E. and Leland/Leland, Mrs. Taylor	Louisville	KY	137 (1922-1923)	1922-1924
05104	Todd, J. Ross	Louisville	KY	1 (1911)	1911
06305	Vogt, Ben F.	Louisville	KY	0	1915
10191	Watkins, Mrs. Lowry	Louisville	KY	9 (1965)	1958-1965
09821	Whitley, M. G.	Louisville	KY	13 (1957-1959)	1948-1958
07617	Witty, A. P./Witty, Alex P.	Louisville	KY	10 (1926-1928)	1926-1928
07815	Witty, Alex P./Residence/Alta Vista Subdivision	Louisville	KY	0	1927-1928
03114	Wood, George T.	Louisville	KY	0	1906
09952	Woodland Farm	Louisville	KY	11 (1953-1957)	1952-1957
09767	Parrish, Douglas Mrs.	Paris	KY	73 (1947-1952)	1947-1952
07046	Edwards, James P.	Prospect	KY	24 (1922-1923)	1922-1928
09820	Ethridge, Mark	Prospect	KY	4 (1948; 1950)	1948-1950
10072	Hickman, Baylor	Prospect	KY	1 (N.D.)	1958
03214	Chess, W. E./Giles, Glover/Boxhill	Woodside	KY	4 (1906-1907)	1906-1909; 1946
06787	Stern, Mrs. Maurice - Memorial	New Orleans	LA	0	1919-1920
01549	Warren, Mrs. Cornelia		MA	0	1904
10637	Weiner, Dr. Alan	Abington	MA	0	
10629	Becklean, Mr. & Mrs. William	Acton	MA	0	1978
10406	O'Grady, Mr. & Mrs. Donald	Acton	MA	0	1972
10374	O'Grady, Mr. and Mrs. Donald	Acton	MA	0	1971
10414	Richmond House/Yankee Construction	Acton	MA	0	
10299	Rosenberg, Dr. and Mrs. Albert	Acton	MA	7 (1969)	1969
03161	Churchill, George B.	Amherst	MA	9 (1906-1907)	1906-1909; 1913
03382	Edward, Miss/Edwards, Miss	Amherst	MA	0	1907
12137	Hills, Henry F.	Amherst	MA	4 (N.D.)	1875
06890	Foss, Alden S.	Andover	MA	0	1920
07515	McLanathan, F. W./McLanathan, Frank W./Brown, Rodney	Andover	MA	0	1925-1927; 1954
09529	Nunez, Mrs. V. E.	Andover	MA	0	1938
09358	Penniman, S. E. Miss	Andover	MA	17 (1928; 1934)	1933-1934
00177	Ripley, Alfred L.	Andover	MA	36 (1930; 1936)	1900; 1930-1936
10461	Russem, Mr. & Mrs. Theodore L.	Andover	MA	0	

Job #	Job Name/Alternative Name	Job Location		Plans	Correspondence
03394	Towle, John A.	Andover	MA	4 (1907-1908)	1907-1908
06927	Burke, W. S. Mrs./Burke, W. S.	Annisquam	MA	3 (1921)	1921
07454	Tifft, Frances B./Tifft, Lewis E.	Annisquam	MA	10 (1925-1926)	1925-1926
10469	Berens, Dr. & Mrs. Howard R.	Arlington	MA	0	
07819	Bullock, Mrs. A. R./Bullock, A.L.	Arlington	MA	0	1927
06155	Fairchild, William A.	Arlington	MA	0	1915-1917; 1947-1948
09510	Gargill, Mrs. D. R.	Arlington	MA	0	1937
05251	Wick, Mr. F.	Ashland	MA	0	1919
02525	Clarke, L. Absolom	Athol	MA	3 (1941; 1962-1964)	1962-1963
09901	Carroll, Paul T.	Barre	MA	1 (1951)	1951-1954
00450	Bingham, A. E.	Beach Bluff	MA	0	1901
10142	Henkels, M. M. Mrs.	Bedford	MA	1 (1962)	N.D.
07562	Pickman, Dudley L.	Bedford	MA	0	1925
10654	Aguilar, Mr. & Mrs. Frank	Belmont	MA	0	
09093	Carpenter, F. I.	Belmont	MA	2 (1929)	1929
10338	Coolidge, Mr. and Mrs. Charles A. Jr.	Belmont	MA	2 (1970)	1970
10275	Erwin, Mr. and Mrs. Robert	Belmont	MA		
10292	Fahey, Mr. and Mrs. Robert J.	Belmont	MA	0	
10388	Frissora, Mr. & Mrs. Joseph	Belmont	MA	3 (1972)	1972
10510	Fuller, Mrs. Virginia	Belmont	MA	2 (1974)	1974
10484	Goldsmith, Mr. & Mrs. Robert	Belmont	MA	0	1973
10524	Grammont, Mr. & Mrs. Ronald	Belmont	MA	0	
06389	Greenough, Chester N. Mrs./Churchill, L./Atkins, R.W./Churchill, Laurence/The Cedar	Belmont	MA	250 (1916-1964)	1916-1965
06735	Henshaw, C. S.	Belmont	MA	0	1919
10670	Heskett, Mr.& Mrs. James	Belmont	MA	0	
09663	Hines, F. J. Mrs.	Belmont	MA	8 (1944)	1944
10504	Hofer, Mr. & Mrs. Philip	Belmont	MA	3 (1975)	1974-1975
10041	Hosmer, W. Arnold	Belmont	MA	0	1956
10269	Kaufmann, Mr. and Mrs. Robert	Belmont	MA	13 (1969-1970)	1968-1979
10300	MacDonald, Mr. and Mrs. Samuel	Belmont	MA	1 (1969)	1969-1970
07433	Vaughan, John F.	Belmont	MA	23 (1923-1926)	1925-1926
06610	Blodgett, John	Beverly	MA	0	1917-1918
06595	Edwards, Hannah Miss	Beverly	MA	5 (1917-1920)	1917-1920
01011	Gurney, EW	Beverly	MA	2 (1881-1884)	1884
00209	King, H. P./Exchange Building	Beverly	MA	0	1897-1899
01720	Peabody, H. W./Montserrat	Beverly	MA	11 (1894-1897)	1896-1899
12297	Phillips, J.C./Batchelder, George L./Moraine Farm	Beverly	MA	83 (1880-1881)	1879-1884
00131	Pierce, H. C.	Beverly	MA	0	1895-1899
03156	Ayer, Frederick	Beverly Farms	MA	21 (1906-1910)	1906-1910
09074	Hodges, Wetmore Mrs./Hodges, Wetmore	Beverly Farms	MA	13 (1927; 1929)	1929-1931

Top: View toward the house along garden path, "Thornewood," July 1911. Job #3494 – Chester Thorne (listed as American Lake, WA).

Bottom: Main axis of "Thornewood" garden with Mt. Rainier added off-center, April 20, 1911. Job #3494 – Chester Thorne (listed as American Lake, WA).

Job #	Job Name/Alternative Name	Job Location		Plans	Correspondence
02062	Pierce, H. C.	Beverly Farms	MA	13 (1897-1899)	1896-1908
09899	Chapin, Alfred H./Camerota, Anthony C./Summer Place	Blanford	MA	34 (1950-1951)	1951-1958
	* See also Brighton, Chestnut Hill, Dorchester, Hyde Park, Jamaica Plain, Mattapan, Readville and West Roxbury	Boston	MA		
12147	Beebe, E. Pierson	Boston	MA	0	1891; 1894
02918	Child, Stephen	Boston	MA	0	1904-1905; 1919
06310	Curley, James Hon./Curley, James M.	Boston	MA	2 (1915-1916)	1915-1916
10258	Currens, Dr. and Mrs. James H.	Boston	MA	0	1968
10332	Diamond, Dr. and Mrs. Israel	Boston	MA	0	
06534	Frothingham, F. C.	Boston	MA	0	1917
03294	Gallagher, Charles T./Gallagher, Charles F.	Boston	MA	1 (1919)	1907
06321	Heathfield, H. D./Property on Charles River	Boston	MA	0	1915
10186	Morison, Admiral and Mrs. Samuel E.	Boston	MA	3 (1964-1965)	1965-1976
06944	Price, Charles Pearl/Housing Projects	Boston	MA	0	1921-1922
10262	Rice, Mr. and Mrs. Jerry S.	Boston	MA	0	1968
10405	Rowe, Miss Dorothy	Boston	MA	2 (1972)	1972-1973
02949	Shaw, William	Boston	MA	0	1904
10450	Sullivan, Mr. & Mrs. John J.	Boston	MA	2 (1973)	1973
05764	Walker, Charles	Boston	MA	8 (1913-1925)	1912-1925
07123	Wells, A. B.	Boston	MA	0	1923
09201	Wells, Channing/Wells, Channing M.	Boston	MA	2 (1930)	1930
09849	Spilhaus, Athelstan F.	Bourne	MA	0	1949
10416	Carriage House/Yankee Construction	Boxboro	MA	0	
03013	Morse, L. K. H.	Boxford	MA	0	1904-1905
06216	Huntington, P. O.	Brighton	MA	0	1915
01238	Morton, A. M.	Brighton	MA	2 (1892)	1892-1894
10310	Towne Estates	Brighton	MA	0	1970
10493	Goldberg, Mr. David	Brockton	MA	0	1974
10254	Green, Mr. and Mrs. Robert	Brockton	MA	13 (1930; 1969-1971)	1962-1973
10399	Rubin, Mr. and Mrs. Harold	Brockton	MA	2 (1972)	1972
10483	Schull, Dr. & Mrs. Robert	Brockton	MA	0	
10691	Siskind, Mr. & Mrs. Lawrence	Brockton	MA	0	1979
10391	Stone, Mr. & Mrs. Dewey	Brockton	MA	0	1970-1972
10261	Weiner, Dr. and Mrs. Alan	Brockton	MA	5 (1969)	1968-1969
00022	White, F. E./White, Frank E.	Brockton	MA	6 (1892-1901)	1892-1903
10318	Wolozin, Mr. and Mrs. Allen	Brockton	MA	0	1970
	* See also Chestnut Hill	Brookline	MA		
09954	Allen, Edward	Brookline	MA	10 (1952-1953)	1952-1953
07703	Almy/Almy, William	Brookline	MA	1 (1909)	1926-1927

Job #	Job Name/Alternative Name	Job Location		Plans	Correspondence
10178	Altschuler, Mr. and Mrs.	Brookline	MA	12 (1952-1970)	1964; 1970-1971
00300	Anderson, Mrs. Larz	Brookline	MA	0	1980
07462	Apthorp, H. O.	Brookline	MA	0	1925
01077	Armstrong, G. W./Armstrong, George W.	Brookline	MA	16 (1887-1901)	1888-1903; 1911-1912
10145	Baldini, Dr. and Mrs. Mario	Brookline	MA	12 (1962)	1962-1963
02069	Beck, Fred	Brookline	MA	2 (1895-1898)	
00454	Beck, Frederick	Brookline	MA	0	1889; 1898-1900
09982	Beckerman, F. M.	Brookline	MA	45 (1954-1955)	1954-1956
10633	Begien, Mr. & Mrs. Martin	Brookline	MA	0	1978
01436	Belcher, J. W./Belcher, John W.	Brookline	MA	4 (1895)	1895-1896
02285	Bemis, John W./Wilson, W. R.	Brookline	MA	1 (1896)	
07506	Bennett, Louis N./Bennett, Louis	Brookline	MA	18 (1925-1926)	1925-1926
07807	Bigelow, Albert/Sewall Park	Brookline	MA	0	1927
01324	Bigelow, Prescott	Brookline	MA	5 (1892)	1892-1896; 1902-1905
01019	Blake Estate	Brookline	MA	44 (1882-1886)	1878; 1886-1890
01389	Blake, A. W.	Brookline	MA	0	1892-1895
10320	Brendze, Dr. and Mrs. Robert	Brookline	MA	0	1970-1971
10311	Bright, Mr. and Mrs. Alexander	Brookline	MA	0	
12037	Brimmer, Martin	Brookline	MA	0	1882; 1886
09397	Brown, George R.	Brookline	MA	81 (1927-1946)	1936-1946
10661	Brown, Mr. & Mrs. Kingsbury Jr.	Brookline	MA	0	1979
09320	Bryant, John Dr./Sargents Estate	Brookline	MA	15 (1932-1935; 1939)	1932-1949
09864	Bryant, John Mrs.	Brookline	MA	5 (1949-1950)	1949-1955
09813	Bryant, John Mrs./Walcott Land	Brookline	MA	81 (1938-1949)	1948-1949
10223	Buell, Mr. and Mrs. George	Brookline	MA	1 (1967)	1897; 1967-1969
09808	Burrage, Walter S.	Brookline	MA	1 (1948)	1948
10306	Butler, Mr. and Mrs. Richard A.	Brookline	MA	7 (1969)	1969
07296	Cabot, Henry B.	Brookline	MA	1 (1924)	1924
00685	Cabot, Walter C.	Brookline	MA	0	
10281	Cahners, Mr. and Mrs. Walter	Brookline	MA	0	1969
10040	Campbell, A. J.	Brookline	MA	0	N.D.
10411	Caperton, Mr. & Mrs. Hugh	Brookline	MA	0	1973
02230	Channing, Walter Dr.	Brookline	MA	4 (1899)	1891; 1899
10293	Chapman, Dr. and Mrs. Earle M.	Brookline	MA	0	
10303	Chasdi, Mr. and Mrs. Simon	Brookline	MA	1 (1969)	1969
10488	Chute, Dr. & Mrs. Richard	Brookline	MA	0	
09747	Claflin, Mr. and Mrs. Thomas	Brookline	MA	0	1946
09483	Clark, Paul F.	Brookline	MA	105 (1936-1944)	1937-1944
12511	Cliffton Estate/Clifton Estate	[Brookline?]	MA	2 (1884)	
01049	Cobb, A. A.	Brookline	MA	25 (1886)	1886
09555	Cobb, Clarence M.	Brookline	MA	8 (1936)	1936-1939; 1944
10297	Cochrane, Mr. and Mrs. David D.	Brookline	MA	0	

Job #	Job Name/Alternative Name	Job Location		Plans	Correspondence
00226	Coffin, F. S.	Brookline	MA	8 (1902)	1902-1903
10039	Colby, Charles	Brookline	MA	22 (1935; 1965; 1967)	1956; 1966
09708	Colford, Mrs. E. O.	Brookline	MA	0	1950-1955
10159	Converse, Mr. and Mrs. Roger W.	Brookline	MA	0	1963
09732	Cooley, R. Howard	Brookline	MA	0	1946
00323	Coolidge, J. R. Jr./Coolidge, J. Randolph	Brookline	MA	63 (1885-1926)	1886-1895; 1903; 1911
06921	Corbett, F. A.	Brookline	MA	0	1921
07790	Cousens, J. A. Dr.	Brookline	MA	8 (1912-1927)	1927
09366	Cunningham, Alan/Sargent Estate	Brookline	MA	11 (1934)	1934-1952
09492	Cunningham, C. C. Jr./Jenckes, Mrs. Marcien/Trowbridge, E.Q.	Brookline	MA	9 (1963; 1966)	1951-1966
07775	Curran, Joseph F.	Brookline	MA	5 (1927)	1927
09009	Curtis, Louis Mrs./Parsons, Ernst M./Curtis, Louis	Brookline	MA	24 (1928-1936)	1929-1930; 1936
03731	Cutler	Brookline	MA	0	
09532	Cutler, Dr. Elliott C.	Brookline	MA	0	1938
07992	Cutler, Sewall Mr./Sargent Estate	Brookline	MA	18 (1927-1928)	1928-1929
09752	Dane, John Jr.	Brookline	MA	34 (1946-1956)	1946-1956
09454	Davis, David Dr.	Brookline	MA	3 (1936)	1936
02953	Davis, Mary S.	Brookline	MA	1 (1899)	1899
10415	Davis, Mrs. Sylvia	Brookline	MA	4 (1972)	1972-1973
10274	Davlin, Mr. and Mrs. Louis	Brookline	MA	0	
09694	Davlin, Mrs. Louis	Brookline	MA	0	1945
10448	DeSantis, Mr. & Mrs. Louis	Brookline	MA	0	1973
10343	Dexter, Dr. and Mrs. Lewis	Brookline	MA	0	
01132	Doliber, Thomas	Brookline	MA	33 (1889-1894)	1889-1899
12047	Dorr, Henry G.	Brookline	MA	0	1891
04010	Douglas, Alfred/Fernwood	Brookline	MA	164 (1909-1912)	1910-1914; 1922-1926; 1937
02061	Duryea, Herman B. & Ellen W.	Brookline	MA	2 (1897-1899)	1897-1899
01046	Eaton, Charles S.	Brookline	MA	36 (1886-1887)	1886-1903
07634	Elliot, G. F.	Brookline	MA	6 (1926)	1926
10446	Emerson, Mr. & Mrs. Bigelow	Brookline	MA	0	1973
10395	Engle, Dr. & Mrs. Ralph P. Jr.	Brookline	MA	0	1972
02993	Estey, Clarence H.	Brookline	MA	2 (1904)	1904
02281	Fabyan, George F.	Brookline	MA	8 (1901)	1901-1902
07266	Fahey, Frank J./Fisher Hill Residence	Brookline	MA	63 (1923-1928)	1924-1930; 1941
09151	Faulkner, Dr. J.M.	Brookline	MA	72 (1929-1951)	1929-1931; 1940; 1951-1969
10024	Faxon, Henry Dr.	Brookline	MA	0	1955-1956
09388	Fine, Jacob Dr./Chestnut Hill	Brookline	MA	13 (1935-1937)	1935-1937
09770	Finkel, Dr. Henry	Brookline	MA	0	1946-1947

Job #	Job Name/Alternative Name	Job Location		Plans	Correspondence
10671	Fox, Mr. & Mrs. Joseph	Brookline	MA	0	
10206	Frost, Mr. and Mrs. Thomas B.	Brookline	MA	0	1966
10009	Fuller, Peter	Brookline	MA	30 (1955-1956)	1955-1956; 1967; 1971
10334	Gabriel, Mr. and Mrs. Charles H.	Brookline	MA	3 (1970; 1973)	1970-1973
01044	Gardner, J. L./Green Hill	Brookline	MA	17 (1886-1887)	1895
10659	Gardner, Mr. & Mrs. George P.	Brookline	MA	0	1978
10344	Gardner, Mr. and Mrs. Robert	Brookline	MA	8 (1970-1971)	1969-1973
10538	Georgaklis, Mr. & Mrs. Arthur	Brookline	MA	0	
01043	Goddard Estate	Brookline	MA	0	1884-1894
09916	Goldberg, Carney Mrs.	Brookline	MA	12 (1951)	1951
10316	Gordon, Mr. and Mrs. Ellis	Brookline	MA	0	1970-1977
12067	Hamlen, N.P.	Brookline	MA	0	1882; 1896; 1899
09236	Hansel, L. H.	Brookline	MA	0	
10049	Harte, Richard	Brookline	MA	11 (1956-1957)	1956-1958
03796	Hartt, Arthur W.	Brookline	MA	13 (1896-1934)	1909-1911; 1927-1934
07380	Harwood, John H.	Brookline	MA	10 (1924-1929)	1924-1929; 1937
10491	Heard, Mr. & Mrs. Edward S.	Brookline	MA	0	
09980	Henderson, R. L.	Brookline	MA	111 (1943-1972)	1951-1972
09542	Hennessy, M. E.	Brookline	MA	0	
09719	Hill, Lucius T.	Brookline	MA	12 (1945)	1945-1946
09026	Holdsworth, Frederick	Brookline	MA	7 (1928-1929)	1929
09646	Hood, Donald/Hood, H.P./Tripp, W.V./ Brooks Est	Brookline	MA	23 (1927; 1942-1946)	1942-1947; 1962
02276	Hood, F. C.	Brookline	MA	2 (1901)	1901-1902
01166	Hopkins, C. A.	Brookline	MA	15 (1906)	1890-1893; 1906
06971	Howe, A. S./Howe, Albert S.	Brookline	MA	9 (1921)	1921-1922
00465	Hunt, W. N. Estate	Brookline	MA	0	
12512	Jacques, Herbert	Brookline	MA	2 (N.D.)	
10146	Jenckes, Mr. and Mrs. Marcien	Brookline	MA	0	1962-1971
09490	Jenney, Charles S.	Brookline	MA	79 (1937-1950)	1937-1940
09538	Jenney, Malcolm	Brookline	MA	12 (1928-1939)	1938-1940
09911	Jenney, Robert M.	Brookline	MA	6 (1951)	1951-1952
10613	Jepson, Mrs. I.	Brookline	MA	2 (1977)	1977-1979
09927	Kane, David	Brookline	MA	68 (1952-1953)	1952-1960
10550	Kay, Mr. & Mrs. Reed	Brookline	MA	0	1975
09602	Kelley, Edmund S. Mrs./Buckminster Road	Brookline	MA	10 (1940)	1940-1941
09586	Kelsey, Robert P.	Brookline	MA	0	1939
01125	Kennard, Martin P.	Brookline	MA	8 (1894-1895; 1911)	1894-1895
09796	Kennedy, A. K. Mrs./Sargent Estate/Kennedy, Audrey K.	Brookline	MA	22 (1947-1948)	1947-1948
09349	King, Franklin/Hillfields Subdivision, in	Brookline	MA	37 (1933-1934)	1934-1937
01161	Kingsbury Estate/Kingsbury, J.F.	Brookline	MA	11 (1889-1890)	1890-1898

Job #	Job Name/Alternative Name	Job Location		Plans	Correspondence
10711	Kirshner, Dr. & Mrs. Lewis	Brookline	MA	0	1979
10539	Klaussen, Mrs. Anita R.	Brookline	MA	0	1976
10410	Lacy, Mr. & Mrs. Benjamin H.	Brookline	MA	0	
06435	Lapham, H. G./Lapham, Henry G./Louis Cabot Place	Brookline	MA	110 (1916-1917)	1916-1921; 1941
00270	Lee, George	Brookline	MA	8 (1899-1900)	1899-1900
09622	Lee, Halfdan Mrs./Lee, Halfdan	Brookline	MA	4 (1941)	1941
10501	Leibel, Dr. & Mrs. Rudolph I.	Brookline	MA	0	
10295	Lewis, Dr. and Mrs. Charles	Brookline	MA	0	1969
10207	Linden, Mrs. Benjamin	Brookline	MA	2 (1966; 1969)	1966-1969
06195	Lord, H. C.	Brookline	MA	0	1915
05496	Loring, Atherton	Brookline	MA	70 (1912-1930)	1912-1916; 1921-1923; 1928-1935
02885	Maddock, Miss A. F.	Brookline	MA	0	1904
07096	Mailman, Charles/Mailman, Charles A.	Brookline	MA	9 (1922)	1922
10553	Marks, Mr. & Mrs. Harry L.	Brookline	MA	0	1976
09853	Mason, Charles E.	Brookline	MA	9 (1949)	1949; 1960-1966; 1979
09582	Mason, Charles E./Sargent Estate	Brookline	MA	0	1939
09714	Mason, Harold F.	Brookline	MA	8 (1937; 1945-1946)	1945-1947
10002	Mason, Mrs. Harold F.	Brookline	MA	6 (1955)	1955
09615	Matz, Charles H.	Brookline	MA	13 (1941)	1941
10224	Maynard, Mr. and Mrs. Edwin P. 3rd	Brookline	MA	0	1967
10210	McCrea, Vice Admiral and Mrs. John L.	Brookline	MA	0	1966-1968
09778	McKittrick, Leland S. Dr.	Brookline	MA	7 (1931; 1947; 1952)	1947-1953
10339	Merrill, Dr. and Mrs. Keith Jr.	Brookline	MA	1 (1970)	1970
10707	Miller, Mr.& Mrs. Allen J.	Brookline	MA	0	
07820	Mitton, George W.	Brookline	MA	42 (1926-1929)	1927-1928
10625	Moore, Mr. & Mrs. Ronald R.	Brookline	MA	0	
03215	Morss, Charles A./Morss, John	Brookline	MA	12 (1907-1926)	1907; 1920; 1976-1977
10151	Mr. and Mrs. Augustus H. Vogel	Brookline	MA	0	1963-1966; 1975
07358	Nash, E. R.	Brookline	MA	14 (1913-1925)	1924-1929
09776	Nelson, Arthur T.	Brookline	MA	77 (1925; 1947)	1947-1948; 1957
10526	Nyman, Mr. & Mrs. Philip	Brookline	MA	0	1975
06625	Oakes, F. J. Jr./Schlesinger Estate/Oakes, Francis J., Jr.	Brookline	MA	30 (1918-1946)	1918-1922; 1946; 1957
00673	Olmsted, F. L. Estate/99 Warren St. (office property)/Fairsted	Brookline	MA	160 (1880-1968)	1883-1899; 1904-1907; 1918-1950; 1960-1980
01030	Olmsted, J. C.	Brookline	MA	0	1899; 1908
01363	Paine, Frederick W.	Brookline	MA	3 (1895; 1926)	1895-1898; 1926
01364	Paine, L.C.	Brookline	MA	1 (1893)	1893
03341	Paine, R. T. 2nd Mrs./Paine, Ruth C./Paine, Mrs. Robert Treat/estate on Cabot Hill	Brookline	MA	7 (1893-1907)	1907; 1917

Job #	Job Name/Alternative Name	Job Location		Plans	Correspondence
05659	Parks, F. R./Whitcomb, L.E.	Brookline	MA	5 (1903-1913)	1912-1913
10527	Perry, Mr. & Mrs. Lee	Brookline	MA	3 (1975)	1975-1978
10507	Pettus, Mr. & Mrs. Peter	Brookline	MA	0	1974
09521	Pfaelzer, Franklin T. Jr.	Brookline	MA	56 (1936-1948)	1938-1947
09994	Pierce, H. W.	Brookline	MA	13 (1954-1955)	1954-1955
10277	Plimpton, Mr. and Mrs. Hollis	Brookline	MA	0	1969-1970
05889	Prouty, Lewis J./BennettBennett, H.D.	Brookline	MA	136 (1913-1936; 1950)	1912-1913; 1927-1943; 1950
10476	Rees, Dr. Michael	Brookline	MA	0	
03556	Rice, Mrs. Dunn Hall/Rice, Dana Hall	Brookline	MA	0	1908
10180	Richardson, Dr. and Mrs. George	Brookline	MA	0	1893; 1964
10447	Robbins, Dr. & Mrs. Peter G.	Brookline	MA	5 (1973-1974)	1973-1974
10360	Rodman, Mr. and Mrs. Benjamin	Brookline	MA	0	
05514	Rogers, A. M./Rogers, A. H.	Brookline	MA	3 (1912)	1912
10398	Rogers, Mr. & Mrs. E.W.	Brookline	MA	1 (1972)	1895-1892; 1972
09884	Rolde, L. R.	Brookline	MA	10(1948; 1950)	1950
10644	Rosen, Mr. & Mrs. Albert	Brookline	MA	0	1978
10355	Rosen, Mr. and Mrs. Maurice T.	Brookline	MA	0	1971
10579	Ross, Mr. & Mrs. John	Brookline	MA	0	1976-1977
09572	Rowley, Charles F.	Brookline	MA	42 (1939-1959)	1939-1966
09936	Rubel, C. Adrian	Brookline	MA	17 (1952-1953)	1952-1953
06280	Ruhl, Edward/Curtis, R.W. Mrs.	Brookline	MA	3 (1905)	1915-1916
10294	Runyon, Dr. and Mrs. Robert C.	Brookline	MA	0	
03044	Rutan, C. H./Rutan, Charles H.	Brookline	MA	1 (1905)	1905-1908
10152	Ryerson, Mrs. M. D.	Brookline	MA	5 (1963)	1895; 1963
07901	Samson, E. J.	Brookline	MA	10 (1928-1929)	1929
06264	Sanger, Sabin B.	Brookline	MA	2 (1915)	1915-1917
01056	Sargent Estate	Brookline	MA	20 (1885-1893)	1927
09508	Sargent, Adelaide/Sargent, E. Adelaide	Brookline	MA	3 (1937)	1937-1938
10168	Sargent, Mrs. Ann	Brookline	MA	4 (1964)	1964-1965
10572	Saunders, Mr. & Mrs. Roger	Brookline	MA	0	
00614	Schlesinger, B.	Brookline	MA	116 (1880-1881)	1879-1890
10457	Selle, Mr. & Mrs. Robert W.	Brookline	MA	2 (1973-1974)	1973-1974
09996	Shactman, Arthur	Brookline	MA	21 (1954-1955)	1955
09960	Shapiro, Sidney	Brookline	MA	7 (1953)	1953
09584	Shaw, Francis G. Jr.	Brookline	MA	10 (1939-1962)	1930-1971
09845	Shepard, John III	Brookline	MA	14 (1928; 1929; 1948; 1949)	1929-1950
01055	Shepley, George	Brookline	MA	11 (1888-1902)	1888-1889; 1902-1903
10324	Sloane, Dr. and Mrs. Robert E.	Brookline	MA	0	1893-1894; 1970
07899	Snow, Wm. B. Jr./Snow, William B.	Brookline	MA	8 (1927-1928)	1927-1929
00299	Sprague, C. F.	Brookline	MA	19 (1886-1895)	1893-1895
10624	Starkey, Dr. & Mrs. George W.B.	Brookline	MA	0	1978

Job #	Job Name/Alternative Name	Job Location		Plans	Correspondence
09737	Stephenson, Preston	Brookline	MA	18 (1930-1947)	1946-1947
09601	Stodder, Clement Mrs.	Brookline	MA	7 (1940)	1940-1973
09053	Stone, R. G./Stone, Robert G.	Brookline	MA	13 (1929-1931)	1929-1931
00629	Storrow, Charles	Brookline	MA	36 (1882; 1886)	1882-1884; 1917
07421	Stuart, Harold Dr.	Brookline	MA	7 (1925)	1925
09383	Sullivan, John B. Jr. Mrs.	Brookline	MA	21 (1926; 1935-1939)	1935-1938
09981	Sweet, William Dr.	Brookline	MA	12 (1954-1955)	1954-1955
10419	Talcott, Mr. & Mrs. Hooker Jr.	Brookline	MA	6 (1972-1974)	1972-1974
10549	Taube, Dr. & Mrs. Irvin	Brookline	MA	0	1975
10273	Taylor, Mr. and Mrs. Thomas	Brookline	MA	0	
10216	Thayer, Mr. and Mrs. Sherman R.	Brookline	MA	0	1966
07719	Thompson, R.E.	Brookline	MA	72 (1923-1929)	1928-1931
09380	Tripp, W. V.	Brookline	MA	20 (1932; 1935)	1935
09783	Tripp, W. V.	Brookline	MA	10 (1947-1948)	1947
09645	Tripp, W. V.	Brookline	MA	1 (1937)	
09923	Tripp, W. V./Lamb Property	Brookline	MA	9 (1937-1952)	1951-1952

View across the iris garden to the house, Cluett garden, October 1926. Job #7099 – George A. Cluett (Williamstown, MA).

Job #	Job Name/Alternative Name	Job Location		Plans	Correspondence
09549	Tripp, William V./Codman Road Property	Brookline	MA	9 (1938)	1938-1940
06220	Trombly, Mrs. John Fogg	Brookline	MA	0	N.D.
10101	Trustman, Alan	Brookline	MA	27 (1959-1960)	1959-1961; 1972
10213	Tucker, Dr. and Mrs. Arthur W. Jr.	Brookline	MA	3 (1966)	N.D.
10284	Tyler, Dr. and Mrs. H. Richard	Brookline	MA	0	1969
10064	Vanderbilt, W. H.	Brookline	MA	200 (1956-1960)	1958-1961
10158	Viaux, Mr. and Mrs. Frederic	Brookline	MA	0	1963
10611	Von Lichtenburg, Mr. & Mrs. Franz	Brookline	MA	0	1977
10193	Wardwell, Mrs. Sheldon E.	Brookline	MA	0	1893; 1965-1968
00460	Washburn/Taylor Estate/Washburn - Taylor Estate	Brookline	MA	0	1902
06686	Watts, John R.	Brookline	MA	3 (1920-1921)	1919-1922
02237	Welch, Francis W.	Brookline	MA	1 (1900)	
10442	Wetherbee, Mrs. Winthrop	Brookline	MA	0	1973
02881	Whipple, Sherman L./Brookline Parks	Brookline	MA	15 (1902-1919)	1894-1896; 1904-1921
07291	Whitcomb, Mrs. Arthur	Brookline	MA	0	1924
01079	White, John H.	Brookline	MA	42 (1887-1888)	1887-1895
00463	White, Jonathan	Brookline	MA	0	1883; 1895; 1978
00626	White, Joseph H./Stone, Galen L.	Brookline	MA	122 (1880-1931)	1877-1895
07811	White, Webb B./Hillfields	Brookline	MA	22 (1927-1941)	1927-1928; 1941; 1978
12167	Whitney, Henry M.	Brookline	MA	0	1890-1898
04019	Wightman, G. H./Wightman, George H.	Brookline	MA	7 (1907-1911)	1902; 1910-1911
00223	Wightman, G. H./Wightman, George H.	Brookline	MA	15 (1901-1902; 1921)	1901-1911; 1921-1922
02392	Willetts, George F./Willett, George F.	Brookline	MA	1 (1903)	1904-1907
00464	Williams, Moses	Brookline	MA	38 (1875-1886)	1886-1890
01023	Williams, Moses	Brookline	MA	0	1888
01438	Wilson, W. R./Bemis, John W	Brookline	MA	5 (1898)	1896-1898
00457	Worthley, George H.	Brookline	MA	0	1901
07651	Wright, George Dr.	Brookline	MA	14 (1926-1931)	1926; 1931-1934
00224	Wright, J. G./Wright Garden and Details	Brookline	MA	19 (1895-1909)	1895-1909
10712	Factor, Mr. & Mrs. Robert	Burlington	MA	0	N.D.
07645	Davis, E. B./Davis, Edgar B.	Buzzards Bay	MA	8 (1925-1926)	1926
07595	Harrison, Mrs. C. L.	Buzzards Bay	MA	0	1925
09769	Barton, Francis L.	Cambridge	MA	4 (1947)	1947
06047	Beach, R. W./Beach, Ruel W.	Cambridge	MA	5 (1914)	1914
12506	Brewster, William	Cambridge	MA	9 (1887)	1885
07060	Cogswell, G. P. Dr./Cogswell, George P.	Cambridge	MA	7 (1922)	1922-1923
10190	Cohen, Mr. and Mrs. Carl	Cambridge	MA	0	1965
10066	Cox, Gardner	Cambridge	MA	0	1957-1958
09643	Farr, William Sharon	Cambridge	MA	4 (1941)	1941-1942
10268	Freedberg, Mr. and Mrs. Sidney	Cambridge	MA	0	

Job #	Job Name/Alternative Name	Job Location		Plans	Correspondence
10593	Grobman, Dr. & Mrs. Jerald	Cambridge	MA	0	
06142	Hall, W.S.	Cambridge	MA	6 (1915)	
07470	Hart, J. G.	Cambridge	MA	1 (1926)	1925-1926
09972	Hawkins, J. F. Mrs.	Cambridge	MA	15 (1922; 1929; 1954)	1954-1975
07569	Howe, Katherine/Gray Gardens East, Lot 13	Cambridge	MA	0	1925
07214	Howe, Lucien Mrs./Howe, Katherine M.	Cambridge	MA	25 (1923-1939)	1923-1924; 1930; 1936-1939
06258	Jewett, J. R. Prof./Jewett, James R.	Cambridge	MA	0	1915-1916
01807	Kelley, Stillman F.	Cambridge	MA	2 (1895)	1895-1900
10684	Longwell, Mr. & Mrs. John P.	Cambridge	MA	0	
10102	Luther, Willard	Cambridge	MA	1 (1959)	1959
01805	Mellen, J. A.	Cambridge	MA	1 (1895)	1895
09530	Millett, Mrs. Joseph B.	Cambridge	MA	0	1937-1941
06996	Morrison, Alva	Cambridge	MA	8 (1921-1922; 1944; 1958)	1921-1922; 1938-1939; 1958
09182	Nichols, R. B.	Cambridge	MA	0	1930
01398	Norton Estate	Cambridge	MA	16 (1894-1895)	1894-1895
05454	Norton, Grace Miss	Cambridge	MA	2 (1912-1913)	1912-1913
03010	Norton, Grace Miss	Cambridge	MA	1 (1914)	1904; 1910-1915
02041	Noyes, J. Atkins/Noyes, James A,tkins	Cambridge	MA	9 (1894-1903)	1894-1902; 1907-1910
07466	Porter, Kingsley/Porter, A. Kingsley/Elmwood	Cambridge	MA	3 (1925-1926)	1926-1934
07300	Robinson, Mrs. B. L.	Cambridge	MA	0	1925
10148	Rubinfein, Mr. and Mrs. David	Cambridge	MA	0	1962
06822	Sachs, P. J.	Cambridge	MA	0	N.D.
10175	Scott, Donald	Cambridge	MA	30 (1961-1966)	1964-1967
06449	Sharples, S. P.	Cambridge	MA	0	1916
10541	Sharpless, Mr. & Mrs. Barry	Cambridge	MA	0	N.D.
10230	Wise, Mr. and Mrs. Henry	Cambridge	MA	0	1967
03696	Keith, Harold C.	Campello	MA	2 (1909)	1896; 1909-1910; 1924
07644	Plymouth County Development Company Garden/Davis, E. B. Park/White, Carleton	Campello	MA	17 (1926)	1926
09194	Chase, Barbara S.	Canton	MA	0	1930
10585	Dadasis, Mr. & Mrs. Louis	Canton	MA	0	
10021	Gilfords, Brewster	Canton	MA	0	
10169	Salah, Mr. James M.	Canton	MA	12 (1963-1964)	1964-1968
10631	Sifakis, Dr. & Mrs. John	Canton	MA	0	
10571	Vinios, Mr. & Mrs. Nicholas	Canton	MA	0	
10471	Andereog, Mr. & Mrs. John S.	Carlisle	MA	0	
10474	Anderson, Mr. & Mrs. Ralph P.	Carlisle	MA	0	1974
10475	Cameron, Mr. & Mrs. Alan G.	Carlisle	MA	0	1973

Job #	Job Name/Alternative Name	Job Location		Plans	Correspondence
10664	Cattacchio, Mr. & Mrs. Vincent	Carlisle	MA	0	1978
10499	Petroskey, Mr. & Mrs. Frederick	Carlisle	MA	0	
10472	Tully, Mr. & Mrs. Sean	Carlisle	MA	0	
07927	Dean, Paul	Cataumet	MA	5 (1928)	1928
10722	Savage - Roney/Arccon, Inc.	Cataumet	MA	0	N.D.
09134	Warner, Mrs. Richard	Cataumet	MA	0	1929
03608	Marston, Howard	Centerville	MA	0	1909; 1914
10381	Arkin, Mr. & Mrs. Marshall	Chelmsford	MA	0	1972
10260	Klemmer, Mr. and Mrs. Howard W.	Chelmsford	MA	4 (1968)	1968
10454	Loiselle, Mr. & Mrs. Edmund	Chelmsford	MA	0	
01329	Adams, C. R.	Chestnut Hill	MA	6 (1895-1896)	1895-1898
10331	Barletta, Mr. and Mrs. Frederick J. Jr.	Chestnut Hill	MA	0	
02629	Bliss, E. J.	Chestnut Hill	MA	5 (1904-1905)	1903-1905
10518	Buell, Mr. & Mrs. George	Chestnut Hill	MA	0	1897; 1975
03139	Burr, Allston	Chestnut Hill	MA	0	1906
10630	Deland, Mr. & Mrs. Frank Stanton Jr.	Chestnut Hill	MA	0	1978
07710	Falvey, Donald	Chestnut Hill	MA	5 (1926)	1926
07078	Fay, Edgar E.	Chestnut Hill	MA	0	1922
10321	Freeman, Mr. and Mrs. Benjamin	Chestnut Hill	MA	2 (1970)	1970
10251	Green, Mr. and Mrs. Arnold	Chestnut Hill	MA	0	
10668	Harrison, Mr. & Mrs. Irwin	Chestnut Hill	MA	0	
03677	Jones, A. Marshall	Chestnut Hill	MA	0	1910
10628	Kirkendall, Mr. & Mrs. Ralph	Chestnut Hill	MA	0	1978
10632	Krentzman, Mr. & Mrs. Harvey	Chestnut Hill	MA	0	1978
10076	Kuehn, G. W.	Chestnut Hill	MA	3 (1958)	1958-1960
00680	Lawrence, A. A.	Chestnut Hill	MA	18 (1881-1885)	1885
09964	Livingstone, M. Eli	Chestnut Hill	MA	19 (1951-1954)	1953-1957; 1977
10503	Myerson, Mr. & Mrs. Sumner	Chestnut Hill	MA	0	1978
10621	Narva, Mr. & Mrs. Morton	Chestnut Hill	MA	0	1978
09356	O'Malley, Charles J.	Chestnut Hill	MA	3 (1934)	1934
10140	Prout, Mr. & Mrs. Henry	Chestnut Hill	MA	5 (1964)	1960-1973
12513	Rogers, W.S.	Chestnut Hill	MA	4 (1891-1892)	
10383	Rudman, Mr. & Mrs. Stanley H.	Chestnut Hill	MA	0	
10622	Shipley, Dr. & Mrs. William	Chestnut Hill	MA	0	1977
10329	Sibley, Mrs. George	Chestnut Hill	MA	0	1970-1971
10177	Swensrud, Mr. and Mrs. Stephen B.	Chestnut Hill	MA	0	1964-1965
07513	Tuttle, Morton C.	Chestnut Hill	MA	0	
01024	White, R.H./White, Ralph H.	Chestnut Hill	MA	43 (1879-1897)	1886-1891
10623	Wolfe, Mr. & Mrs. Stanley	Chestnut Hill	MA	0	1977
10517	Benson, Mr. & Mrs. Robert	Cohasset	MA	0	
00631	Bigelow, A. S.	Cohasset	MA	4 (1892-1893)	1893-1894
06481	Bigelow, Alanson Jr.	Cohasset	MA	0	1916

Job #	Job Name/Alternative Name	Job Location		Plans	Correspondence
00144	Bigelow, Joseph S. Mrs.	Cohasset	MA	10 (1901)	1893; 1900-1901
07996	Blake, Robert F.	Cohasset	MA	0	1928
12187	Bryant, John	Cohasset	MA	0	1880-1882; 1894
01207	Crocker, G. G.	Cohasset	MA	0	1890
09742	Howes, E. G.	Cohasset	MA	15 (1917; 1919; 1946)	1946
10592	Lantz, Mr. & Mrs. Henry	Cohasset	MA	0	
03705	Long, Harry V.	Cohasset	MA	36 (1907-1926)	1909-1916; 1926; 1935
09196	Plant, C. G. Mrs./Plant, C. G.	Cohasset	MA	5 (1930)	1930
09362	Stampleman, S. C./Stanpleman, Samuel C.	Cohasset	MA	0	1934
10429	Thayer, Mr. & Mrs. Sherman	Cohasset	MA	0	
03046	Adams, Charles Francis 2nd	Concord	MA	0	1905
10226	Bramhall, Mr. and Mrs. George	Concord	MA	0	
10537	Dunfey, Mr. & Mrs. Gerald F.	Concord	MA	0	
10233	Hall, Mr. and Mrs. Bruce	Concord	MA	0	1968
09505	Laughlin, Henry A.	Concord	MA	247 (1931-1941)	1937-1958
10087	Morrison, Alva Jr.	Concord	MA	11 (1926; 1958)	1958-1959
10468	Nelson, Mr. & Mrs. Bruce E.	Concord	MA	0	1896
10635	Nestory, Mr. & Mrs. John	Concord	MA	0	1978
10225	Porter, Mr. and Mrs. David B.	Concord	MA	0	
10591	Rabinowitz, Mr. & Mrs. Peter A.	Concord	MA	0	1977
09772	Rodd, David B.	Concord	MA	10 (1947)	1947
10010	Rowley, F. H.	Concord	MA	3 (1955)	1955; 1959
10153	Rowley, Mr. amd Mrs. F. Hunter	Concord	MA	0	1963
10685	Tilney, Mr. & Mrs. John	Concord	MA	0	1979
10478	Trustman, Mr. & Mrs. Alan	Concord	MA	0	1973-1976
10652	Weeks, Mr. & Mrs. Sinclair	Concord	MA	0	1978
06943	Wing, D. G.	Concord	MA	23 (1920-1921)	1920-1922
09733	Barton, F. O. Mrs.	Cotuit	MA	10 (1946-1948)	1946-1950
00053	Bryant, Henry	Cotuit	MA	1 (1893)	1895
09907	Jones, Cyril H.	Cotuit	MA	76 (1951-1953)	1951-1953
09710	Kirkman, Mary Lewis	Cotuit	MA	60 (1919; 1945-1949)	1945-1949
09689	McIver, Monroe A. Mrs.	Cotuit	MA	2 (1945)	1944-1945
09592	Morrison, Alva	Cotuit	MA	12 (1923-1945)	1944-1945
09840	Putnam, C. D. Mrs./Putnam, Charlton D.	Cotuit	MA	6 (1949)	1949
09682	Ropes, James H. Mrs.	Cotuit	MA	4 (1908; 1944)	1944
09684	Taussig, H. B. Dr./Taussig, Helen B.	Cotuit	MA	2 (1944)	1944
09683	Taylor, Warren	Cotuit	MA	2 (1944)	1944
09681	Wesson, Cynthia M.	Cotuit	MA	15 (1944-1945)	1944-1950
09680	Wesson, Frank H.	Cotuit	MA	83 (1944-1950)	1944-1951
10108	Whitcomb, Pemberton	Cotuit	MA	2 (1959)	1959

Job #	Job Name/Alternative Name	Job Location		Plans	Correspondence
01388	Bryant, William Cullen	Cummington	MA	2 (1891)	1891
10105	Crane, Arthur	Dalton	MA	34 (1949; 1959-1960; 1967-1969)	1959-1969
10075	Crane, W. M. Jr.	Dalton	MA	31 (1957-1960; 1970)	1958-1960; 1970
09128	Crane, Winthrop/Crane, Winthrop M. Jr.	Dalton	MA	20 (1929-1931)	1929-1934
05768	Crane, Z./Crane, Z.M.	Dalton	MA	0	1912
00027	Crane, Zenas	Dalton	MA	10 (1897-1903)	1896-1903
07103	Sawyer, Charles F.	Dalton	MA	49 (1922-1924)	1922-1924
01425	Endicott, William C.	Danvers	MA	6 (1894)	1894-1895; 1975-1977
10236	Archibald, Mr. and Mrs. Frederick A.	Dedham	MA	0	
02992	Barrows, Miss Fanny	Dedham	MA	0	1904
02387	Bullard, Harold	Dedham	MA	1 (1901)	1902
10690	Carlson, Mrs. Barbara	Dedham	MA	0	1979
00627	Endicott, H. Wendell/Platt, C. A./Weld, S.M.	Dedham	MA	41 (1882-1934)	1882-1884; 1931-1934
10305	Jenckes, Mr. and Mrs. C. Webb	Dedham	MA	0	1970-1975
10333	Leach, Mr. and Mrs. Malcolm	Dedham	MA	0	1970
09347	Murchie, Guy	Dedham	MA	25 (1933-1934)	1933-1935; 1941; 1953
01122	Nickerson, A. W.	Dedham	MA	53 (1851-1888)	1887-1895
10390	Raymond, Mr. & Mrs. Edward H.	Dedham	MA	0	
10301	Soule, Mr. and Mrs. Horace H.	Dedham	MA	3 (1969-1970)	1969-1971
09905	Stimpson, H. F.	Dedham	MA	9 (1928; 1951)	1951
10397	Thayer, Mrs. John E.	Dedham	MA	0	1894; 1972-1975
10372	Webber, Mr. and Mrs. Ralph B. Jr	Dedham	MA	3 (1972)	1896; 1972-1973
05918	Wrenn, Philip	Dedham	MA	15 (1903-1904; 1926)	1913; 1926; 1938
07633	Adams, R. M./Miramar Park Subdivision	Dennisport	MA	6 (1926)	1926-1930
06874	Dreyfus, Carl	Devereux	MA	30 (1920-1929)	1920-1921
12507	Capen Farm	Dorchester	MA	1 (1872)	1885
03406	Gallagher, E. B.	Dorchester	MA	0	N.D.
02227	Holbrook, S. P.	Dorchester	MA	0	1899
01361	Rogers, Dr. O.F./Rogers, Orville F.	Dorchester	MA	1 (1893)	1893
05998	Benson, Miss/Benson, Ethel	Dover	MA	0	1914
10544	Buonocore, Mr. & Mrs. John	Dover	MA	2 (1975)	1975
03585	Davis, Arthur E./Greystone Farm	Dover	MA	69 (1902-1928)	1907-1914; 1924-1926; 1938

Left, Inset: Arbor in the garden, Gardiner Lane estate "The Chimneys," 1930. Job #273 – G.M. Lane (Manchester, MA). Listed in Subdivisions and Suburban Communities.

Left: View across the water garden to the iris border, Gardiner Lane estate "The Chimneys," 1930. Job #273 – G.M. Lane (Manchester, MA). Listed in Subdivisions and Suburban Communities.

Job #	Job Name/Alternative Name	Job Location		Plans	Correspondence
05108	Davis, L. Shannon	Dover	MA	0	1911
03364	Fay, J. S. 3rd/Fay, Joseph S III	Dover	MA	6 (1907)	1907-1908
10302	McGrath, Mr. and Mrs. Robert D.	Dover	MA	0	1969-1970
07698	Parker, Mrs. A. H.	Dover	MA	0	1926
09503	Porter, Dr. William J./Porter, William T.	Dover	MA	0	1937
10245	Walker, Mr. and Mrs. James	Dover	MA	0	
10358	Wylde, Mr. and Mrs. John H.	Dover	MA	0	
10237	Archibald, Mr. and Mrs. Frederick A.	Duxbury	MA	0	
09739	Clifford, Stewart Dr.	Duxbury	MA	7 (1946)	1946-1947
09691	Harwood, Sydney/Powder Point	Duxbury	MA	0	1945
10642	Kopald, Mrs. Martha	Duxbury	MA	0	1978
10643	Langeland, Mr. & Mrs. A. Wesley	Duxbury	MA	0	1978
03165	Loring, Atherton	Duxbury	MA	3 (1902-1923)	1906; 1931
10536	Soule, Mr. & Mrs. Horace	Duxbury	MA	0	
10688	Wakefield, Mr. & Mrs. Scott	Duxbury	MA	0	1979
06379	Murphy, H. D./Murphy, Herman D.	East Lexington	MA	0	1916-1919
09726	Lawrence, Raymond E.	East Longmeadow	MA	23 (1945-1947)	1946-1947
09022	Wilder, W. O. Dr.	East Longmeadow	MA	0	1928-1932
10496	Kenney, Dr. & Mrs. Francis R.	East Orleans	MA	0	1894; 1974
09651	Beach, Ruel W.	East Weymouth	MA	6 (1943)	1943
05677	Slade, Leonard N.	Fall River	MA	0	1912
12197	Beebe, Frank	Falmouth	MA	0	1892-1893
09518	Cobb, Clarence	Falmouth	MA	58 (1938)	1938-1940
10308	Hiam, Edwin W.	Falmouth	MA	3 (1969)	1970
07708	Janney, Walter C.	Falmouth	MA	18 (1920-1929)	1926-1929
07567	Leatherbee, R. W.	Falmouth	MA	45 (1925-1926)	1919; 1925-1926
09727	Lovell, Hollis	Falmouth	MA	13 (1945-1946)	1946-1947
00412	Pierce, Edgar	Falmouth	MA	9 (1900-1902)	1901-1902
12337	Smith, John H.	Falmouth	MA	8 (1891)	1884-1897
01293	Crocker, Alvah	Fitchburg	MA	28 (1892-1923)	1894-1897; 1912-1916; 1923-1925; 1938; 1952
01133	Cross, A. J.	Fitchburg	MA	1 (1889)	1889
01292	Cross, Chas. A.	Fitchburg	MA	8 (1892)	1892
10012	Babbott, Frank L. Jr	Framingham	MA	10 (1955-1957)	1955-1960
10267	Cohen, Mr. and Mrs. Gerard	Framingham	MA	0	
10417	Frieband, Mr. & Mrs. Neil	Framingham	MA	2 (1975)	1975
10234	Frieband, Mr. and Mrs. Neil	Framingham	MA	5 (1967)	1967
10242	Kelber, Mr. and Mrs. Karl	Framingham	MA	2 (1968)	1968
10453	Kim, Dr. & Mrs. Il	Framingham	MA	0	1973-1975
01395	Perkins, R.F.	Framingham	MA	10 (1894; 1942)	1893-1894
10502	Welch, Mr. & Mrs. Mervyn D.	Framingham	MA	0	
10163	Ferrucci, Dr. and Mrs. Joseph	Framingham Centre	MA	8 (1961; 1963)	1963-1964

Job #	Job Name/Alternative Name	Job Location		Plans	Correspondence
01239	Morrill, Amos	Gardner	MA	9 (1891)	1891-1898
00459	Clay, John	Gloucester	MA	0	1903
00435	Clay, Mrs. John	Gloucester	MA	0	
09008	Davis, Arthur E. Mrs./Davis, Arthur	Gloucester	MA	4 (1928)	1928
06452	Jones, Emma C.	Grafton	MA	15 (1915-1917)	1916-1917
06802	Pond, George K.	Greenfield	MA	24 (1917-1920)	1920-1921
10636	Andrews, Mr. & Mrs. John B.	Groton	MA	0	1978
10288	Berry, Mr. and Mrs. Phillip	Groton	MA	0	1969
01129	Gardner, W. A.	Groton	MA	6 (1887-1889)	1888-1890
01124	Laurence, J.	Groton	MA	4 (1889)	1889-1892
06661	Norton, Charles D.	Groton	MA	5 (1919)	1919
07812	Parsons, J. Lester	Groton	MA	0	1927-1928
01347	Sears, Miss C. E.	Groton	MA	7 (1893)	1893
10353	Staub, Dr. and Mrs. Richard	Groton	MA	2 (1971)	1971
03148	Ayer, C. F./Ayer, Charles F.	Hamilton	MA	60 (1906-1919)	1906-1919
06578	Burrage, A. C./Burrage, A.C. Jr.	Hamilton	MA	7 (1917-1918)	1917-1919
07894	Ramsdell, C. C.	Hampden	MA	3 (1928)	1927-1928
00633	Beal, J. Williams	Hanover	MA	3 (1893)	1893-1894
03591	Mitchell, T. S.	Hanson	MA	0	1909
05782	Fiske, Warren	Harvard	MA	0	
09618	Willett, Hurd C.	Harvard	MA	20 (1940-1941)	1940
09968	Leavitt, M.	Haverhill	MA	0	1953
01222	Andrews, J. F./Andrew, John F.	Hingham	MA	24 (1891-1892)	1890-1895
10598	Casey, Mr. & Mrs. John Jr.	Hingham	MA	0	
10443	Davis, Mr. & Mrs. Brewster	Hingham	MA	0	
10250	Davis, Mr. and Mrs. Lucius P.	Hingham	MA	2 (1968-1969)	1968-1969
10402	Frederickson, Dr. & Mrs. E. Allen	Hingham	MA	7 (1972-1973)	1972-1973
10481	Michon, Dr. & Mrs. Joseph	Hingham	MA	0	
10480	Papuga, Dr. & Mrs. David G.	Hingham	MA	1 (1973)	1973-1974
05503	Dawson, H. S./Eastern Nurseries	Holliston	MA	7 (1904-1912)	
03596	Dunham, Carroll Dr.	Holliston	MA	3 (1909-1911)	1909-1913
07389	Prentiss, George W.	Holyoke	MA	0	1924
06151	Prentiss, William A.	Holyoke	MA	8 (1915)	1915
07087	Skinner, William	Holyoke	MA	5 (1917-1922)	1922
07305	Steiger, Albert	Holyoke	MA	11 (1924)	1924-1926
07227	Towne, Edward S.	Holyoke	MA	4 (1918-1924)	1923-1924
07357	Towne, Joseph Mrs./Towne, Joseph S.	Holyoke	MA	12 (1924-1925)	1923-1925
07226	Twing, Edward L./Mt. Tom	Holyoke	MA	8 (1923)	1923-1924
07391	Twing, Edward L./Wycoff Park Lot	Holyoke	MA	4 (1924-1925)	1925
07309	Wakelin, James H.	Holyoke	MA	0	1924
10080	Whiting, William	Holyoke	MA	0	1958; 1965
07225	Woodruff, J. B.	Holyoke	MA	4 (1923)	1923-1924

Job #	Job Name/Alternative Name	Job Location		Plans	Correspondence
07475	Wyckoff, J. Lewis	Holyoke	MA	5 (1927)	1925-1928
01205	Draper, G. A.	Hopedale	MA	6 (1890)	1890-1891
09692	West, Thomas H.	Hopedale	MA	29 (1944-1945)	1945
10731	Kieger, Mr. & Mrs. A. Bill	Hopkinton	MA	0	N.D.
06415	Maxwell, G. H.	Hull	MA	1 (1916)	1916
05910	Dunn, H. T.	Hyannisport	MA	77 (1913-1916)	1913-1917; 1922-1923
09199	Kennedy, Joseph P.	Hyannisport	MA	16 (1930-1932)	1930-1932
09754	Laughlin, J. B. Mrs.	Hyannisport	MA	13 (1946-1947)	1946-1947
01367	Longfellow, A.W.	Hyannisport	MA	3 (1893)	1897
06432	Taggart, Lucy M. Miss	Hyannisport	MA	22 (1916-1918)	1916-1919
02066	Grew, Henry S.	Hyde Park	MA	5 (1894-1898)	1898-1903
03793	Crane, Richard T. Jr./Crane, Richard T./Castle Hill	Ipswich	MA	60 (1903-1913)	1909-1920; 1937; 1967; 1976
02934	Harrington, F. B. Dr.	Ipswich	MA	0	1904
06637	Moseley, Ben P. P. Mrs./Thomas, I. son-in-law	Ipswich	MA	7 (1917-1925)	1918-1925
05928	Bowditch, Alfred	Jamaica Plain	MA	0	1894; 1913
06665	Farrington, H. J.	Jamaica Plain	MA	8 (1919)	1919-1920
00298	Heald, S. C.	Jamaica Plain	MA	12 (1892-1903)	1892-1896; 1903-1904
01230	Reuter, H.H./Reuter, Henry H.	Jamaica Plain	MA	4 (1891-1894)	1893-1894
09848	Scanlon, Geraldine Miss	Jamaica Plain	MA	8 (1949)	1949
00432	Thayer, Mrs. John E.	Lancaster	MA	0	1894-1898
09169	Ashton, John	Lawrence	MA	2 (1929)	1929-1930
05996	Walworth, C. W.	Lawrence	MA	0	1914
10562	Lapierre, Mr. & Mrs. Armond	Leicester	MA	2 (1976)	1967; 1976
01022	Appleton, Julia S./Appleton, Julia A.	Lenox	MA	11 (1883-1884)	1883-1884
01295	DeHeredia, Carlos M. Mrs./Wheatleigh/H.H. Cook/Cook, Henry H.	Lenox	MA	47 (1892-1919)	1892-1894; 1919
03381	Field, Mrs. William/Sloane, W. D. & Mrs. William Field	Lenox	MA	0	1907
01131	Freylinghausen, F.	Lenox	MA	59 (1887-1888)	1887-1888
01041	Jessup, Morris K.	Lenox	MA	12 (1888)	1885-1889
01346	Sloane, John	Lenox	MA	18 (1893-1894)	1893-1895
01229	Sloane, W. M.	Lenox	MA	9 (1891-1894)	1887-1895
01027	White, Henry D. Mrs./Sloane, W.D./Sloane, William D.	Lenox	MA	92 (1885-1886; 1924-1925)	1885-1899; 1924-1927
02267	Emery, F. L./Emery, Frederick L.	Lexington	MA	4 (1900-1904)	1899-1905
02936	Hayden, Richard	Lexington	MA	0	1903
10559	Ireland, Mr. & Mrs. Blake	Lexington	MA	0	
10677	Jackson, Mr. & Mrs. Kenneth	Lexington	MA	0	N.D.
10387	Peters, Mr. & Mrs. Robert	Lexington	MA	0	1972
10558	Plank, Mr. & Mrs. Richard B.	Lexington	MA	0	
09332	Richards, Thomas V. Dr.	Lexington	MA	107 (1930-1941; 1962)	1933-1941

Job #	Job Name/Alternative Name	Job Location		Plans	Correspondence
07072	Scheibe, E. F.	Lexington	MA	0	
09962	Shearer, James	Lexington	MA	12 (1949-1956)	1953-1957
03080	Tower, A. L. Miss	Lexington	MA	1 (1905)	1905
00258	Whipple, J. Reed	Lexington	MA	18 (1903-1908)	1902-1914
03053	Adams, Charles Francis/Burnham, W. A.	Lincoln	MA	44 (1888-1892)	1891; 1905
10276	Birkett, Mr. and Mrs. James	Lincoln	MA	0	
09623	Booth, Robert H.	Lincoln	MA	0	1941
10286	Brown, Mr. and Mrs. John B.	Lincoln	MA	0	
01134	Burnham, W. A.	Lincoln	MA	0	1888-1892
10205	D'Autremont, Dr. and Mrs. Chester	Lincoln	MA	11 (1966)	1966
10392	Downey, Mr. & Mrs. Edward F. Jr.	Lincoln	MA	3 (1972)	1888; 1972
10681	Golden, Mr. & Mrs. Marvin	Lincoln	MA	0	1978-1979
07806	Macomber, Donald Dr.	Lincoln	MA	4 (1890; 1927)	1927-1929
10285	Pugh, Mr. and Mrs. Alexander	Lincoln	MA	0	1969
10271	Thurmond, Mr. and Mrs. G. Bruce	Lincoln	MA	1 (1969)	1969
10726	Weyl, Mr. & Mrs. Alan	Lincoln	MA	0	1979
02239	Simmons, Sally M.	Little Nahant	MA	5 (1900-1901)	1900-1901
09614	Booth, Richard A./Booth, Joseph C.	Longmeadow	MA	4 (1940-1943)	1940-1944
09381	Brooks, John C.	Longmeadow	MA	15 (1935)	1935-1939
09908	Brooks, John C. Mrs.	Longmeadow	MA	4 (1951)	1951-1952
09959	Chapin, A. H./Glen Arden	Longmeadow	MA	8 (1953)	1959
09355	Cruttenden, Walter B. Mrs.	Longmeadow	MA	1 (1934)	1933-1934
09947	Ellis, H. B.	Longmeadow	MA	11 (1952-1954)	1953-1955
09001	Harrington, John S.	Longmeadow	MA	12 (1928)	1928-1930
03647	Haynes, Stanford L.	Longmeadow	MA	5 (1906-1909)	1909-1910
09059	Hooker, Richard	Longmeadow	MA	6 (1928-1929)	1929
09762	Hoyt, Dr. W. Fenn	Longmeadow	MA	0	1947
09211	Irwin, Robert Mrs./Irwin, Robert	Longmeadow	MA	4 (1930)	1930
07606	Kibbe, C. W.	Longmeadow	MA	0	1926
09616	Palermo, Alfonso A. Dr./Palermo, Alphonson	Longmeadow	MA	16 (1941-1944)	1940-1944
09141	Robinson, Homans	Longmeadow	MA	12 (1929)	1929-1931
09883	Schlesinger, Frank A.	Longmeadow	MA	0	1949-1950
09814	Smith, William H. 2d	Longmeadow	MA	6 (1948; 1951)	1948-1953
09949	Stoughton, Edward	Longmeadow	MA	11 (1952-1954)	1952-1955
09248	Wesson, Harold	Longmeadow	MA	10 (1930-1931)	1930-1933; 1941
02048	Tower, Abner J.	Longwood	MA	3 (1898)	1898-1899
00632	Bent	Lowell	MA	1 (1893)	
05339	Pierce, Edward B.	Lowell	MA	0	1911
03729	Putnam, Frank P.	Lowell	MA	0	1909
03142	Baker, F. E./Little Nahant	Lynn	MA	0	1906
12237	Rollins, Royal	Lynn	MA	0	1892
10687	Leskiewicz, Mr. & Mrs. Walter	Lynnfield	MA	0	1979

Job #	Job Name/Alternative Name	Job Location		Plans	Correspondence
10364	Travalini, Dr. and Mrs. J. Robert	Lynnfield	MA	0	1971
07846	Farnum, H. W.	Magnolia	MA	43 (1927-1932)	1927-1932
07993	Paine, R. T.	Magnolia	MA	0	1929
06707	Voorhees, Flora/Green Gables	Magnolia	MA	2 (1919)	1919-1921
12247	Baxter, Sylvester	Malden	MA	0	1889
00320	Bigelow, Prescott	Manchester	MA	3 (1902)	1892-1894; 1902
03278	Bradbury, Frederick T. Mrs./Bradbury, Frederick T.	Manchester	MA	6 (1907-1912)	[1903]-1912; 1925-1927
01895	Bullard Estate	Manchester	MA	4 (1896-1897)	1896-1897
10194	Cunningham, Mr. and Mrs. Alan	Manchester	MA	0	1963-1966
09157	Febiger, W./Febiger, William S.	Manchester	MA	0	1929-1930
09258	Hanks, Stedman S.	Manchester	MA	21 (1930-1931)	1930-1931
05958	Lancashire, Dr. J. H.	Manchester	MA	0	1912-1914
10525	Lothrop, Mr. & Mrs. Francis B.	Manchester	MA	0	1975-1977
06740	Mann, Isaac	Manchester	MA	0	1919
09344	McKenna, William J. Mrs.	Manchester	MA	3 (1933)	1931-1934
00307	McMillan, James Mrs.	Manchester	MA	8 (1903)	1903
10662	Stone, Mr. & Mrs. Edward L.	Manchester	MA	2 (1978)	1978
01773	Towne Estate/Towne, Henry R./Eagle Head	Manchester	MA	8 (1895)	1893-1896
00237	Walker, Charles C./Walker, W.B.	Manchester	MA	2 (1899)	1896-1926
02213	Wetherbee, J. O.	Manchester	MA	8 (1899-1900)	1899-1900
00418	White, George R. Estate	Manchester	MA	72 (1898-1929)	1897-1929
03060	Wick, Morrow C./Wick, Myron C.	Manchester	MA	0	1905
09473	Williamson, W. B.	Manchester	MA	10 (1936-1937)	1936-1937
00686	Black, G. N.	Manchester-by-the-Sea	MA	13 (1882-1883)	1884
07546	Appleton, Samuel	Marblehead	MA	5 (1925)	1925
01433	Burlen, L.W.	Marblehead	MA	1 (1894)	1894-1895
06683	Dana, Harold W. Dr.	Marblehead	MA	5 (1915-1920)	1919-1921
01427	Eaton, C. S.	Marblehead	MA	5 (1894; 1900)	1894-1899
07281	Fahey, Frank J.	Marblehead	MA	11 (1923-1924)	1924
10079	Ladd, Mrs. Harold	Marblehead	MA	0	
10030	Merrill, Mrs. E. M.	Marblehead	MA	6 (1930; 1956)	1956
10573	Sibley, Mr. & Mrs. Gerald	Marblehead	MA	0	1977
07356	Tutein, E. A. Mrs./Tutein, E.A.	Marblehead	MA	14 (1924-1930)	1924-1926
00636	Wheeler, Elbert Gen.	Marblehead	MA	5 (1894-1902)	1894-1896; 1902
10129	Zimman, Harold O.	Marblehead	MA	13 (1961)	1961
07583	Bennett, H. W.	Marion	MA	0	1925
03380	Bennett, H. W.	Marion	MA	0	1907
10477	Butler, Mr. & Mrs. Richard A.	Marion	MA	3 (1974)	1973
12257	Coolidge, C.A.	Marion	MA	0	1889; 1892-1893; 1896
10077	Kuehn, G. W.	Marion	MA	12 (1958-1960)	1958-1961

Front entrance, carriage drive and Hutchinson garden, December 1904. Job #416 – C.L. Hutchinson (Lake Geneva, WI).

Job #	Job Name/Alternative Name	Job Location		Plans	Correspondence
10695	Norweb, Mr. & Mrs. R. Henry III	Marion	MA	0	N.D.
09062	Prouty, Lewis I.	Marion	MA	6 (1927; 1929)	1929; 1937
03712	Stone, Galen	Marion	MA	0	1909
10699	Tomlinson, Mr. & Mrs. Joseph	Marion	MA	0	
10511	Wellman, Mr. & Mrs. Arthur O. Jr.	Marion	MA	22 (1974-1975)	1974-1979
00451	Sherman, George M.	Marshfield	MA	0	1903
07933	Davis, Edward Kirk	Marstons Mills	MA	131 (1921-1950)	1928-1952
12077	Poor, Henry V.	Mattapan	MA	0	1884; 1887
10369	Austin, Mr. and Mrs. Charles A.	Medfield	MA	0	
10298	Carter, Mr. Dwight	Medfield	MA	2 (1969)	1969
10365	McCurdy, Mr. and mrs. Edward	Melrose	MA	0	1971
03818	Page, E. S.	Melrose	MA	0	1909
10720	Razvi, Dr. & Mrs. Syed A.	Mendon	MA	0	
09723	Paine, Stephen	Millis	MA	33 (1925; 1946)	1945-1946
10243	Boylan, Mr. and Mrs. Dean M.	Milton	MA	0	N.D.
06824	Brooks, Walter	Milton	MA	1 (1923)	

Job #	Job Name/Alternative Name	Job Location		Plans	Correspondence
09036	Cobb, John C.	Milton	MA	3 (1929)	1928-1929
09096	Cobb, John Candler	Milton	MA	0	1929
09721	Collins, R. P.	Milton	MA	31 (1946)	1945-1946
07523	Halbritter, John	Milton	MA	0	1925
10708	Herbert, Mr. & Mrs. J. Kingston	Milton	MA	0	
05852	Kennedy, Harris	Milton	MA	0	1913
10001	Kennelly, R. G.	Milton	MA	17 (1954-1955)	1955-1956
07548	Kimball, Rev. Thatcher R.	Milton	MA	0	1925
10462	Mackenzie, Dr. & Mrs. John M.	Milton	MA	0	1973
10407	Musgrave, Mr. & Mrs. William G.	Milton	MA	0	1972
09965	O'Connor, Thomas Jr.	Milton	MA	8 (1937-1953)	1953-1960
01146	Olney, Richard	Milton	MA	8 (1865-1889)	1889-1895
02218	Russell, H. S.	Milton	MA	1 (1899)	1899
05834	Slater, H. N.	Milton	MA	0	1913
10657	Ward, Mr. & Mrs. Richard P.	Milton	MA	0	1978
07786	Whitney, G. G.	Milton	MA	191 (1920-1934)	1927-1934; 1950-1952; 1976
09067	Whitney, Theodore T. Jr.	Milton	MA	7 (1929)	1929-1933
00635	Wigglesworth, George	Milton	MA	2 (1894)	1894-1896
02065	Judd, Curtis S./Judd, Curtis J.	Monterey	MA	0	1898-1899
01076	Blanchard, J. A. Mrs./Duncan, Geo. A.P.H. Mrs.	Nahant	MA	6 (1887)	1887; 1898
01075	Cameron, Sir Roderick	Nahant	MA	23 (1887-1888)	1888-1889
00625	Duncan, George A.P.H. Mrs./Blanchard, J.A. Mrs.	Nahant	MA	9 (1898)	1898
12267	Guild, Mrs. E.G.	Nahant	MA	0	1882
00645	Guild, S.E.	Nahant	MA	21 (1881-1882)	1881-1882
09743	Hall, Dr. Francis C.	Nahant	MA	0	1946
02959	Bates, Jacob P./Bates, J.P.	Nantasket	MA	5 (1904-1905)	1904-1906
09705	Blake, Mrs. Sarah Weld	Natick	MA	0	1945
10732	Bratko, Bart	Natick	MA	0	
10244	Foley, Mr. and Mrs. Richard	Natick	MA	5 (1968; 1974)	1968-1974
09357	Ketchum, Phillips	Natick	MA	12 (1932-1935)	1934-1936
01227	Walcott, J. W.	Natick	MA	7 (1890-1894)	1892-1894
10007	Alpert, E.	Needham	MA	2 (1955)	1955
06813	Amory, John Austin/Armory, J.A.	Needham	MA	2 (1920)	1920
10313	Charles Court East	Needham	MA	7 (1970)	1970-1973
10370	Gilpatrick, Mr. and Mrs. Robert B.	Needham	MA	0	
10086	Hiam, Edwin W.	Needham	MA	31 (1953-1959)	1958-1959
09986	Marks, F. W.	Needham	MA	6 (1954-1955)	1954-1956
07935	Moine, John T.	Needham	MA	0	
10160	Strekalovsky, Mr. and Mrs. Nicholas	Needham	MA	0	1963
10325	Vaughan, Mr. and Mrs. Herbert W.	Needham	MA	0	1970

Job #	Job Name/Alternative Name	Job Location		Plans	Correspondence
10467	Wallack, Mr. & Mrs.	Needham	MA	0	
10346	Weyand, Mr. and Mrs. John	Needham	MA	0	
01381	Grinnell, Fred	New Bedford	MA	7 (1893)	1893-1894
00672	Mandell, E. D.	New Bedford	MA	3 (1883)	1883
06291	Paul, Ann Marie	Newbury	MA	0	1915
06812	Burnhome, M. S. Mrs./Burnhome, M.S.	Newburyport	MA	0	1920
07676	Hamilton, Dr. Robert D.	Newburyport	MA	0	1926
	* See also Chestnut Hill, Waban and West Newton	Newton	MA		
10412	Abrams, Mr. & Mrs. Benjamin	Newton	MA	4 (1970-1972)	1972
10589	Ambrosino, Mr. & Mrs. Michael	Newton	MA	3 (1977)	1977
01896	Armstrong, G. E./Jewett, N. M.	Newton	MA	28 (1880-1910)	1874; 1895-1899
01021	Bayley, M.C./Bailey	Newton	MA	4 (1882-1883)	1879 (?); 1884
10157	Beal, Mrs. Willams De Ford	Newton	MA	0	1963
10534	Berg, Dr. & Mrs. Robert B.	Newton	MA	4 (1975)	1975
10235	Briskin, Mr. and Mrs. Gerald	Newton	MA	1 (1967)	1967
10675	Charkoudian, Mr. & Mrs. John	Newton	MA	0	1978
10340	Church, Mr. and Mrs. Gerald B.	Newton	MA	0	N.D.
01208	Cobb, H. S.	Newton	MA	8 (1890-1891)	1889-1893
01294	Cooper, F. J.	Newton	MA	4 (1894-1895)	1898
06554	Cronan, John L.	Newton	MA	0	1917
10373	Dwork, Mr. and Mrs. Bernard	Newton	MA	0	
06436	Ellison, E. H.	Newton	MA	0	1916
12277	Farlow, J.S.	Newton	MA	0	1890
10246	Fenno, Mr. and Mrs. J. Brooks	Newton	MA	0	1968-1979
06085	Ferguson, John C.	Newton	MA	2 (1915)	1914-1916
05882	Ferrin, F. M.	Newton	MA	9 (1907-1914)	1913-1916
10464	Fogel, Dr. & Mrs. Berthram	Newton	MA	1 (1973)	1973-1974
10565	Greytak, Mr. & Mrs. Thomas	Newton	MA	0	
10583	Haffenreffer, Mr. & Mrs. Theodore C. Jr.	Newton	MA	0	1976
10208	Hencken, Mr. and Mrs. O'Neill	Newton	MA	3 (1966; 1969)	1966-1971
06814	Hopewell, Henry C.	Newton	MA	0	1920
10143	Howkins, G. H. Jr. Mrs.	Newton	MA	5 (1962)	1962-1966
10356	Jacobs, Mr. and Mrs. Herman	Newton	MA	0	
01724	Jewett, N. M./Armstrong, G. E.	Newton	MA	4 (1896)	1874; 1889-1896
10384	Kent, Dr. & Mrs. Henry	Newton	MA	0	1972
10555	Kramer, Mr. & Mrs. Clarence Jr.	Newton	MA	4 (1976)	1976
10682	Lamont, Mr. & Mrs. Hayes	Newton	MA	0	1979
01040	Lee, William P.	Newton	MA	4 (1887)	1887
06980	Merrill, K./AyerLacy	Newton	MA	19 (1903-1923)	1921-1924; 1929
10576	Morss, Mr. & Mrs. Philip	Newton	MA	4 (1975-1976)	1976-1977
10594	Moskos, Dr. Vasiliki	Newton	MA	2 (1974)	1977
10440	Moskow, Mr. & Mrs. Abraham	Newton	MA	0	

Job #	Job Name/Alternative Name	Job Location		Plans	Correspondence
10470	Myers, Mr. & Mrs. Herbert J.	Newton	MA	0	
10133	O'Doherty, Miss Elizabeth	Newton	MA	0	
01800	Potter, J.S.	Newton	MA	3 (1893-1895)	1895-1896
07632	Rand, James H.	Newton	MA	3 (1925-1926)	1926
10289	Remensnyder, Dr. and Mrs. John P.	Newton	MA	0	
10349	Roberts, Mr. and Mrs. Simon	Newton	MA	0	
01391	Russell, C. F.	Newton	MA	5 (1894)	1894-1895; 1902
05927	Sheldon, Frank M.	Newton	MA	0	1913
10290	Smith, Mr. and Mrs. Endicott	Newton	MA	0	1969
07422	Sullivan, Frank J.	Newton	MA	14 (1925)	1925
10612	Swartz, Mr. & Mrs. Frederick	Newton	MA	0	
06251	Towle, Loren D./Convent of the Sacred Heart/Academy of the Sacred Heart/Sacred Heart Country Day School	Newton	MA	77 (1914-1925)	1915-1926; 1938; 1948; 1953
00461	Tyler, Dr. H. W.	Newton	MA	0	1897-1898
12509	Ward, John & George	Newton	MA	1 (1890; 1893)	
10279	Wasserman, Mr. and Mrs. Max	Newton	MA	2 (1971-1972)	1972
10363	Wechsler, Mr. and Mrs. Paul	Newton	MA	0	1971-1973
10187	Weisman, Dr. and Mrs. David	Newton	MA	0	1965
02234	Abbott, Samuel W. Dr.	Newton Centre	MA	2 (1898-1900)	1899-1900
02044	Barnes, C. L. & W. H.	Newton Centre	MA	3 (1897)	1897
12287	Bigelow, H. J.	Newton Centre	MA	0	1886; 1888
01221	Bishop, R. R. Judge/Bishop, Robert R.	Newton Centre	MA	16 (1892-1900)	1886-1905
10063	Bornstein, Bernard	Newton Centre	MA	0	
07943	Bunnell, G. W.	Newton Centre	MA	14 (1928-1929)	1928-1930
10638	Burdick, Mr. & Mrs. Lalor	Newton Centre	MA	0	
01430	Casson, R.	Newton Centre	MA	5 (1894)	1894-1896
01296	Colburn, E.T.	Newton Centre	MA	3 (1886-1892)	1892
01386	Crowell, T. Irving	Newton Centre	MA	4 (1893)	1893
10130	Green, Arnold	Newton Centre	MA	0	1961
09809	Howes, Mr. Samuel C.	Newton Centre	MA	0	1948
07853	Jones, Mrs. M. B.	Newton Centre	MA	0	1927
10574	Macomber, Miss Dell	Newton Centre	MA	0	
10430	Marshall, Mr. & Mrs. John	Newton Centre	MA	10 (1970-1973)	1972-1973
10672	McCraith, Mr. & Mrs. Douglas	Newton Centre	MA	0	1978
02289	Parker, W. E.	Newton Centre	MA	1 (1902)	1902
10540	Podolsky, Mr. & Mrs. David	Newton Centre	MA	0	
10424	Seghorn, Dr. & Mrs. Theoharis	Newton Centre	MA	0	
06073	Shaw, Robert G. 2nd/Shaw, Robert Gould	Newton Centre	MA	28 (1908-1914)	1914-1915
10375	Siegel, Dr. and Mrs. Julius	Newton Centre	MA	0	1971
01897	Tyler, H. W. Dr.	Newton Centre	MA	3 (1897-1898)	1897-1899
03649	Davenport, W. N./Davenport, Lizzie M./Davenport, Mrs. W. N.	Newton Highlands	MA	4 (1909)	1893; 1909

Job #	Job Name/Alternative Name	Job Location		Plans	Correspondence
09665	Kowal, Samuel J. Dr.	Newton Highlands	MA	5 (1944)	1944
10319	Soep, Mr. and Mrs. Bernard	Newton Highlands	MA	4 (1970)	1970
06463	Thompson, Sanford E.	Newton Highlands	MA	3 (1917-1918)	1916-1918
10646	Babcock, Miss Martha	Newtonville	MA	0	1978
10004	Brown, Gardner Mrs.	Newtonville	MA	2 (1955)	1955
10314	Collins, Mr. and Mrs. Milton	Newtonville	MA	0	1972
05919	Fulton, W. D.	Newtonville	MA	0	1913
10296	Zalkind, Mr. and Mrs. Norman	Newtonville	MA	0	
03436	Arnold, Moses/Island Grove Park	North Abington	MA	0	1908
06082	Foss, Granville E. Jr./Foss, Granville E.	North Andover	MA	5 (1904-1915)	1914-1916; 1924
05678	Simonds, George H.	North Andover	MA	2 (1908-1928)	1912-1920
10016	Batchelder, George L., Jr./Moraine Farm/ Phillips, J. C.	North Beverly	MA	6 (1955-1967)	
01326	Ames, F. L./Ames, Oliver	North Easton	MA	5 (1891)	1891-1893; 1978
01325	Ames, Hobart/Ames, Oakes A.	North Easton	MA	2 (1890-1892)	1877-1892
01224	Ames, Oliver 2d/Ames, F. L.	North Easton	MA	42 (1891-1892)	1891-1894; 1976-1980
01223	Ames, William	North Easton	MA	0	1891-1897
09798	Parker, Mrs. William Amory	North Easton	MA	0	1947-1950
09912	Parker, William A. Mrs.	North Easton	MA	10 (1951-1952)	1951-1952
09517	Cobb, Clarence/Wild Harbor	North Falmouth	MA	2 (1937)	1938-1939
07580	Rand, James H.	North Falmouth	MA	54 (1921-1928)	1925; 1928
10575	Vaughan, Mr. & Mrs. Herbert W.	North Falmouth	MA	0	1976
06641	Smith, Harry Worcester/Lordvale	North Grafton	MA	0	1918-1923
10557	Williams, Mr. & Mrs. Peter	North Grafton	MA	4 (1976-1977)	1976-1977
09886	Reilly, J. R.	North Scituate	MA	3 (1950)	1950
07297	Collins, Mrs. Joseph	Northampton	MA	0	1924
01775	Schell, Francis	Northfield	MA	4 (1895)	1895-1896
10427	Matthews, Mr. & Mrs. George T.	Norwood	MA	0	1972
03742	Plimpton, G. A.	Norwood	MA	0	
01394	Plimpton, H. M./Plimpton, Herbert L.	Norwood	MA	13 (1894)	1894-1896
02049	Smith, George H.	Norwood	MA	9 (1898-1913)	1897-1916
09255	Willett, George F.	Norwood	MA	0	1930-1931
10282	Davis, George A. Mrs./Mrs. Barton J. Thompson	Orleans	MA	3 (1969)	1969-1972
10698	Chace, Mr.& Mrs. William B.	Osterville	MA	0	
09676	Crossett, E. C.	Osterville	MA	50 (1915; 1944-1947)	1944-1947
09712	Gates, Thomas S. Dr.	Osterville	MA	37 (1945-1947)	1945-1954
09662	Lee, Halfdan Mrs.	Osterville	MA	1 (1944)	1944
09795	Parlett, Miss Mary	Osterville	MA	0	1947
10640	Rabb, Mr. & Mrs. Irving	Osterville	MA	0	1978
10694	Stanhope, Mr. & Mrs. Luther E.	Osterville	MA	0	1978-1979
10610	Thorkilsen, Mr. Harold	Osterville	MA	0	1977-1978

Top: View to the tower over lake in the Mountain Lake development, Spring 1932.
Job #6829 – George M. Laughlin (Mountain Lake, FL).

Bottom: Entrance drive and forecourt, S.Z. Mitchell residence, January 1929.
Job #7778 – S.Z. Mitchell (Mountain Lake, FL).

Job #	Job Name/Alternative Name	Job Location		Plans	Correspondence
05060	Joslin, E. P. Dr./Joslin, Elliott P.	Oxford	MA	0	1910-1914
07752	Marsters, A. A.	Oyster Harbor	MA	11 (1926-1930)	1926-1931
12207	Fiske, G. S. & E. L.	Philadelphia	MA	14 (1894-1916)	1891-1894
07594	Eaton, A. W.	Pittsfield	MA	0	1925-1926
09345	Fox, Alanson G.	Pittsfield	MA	0	1933
09044	Graves, Merle - Community Houses/Graves, Merle D.	Pittsfield	MA	11 (1929)	1929-1930
09108	Graves, Merle - New Homes/Graves, Merle D.	Pittsfield	MA	6 (1929-1930)	1929-1931
07829	Graves, Merle Mrs.	Pittsfield	MA	105 (1927-1929)	1927-1931
01147	Ogden, Mrs. M.D./Ogden & West	Pittsfield	MA	6 (1891)	1891
01092	Walker, W.D./Walker, Wirt D./Brythewood	Pittsfield	MA	75 (1889-1894)	1889-1899
01174	West, F. T.	Pittsfield	MA	4 (1890-1891)	1888-1891
03163	Weston, Franklin	Pittsfield	MA	4 (1906-1907)	1906-1914
09343	Greenough, Chester N. Mrs./Churchill, L./Plimouth Plantation	Plymouth	MA	7 (1933; 1956)	1933; 1956-1960
06704	Hornblower, Henry/Plimouth Plantat./Greenough	Plymouth	MA	39 (1919-1927; 1956)	1919-1936; 1955-1961
05429	Knapp Estate/Marion Olmsted lives here,1939	Plymouth	MA	35 (1939-1940)	1940-1949
10564	Vecchione, Mr. Joseph	Plymouth	MA	0	
10580	Wadsworth, Mr. & Mrs. Lewis L. Jr.	Plymouth	MA	0	1976
00034	Bradley, R. S./Bradley, Robert S.	Prides Crossing	MA	0	1900-1922
05912	Jackson, Charles L.	Prides Crossing	MA	0	1913-1914
00682	Kidder, H.P.	Prides Crossing	MA	1 (1884)	1884
01071	Loring, W. C.	Prides Crossing	MA	66 (1887-1889)	1887-1895; 1903-1906
00206	Spaulding, W. S. & J. P./King, H.P./Spaulding, W.S. & J.T.	Prides Crossing	MA	19 (1897-1898)	1897-1899
05579	Swift, E. C.	Prides Crossing	MA	0	1912
10379	Ewer, Mr. & Mrs. John C.	Princeton	MA	0	1971
10368	Adams, Mr. and Mrs. James F.	Quincy	MA	0	
09847	Faxon, Robert - Homestead	Quincy	MA	20 (1918; 1927; 1947-1950)	1949-1950
07764	Hall, G. F./Hall, George Freeman	Quincy	MA	12 (1924-1927)	1927
03415	Rice, Fred B.	Quincy	MA	0	1907
10458	Ward, Mr. & Mrs. Richard P.	Quincy	MA	0	
01052	Belcher, H. A.	Randolph	MA	45 (1882-1895)	1887-1897
03433	French, Herbert F.	Randolph	MA	0	1908
02963	Burgess, Mrs. G.E.	Readville	MA	0	1904
01072	Hemenway, Mary and Augusta	Readville	MA	2 (1882)	1896
05059	Crane, W. M. Rev.	Richmond	MA	55 (1910-1913)	1910-1913; 1951
06401	Tirrell, James A.	Rockland	MA	0	1916-1920
01434	Calder Estate	Roxbury	MA	4 (1895)	1895
02269	Collar, William C.	Roxbury	MA	1 (1900)	1900
07895	Hersey, Misses	Roxbury	MA	10 (1927-1932)	1928-1935

Job #	Job Name/Alternative Name	Job Location		Plans	Correspondence
01200	Kendricken, P. H.	Roxbury	MA	1 (1891)	1891
06238	Morse, James F.	Roxbury	MA	0	1915
03179	Rudiger, Miss/Rudiger, Marie	Roxbury	MA	2 (1906)	1906-1907
09976	Cummings, Raymond	Salem	MA	14 (1954-1958)	1954-1964; 1975
10486	Koleman, Mr. Donald	Salem	MA	0	1973-1974
00044	Loring Estate	Salem	MA	18 (1895-1904)	1891-1907
07488	Dexter, Charles O.	Sandwich	MA	0	1925-1926
07638	Baukart, Charles F./Bankart, Charles F.	Scituate	MA	0	1926
10710	Plunkett, Mr. & Mrs. Robert J. Jr.	Scituate	MA	0	
07706	Rothery, James	Scituate	MA	0	1926
06357	Schauffler, Robert Haven/Greenbush	Scituate	MA	0	1916
10497	Thibodeau, Dr. & Mrs. Theodore J.	Scituate	MA	0	
10570	Cuming, Mr. & Mrs. William R.	Sharon	MA	0	1978
10393	Gould, Mr. & Mrs. Herbert	Sharon	MA	0	
10577	Grossman, Mr. & Mrs. Theodore	Sharon	MA	1 (1977)	1977
10188	Harris, Mr. and Mrs. F. E.	Sharon	MA	0	1965
10665	Jaye, Dr. & Mrs. Barry	Sharon	MA	0	1978
10394	Shaw, Mr. & Mrs. William T.	Sharon	MA	0	1972
10103	Simonds, Mr. and Mrs. William	Sharon	MA	1 (1959)	1959-1961
07114	Cabot, Walter M.	Sherborn	MA	10 (1924-1925)	1924-1925
10107	Gilmartin, R. D.	Sherborn	MA	4 (1959-1960)	1959-1960
10413	Maulbetsch, Mr. & Mrs. John S.	Sherborn	MA	0	1972-1974
09677	Motley, J. L. Mrs.	Sherborn	MA	5 (1944-1945)	1944-1945
10523	Shepard, Dr. & Mrs. James	Sherborn	MA	0	
03635	Gallagher, W. S./Gallagher, Walter S.	Somerville	MA	1 (1909)	1909
05574	Skinner, Joseph A.	South Hadley	MA	3 (1912-1914)	1912-1914
03478	Smith, Hinsdale	South Hadley	MA	6 (1908-1910)	1908-1910; 1937; 1973-1974
10700	Gardner, Mr. & Mrs. John	South Hamilton	MA	0	N.D.
10701	Whitman, Mr. & Mrs. Peter	South Hamilton	MA	0	1896; 1979
12307	Baker, James E.	South Lincoln	MA	0	1890-1891
10614	Marshall, Mr. & Mrs. John	South Yarmouth	MA	0	N.D.
01366	Mead, E. S.	Southampton	MA	1 (1893)	1893-1894
01141	Sears, J. M.	Southboro	MA	4 (1889)	1889
01432	Burnett, Joseph/Deer foot Farm	Southborough	MA	5 (1894)	1890-1894
09190	Wells, Channing M.	Southbridge	MA	4 (1926-1930)	1930
09106	Wells, J. Cheney et al.	Southbridge	MA	20 (1929-1930)	1929-1934
07379	Wells, J.C. & C.W., A.B.	Southbridge	MA	8 (1909-1924)	1924-1925
00449	Prouty Estate	Spencer	MA	0	1900
07440	Adaskin, H.	Springfield	MA	0	1925
06990	Baker, R. K.	Springfield	MA	6 (1920-1921)	1921-1922
09262	Behan, J. E. Mrs./Behan, J.C.	Springfield	MA	11 (1929; 1931)	1931
09002	Bemis, William	Springfield	MA	3 (1924-1928)	1928-1931

Job #	Job Name/Alternative Name	Job Location		Plans	Correspondence
02887	Bill, Nathan D.	Springfield	MA	0	1901
07900	Bradford, E. S.	Springfield	MA	45 (1928-1929)	1928-1932
07936	Bradford, E. S. Jr./Laurel Manor	Springfield	MA	10 (1928-1930)	1928-1933
09060	Brown, Phelp	Springfield	MA	0	1929
10117	Bulkley, James S.	Springfield	MA	7 (1960-1961)	1960-1961
07603	Burbank, D. E.	Springfield	MA	54 (1926-1930)	1926-1931
09207	Burbank, James B./Pearson Subdivision #3	Springfield	MA	42 (1933-1957)	1948-1955
09930	Carlson, Gunnar	Springfield	MA	8 (1952)	1952
02886	Carver, Eugene P.	Springfield	MA	0	1902
07803	Decker, Edward S. Jr./Colony Hills	Springfield	MA	1 (1927)	1927
09210	Dowley, Kenneth C./Colony Hills	Springfield	MA	16 (1929-1931)	1929-1938
05769	Duryea, J. Frank	Springfield	MA	1 (1913)	1912-1913
09204	Ellis, Dwight W.	Springfield	MA	7 (1928-1930)	1930-1931
09058	Goodell, William Mrs./Goodell, William	Springfield	MA	7 (1929)	1929
06994	Harris, Frederick	Springfield	MA	12 (1921-1923)	1920-1929
09122	Insull, Joseph & Whittlesey, G. E./Holbrook, Emma/Insull, Joseph	Springfield	MA	16 (1928-1931)	1929-1933
09239	Kemater, George H.	Springfield	MA	11 (1930-1931)	1930-1935; 1941
07926	Lyman, John R./Dean, Paul D.	Springfield	MA	4 (1928)	
07441	McElwain, H. E.	Springfield	MA	0	1925
07945	Medlicott, A. G./Colony Hills	Springfield	MA	0	1928
09110	Mitchell, John H.	Springfield	MA	8 (1929)	1929-1930
07352	Paige, Ralph H.	Springfield	MA	5 (1924)	1924
09254	Perry, B. J./Perry, Bertrand J.	Springfield	MA	10 (1931; 1933)	1928-1931
07063	Sargeant, W. H.	Springfield	MA	0	1922
00261	Skinner, H. H.	Springfield	MA	4 (1902; 1910)	1898; 1902-1903; 1910
09228	Tourelotte, Frederick J./Colony Hills	Springfield	MA	0	
07566	Victor Corporation/Munson, Edwin S./Laurel Manor	Springfield	MA	22 (1921-1926)	1925-1931
00419	Wallace, A. B.	Springfield	MA	9 (1901-1902; 1927-1929)	1901-1903; 1927-1929
07355	Wallace, A. B. Mrs./Wallace, A.B.	Springfield	MA	4 (1924)	1924-1925
07818	Wallace, Norman Mrs.	Springfield	MA	75 (1927-1930)	1927-1931; 1950
01016	Choate, J. H.	Stockbridge	MA	3 (1884-1885)	1884; 1919-1920
03070	Hill, Sam	Stockbridge	MA	9 (1905)	1905
05550	Hoffman, Bernard	Stockbridge	MA	0	1912
09395	Stewart, Robert G.	Stockbridge	MA	0	1935-1936
10465	Baker, Miss Myrian	Sudbury	MA	0	1973
10626	Kim, Dr. & Mrs. Il	Sudbury	MA	0	1978
10441	Lee, Mr. & Mrs. Carroll Brown	Sudbury	MA	0	
10560	Saint Germain, Mr. & Mrs. Philip	Sudbury	MA	0	
10603	Todd, Mr. & Mrs. J. Owen	Sudbury	MA	2 (1977)	1977

Farm barn at Shelburne Farms. Job #1031 — William Seward Webb/Shelburne Farms (listed as Burlington, VT).

Job #	Job Name/Alternative Name	Job Location		Plans	Correspondence
09477	Wolbach, S. B. Dr.	Sudbury	MA	111 (1937-1950)	1936-1953
10487	Davis, Mr. & Mrs. Lucius	Sugar Hill	MA	3 (1973)	1973-1975
10717	Perlo, Mr. & Mrs. Bruce S.	Sugar Hill	MA	0	
07624	Atherton, Louis	Swampscott	MA	0	1926-1927
09562	Brown, E. P. Mrs./Brown, Edwin P./Galluop's Point	Swampscott	MA	68 (1925-1947)	1939; 1946-1948
09540	Cohen, Eli	Swampscott	MA	30 (1938-1939)	1938-1939
09657	Cornwall, B. F. Dr.	Swampscott	MA	20 (1943-1944)	1943-1944
06835	Deland, Frank S. - town place	Swampscott	MA	2 (1921)	
06658	Deland, Frank S./Deland, Frank D./Lincoln House Property	Swampscott	MA	22 (1918-1921)	1918-1923; 1942
09536	Eiseman, Sidney	Swampscott	MA	4 (1938)	1938-1939
07314	Evatt, Walter M.	Swampscott	MA	5 (1924-1927)	1924-1927
09534	Proctor, Charles Mrs./Proctor, Charles A.	Swampscott	MA	32 (1936-1939)	1936-1941
09491	Rabinowitz, I.M.	Swampscott	MA	17 (1936-1937)	1937
09587	Remis, H.	Swampscott	MA	0	1939
09537	Smith, Robert	Swampscott	MA	11 (N.D.)	1938
10515	Stahl, Mr. & Mrs. Louis E.	Swampscott	MA	0	1974
10548	Paterson, Mr. & Mrs. Donald R.	Topsfield	MA	0	
07122	Phillips, James Duncan	Topsfield	MA	5 (1923)	1923

*Farm barn at Shelburne Farms in the Autumn. Job #1031 – William Seward Webb/
Shelburne Farms (listed as Burlington, VT).*

Job #	Job Name/Alternative Name	Job Location		Plans	Correspondence
09545	Howard, Sidney/Howard, Sidney C.	Tyringham	MA	4 (1938-1939)	1938-1939
10506	Ault, Mr. & Mrs. Warren O.	Waban	MA	0	
10272	Brisker, Mr. and Mrs. Robert	Waban	MA	1 (1969)	1969-1970
10437	Colten, Mr. & Mrs. Jerome	Waban	MA	0	1973
09325	Congdon, Joseph	Waban	MA	0	
03150	Fisher, Willis R.	Waban	MA	5 (1906-1928)	1910-1911; 1928
10535	Frieze, Mr. & Mrs. Michael	Waban	MA	3 (1975)	1975
10495	Gertman, Mr. & Mrs. Myron S.	Waban	MA	1 (1975)	1974
10095	Glass, George B.	Waban	MA	0	1959
10259	Goldstein, Dr. and Mrs. Michael	Waban	MA	0	
09668	Harris, Russell H.	Waban	MA	0	1944
10042	Itkin, Morris K.	Waban	MA	0	1956
09693	Lyons, Thomas F.	Waban	MA	0	1945
10280	Marran, Mr. and Mrs. C. Charles	Waban	MA	0	1969
10653	Nelson, Dr. & Mrs. Donald	Waban	MA	0	1896
10660	Paul, Mr. & Mrs. Steven	Waban	MA	0	
10247	Pompian, Mr. and Mrs. Stuart	Waban	MA	0	1968
10599	Rendell, Mr. & Mrs. Kenneth	Waban	MA	0	1977-1978
10352	Skinner, Mr. and Mrs. David W.	Waban	MA	2 (1971)	1971

Job #	Job Name/Alternative Name	Job Location		Plans	Correspondence
09854	Wermer, Henry Dr.	Waban	MA	3 (1949)	1949
10357	Wilson, Mrs. Charles M.	Waban	MA	0	1971
10697	Wohlauer, Dr. & Mrs. Peter	Waban	MA	0	
10328	Wolfe, Mr. and Mrs. George	Waban	MA	0	1970
10490	Marshall, Mr. & Mrs. Preston	Walpole	MA	0	
07279	Barker, George W.	Waltham	MA	0	1924
06422	Marcy, Richard	Waltham	MA	0	1916
00677	Paine, R. T.	Waltham	MA	13 (1884-1886)	1884-1887; 1892-1898; 1975-1980
10385	Soltes, Mr. & Mrs. Aaron S.	Waltham	MA	4 (1972-1973)	1972-1973
09094	Duncalf, Frederick	Waquoit	MA	0	1929
00220	Gore, Governor Place	Watertown	MA	56 (1935-1938)	1936-1951
10167	Mikulka, Mr. and Mrs. Charles	Watertown	MA	0	1964-1965
00642	Payson, G.R.	Watertown	MA	7 (1882)	1882
10006	Berberian, J. K.	Wayland	MA	2 (1955)	1955
10513	Emory, Mr. & Mrs. George	Wayland	MA	0	
10185	Harper, George	Wayland	MA	0	1965
10403	Maillet, Mr. & Mrs. Alderice	Wayland	MA	0	
06058	Baltzell, W. H. Dr./Baltzell, William Hewson/Elm Bank	Wellesley	MA	18 (1914-1926)	1914-1916; 1926-1927; 1934; 1938
09649	Brown, Elliot W.	Wellesley	MA	0	1942
10547	Butler, Mr. & Mrs. Richard A.	Wellesley	MA	0	1975
10348	Catinella, Dr. and Mrs. Paul J.	Wellesley	MA	0	
07420	Cumings, Paul L./Lots in Uplands Subdivision	Wellesley	MA	21 (1924-1926)	1925-1926
07487	Cushman, Elton G.	Wellesley	MA	15 (1924-1925)	1925-1926
10062	Dickerson, John G.	Wellesley	MA	0	1957
10605	DiMaggio, Mr. & Mrs. Dominic	Wellesley	MA	0	1977
10445	Dole, Mr. & Mrs. William P.	Wellesley	MA	2 (1973)	
09304	Garon, Frederick R.	Wellesley	MA	0	1931-1932
09678	Goodrich, Richard I.	Wellesley	MA	12 (1944-1945)	1944-1945
09378	Hunnewell, Arnold Mrs. (Louisa)	Wellesley	MA	0	1935
07215	Hunnewell, F. W./Hunnewell, Francis W.	Wellesley	MA	50 (1923-1939)	1923; 1930-1939
00620	Hunnewell, H. S.	Wellesley	MA	6 (1893)	1877-1895
10597	Johnston, Mr. & Mrs. Reed	Wellesley	MA	0	1977
10566	Lapierre, Mr. & Mrs. Gerard	Wellesley	MA	0	1976
10568	Miller, Mr. & Mrs. Alan	Wellesley	MA	0	
03149	Potter Estate/Potter, Fannie/Potter, Mrs. Homer C.	Wellesley	MA	7 (1906)	1906-1908
10455	Robinson, Mr. & Mrs. Powell Jr.	Wellesley	MA	0	1978
07223	Shaw, R. G./Shaw, Robert Gould	Wellesley	MA	21 (1923)	1923-1924
09929	Gavel, J. Murray Dr.	Wellesley Farms	MA	27 (1950-1955)	1952-1956
10022	Adams, Dr. Herbert	Wellesley Hills	MA	0	1955

Job #	Job Name/Alternative Name	Job Location		Plans	Correspondence
10088	Caneo, E. L.	Wellesley Hills	MA	23 (1958-1960)	1958-1960; 1969
10183	Catlin, Dr. and Mrs. Randolph	Wellesley Hills	MA	16 (1963-1968)	1965-1968
10287	Crosby, Dr. and Mrs. William H.	Wellesley Hills	MA	0	1969-1970
10221	Fulham, Mr. and Mrs. John N.	Wellesley Hills	MA	0	1967
10452	Hansen, Mr. & Mrs. Howard E.	Wellesley Hills	MA	0	
10578	Harrington, Mr. & Mrs. Francis A. Jr.	Wellesley Hills	MA	0	
07923	Hayman, S. R. Dr.	Wellesley Hills	MA	0	1928-1929
10264	Ireland, Mrs. Emory	Wellesley Hills	MA	0	1968
09736	Johnson, E. E.	Wellesley Hills	MA	0	1946-1955
03430	Loring, Victor J.	Wellesley Hills	MA	0	1908
10401	Malkasian, Mr. & Mrs. Henry	Wellesley Hills	MA	1 (1972)	1960; 1972
10204	Morrill, Mr. and Mrs. Olney	Wellesley Hills	MA	0	
09240	Morse, Roger E.	Wellesley Hills	MA	7 (1929-1930)	1930-1931
10408	Mulroy, Dr. & Mrs. Richard D.	Wellesley Hills	MA	5 (1972-1973)	1972-1973
09983	Sanders, R. M.	Wellesley Hills	MA	11 (1944; 1945; 1954; 1957)	1954-1957
10426	Steinberg, Mr. & Mrs. Herbert G.	Wellesley Hills	MA	3 (1974)	1972-1976
07522	Sweetser, George	Wellesley Hills	MA	9 (1925-1926)	1925-1928
10113	Visvis, C. A.	Wellesley Hills	MA	0	1960
05349	Whiting, Frederick A.	Wellesley Hills	MA	0	1911; 1916
06919	Wires, E. Stanley/Uplands Subdiv.	Wellesley Hills	MA	6 (1921)	1921-1927
10400	Woods, Mr. & Mrs. Robert	Wellesley Hills	MA	2 (1972)	1972
10584	Frangos, Mr.& Mrs. Michael	Wenham	MA	5 (1975-1977)	1976-1977
09801	Laughlin, Henry A. Jr./Laughlin, Henry Jr.	Wenham	MA	3 (1947)	1947-1948
04050	Edwards, Victor E.	West Boylston	MA	7 (1910)	1910
09751	Hodgson, Fred G. Mrs.	West Falmouth	MA	13 (1943; 1946-1947)	1946-1948
00340	Lyon, William H.	West Falmouth	MA	0	1903
00339	Nash, F. K./Nash, Frank King	West Falmouth	MA	4 (1890-1904)	1903-1904; 1908
05056	Merrill, Sherburne M.	West Gloucester	MA	73 (1907-1926)	1910-1913; 1926
05671	Sinclair, Charles K. Mrs./Sinclair, Charles A.	West Gloucester	MA	13 (1913-1914)	1912-1914
09991	Whittemore, P. W.	West Gloucester	MA	0	1954
00055	Grew, E. S.	West Manchester	MA	12 (1902-1904)	1902-1904
06459	Higginson, Mrs. H. L.	West Manchester	MA	0	1916
07259	Walker, C. C./Shannon, J.B. Mrs./Walker, Charles C.	West Manchester	MA	8 (1923-1924)	1919-1938
09509	Aborn, Pennell N./Brightman, Julian, Mr. & Mrs.	West Newton	MA	14 (1927-1972)	1937-1939; 1972
07799	Beach, R. W.	West Newton	MA	2 (1927)	1927
06713	Beebe, C. C.	West Newton	MA	0	
12317	Carter, J. Richard	West Newton	MA	0	1881-1884
06926	Crimmins, Thomas A. Mrs./Crimmins, Thomas A.	West Newton	MA	3 (1933)	1921; 1928; 1933-1934

Job #	Job Name/Alternative Name	Job Location		Plans	Correspondence
09017	Dowse, W. B. H. Mrs./Dowse, W. B. H.	West Newton	MA	49 (1905; 1910; 1944-1945)	1928-1929; 1944-1945
07587	Hartridge, A. L.	West Newton	MA	4 (1926)	1926; 1929
07640	Kimball, George B.	West Newton	MA	10 (1916-1928)	1926-1930
10404	Levine, Dr. & Mrs. Howard	West Newton	MA	2 (1972-1973)	1972
10512	McDonough, Dr. & Mrs. Francis E.	West Newton	MA	0	1975
10256	Payne, Dr. and Mrs. Edmund C.	West Newton	MA	4 (1968)	1968
10253	Pounds, Mr. and Mrs. William	West Newton	MA	0	
03279	Pratt, F. S.	West Newton	MA	3 (1907-1912)	1907-1912
10048	Robinson, Winifred	West Newton	MA	16 (1956)	1956-1958
10500	Rubin, Mr. & Mrs. Saul	West Newton	MA	0	
10451	Slater, Mr. & Mrs. Paul	West Newton	MA	0	1973
10359	Stein, Dr. and Mrs. Robert Sheldon	West Newton	MA	0	1971
10257	Wagenknecht, Mr. and Mrs. Edward	West Newton	MA	0	1968
07047	Weeks, C. Sinclair	West Newton	MA	6 (1922-1928)	1922-1928
10248	Work, Mr. and Mrs. Frederick	West Newton	MA	0	1891; 1968
06804	Brown, Mary E. Miss Estate	West Roxbury	MA	2 (1919-1920)	1920-1922
10641	Segersten, Mr. & Mrs. Robert	West Roxbury	MA	0	
07809	Walsh, J. F./Walsh, J.R.	West Roxbury	MA	0	1927-1928
10634	Bain, Mr. & Mrs. William	Weston	MA	0	
05445	Blake, Francis	Weston	MA	11 (1911-1912)	1911-1912
10645	Boyle, Mr. & Mrs. Gene	Weston	MA	0	1978
10620	Bridwell, Mr. & Mrs. John	Weston	MA	0	
10647	Brountas, Mr. & Mrs. Paul	Weston	MA	0	1978
10428	Carey, Mr. & Mrs. H. Robert	Weston	MA	0	1972
10639	Clemson, Mr. & Mrs. Daniel	Weston	MA	0	1978
02067	Coburn, A. L./Coburn, Arthur L.	Weston	MA	0	1898-1899
09621	Cuneo, E. L./Rothwell, B. J.	Weston	MA	96 (1940-1963)	1941-1963
09987	Cutler, T. P.	Weston	MA	0	1954
10362	DuMaine, Mr. and Mrs. Frederic C. Jr.	Weston	MA	5 (1971-1973)	1971-1978
10509	Earle, Dr. & Mrs. Ralph Jr.	Weston	MA	2 (1974)	1974
10601	Edmonds, Mr. & Mrs. Dean Jr.	Weston	MA	3 (1975; 1977)	1977-1978
10342	Elmes, Mr. and Mrs. Charles F.	Weston	MA	0	1970
07442	Filene, A. Lincoln Mrs./Filene, A. Lincoln	Weston	MA	2 (1925)	1925
10532	Fulkerson, Mr. & Mrs. Allan W.	Weston	MA	0	
10729	Glass, Mr. & Mrs. George	Weston	MA	0	
10596	Goldstein, Dr. & Mrs. Donald	Weston	MA	0	1977-1978
10606	Gosman, Mr. & Mrs. Abraham D.	Weston	MA	0	1977-1979
05058	Hubbard, Charles W.	Weston	MA	59 (1911-1916)	1910-1917
10485	Jacobs, Mr. & Mrs. Robert	Weston	MA	0	1973
09235	Jones, C. H. "Daughter's Home"/Jones, Charles H.	Weston	MA	5 (1950)	1930-1931
00038	Jones, C. H./Jones, Charles H.	Weston	MA	2 (1901-1913)	1901-1929

Job #	Job Name/Alternative Name	Job Location		Plans	Correspondence
10508	Kanfer, Mr. & Mrs. Jack	Weston	MA	0	
10335	Karofsky, Mr. and Mrs. Sydney	Weston	MA	3 (1970)	1970-1971
09620	Lombard, Richard/Lambard, Richard	Weston	MA	0	1941
10444	Margolies, Dr. & Mrs. Michael	Weston	MA	0	
07524	Noyes, Waldo	Weston	MA	0	
01396	Paine, C. J.	Weston	MA	11 (1883; 1894)	1883; 1894-1898
10666	Paine, Miss Elizabeth	Weston	MA	0	
10551	Paine, Mr. & Mrs. John A. Jr.	Weston	MA	0	
09535	Patterson, Theodore G.	Weston	MA	49 (1928-1971)	1938; 1971
10663	Quinn, Mr John	Weston	MA	0	
10713	Razvi, Dr. & Mrs. Syed Asif	Weston	MA	0	1979
10520	Roney, Mr. & Mrs. J. Edward	Weston	MA	3 (1975)	1975
10519	Ryan, Dr. & Mrs. Kenneth J.	Weston	MA	4 (1974-1975)	1975
10674	Sanger, Mr. & Mrs. Wilbert	Weston	MA	0	
02060	Sears, Horace S.	Weston	MA	0	1898-1899
01348	Sears, P. H.	Weston	MA	1 (1893)	1882; 1889-1894
10529	Slaff, Mr. & Mrs. Allan P.	Weston	MA	6 (1975)	1975
10432	Stambaugh, Mr. & Mrs. A.A.	Weston	MA	6 (1973-1977)	1972-1977
10715	Starr, Mr. & Mrs. Alan	Weston	MA	0	
10667	Strumph, Mr. & Mrs. Joel	Weston	MA	0	1978
09554	Sweet, Homer N.	Weston	MA	27 (1938-1941)	1938-1941
09556	Ursin, Bjarne	Weston	MA	81 (1937-1940)	1938-1940; 1952; 1961
07787	Warren, Fiske/Kendell Green Property	Weston	MA	77 (1917-1932)	1926-1931
07737	Weston Baptist Parsonage/Weston First Baptist Church	Weston	MA	5 (1926)	1926
09568	Wilder, Thomas G.	Weston	MA	3 (1939)	1939
10249	Wilson, Mr. and Mrs. Dennis A.	Weston	MA	0	
03994	Winsor, Robert/Lombard, Richard/Meadow Brook School	Weston	MA	43 (1900-1911)	1910-1916; 1928-1929
10422	Wright, Mrs. Thruston Jr.	Weston	MA	1 (1974)	1972-1977
10013	Bailey, Mr. and Mrs. Vincent R.	Westwood	MA	1 (1955)	1955-1956
10266	Brown, Mr. and Mrs. Clayton	Westwood	MA	3 (1968)	1968
10514	Cabot, Mr. & Mrs. Paul C. Jr.	Westwood	MA	3 (1974-1975)	1974-1979
10433	Chace, Mr.& Mrs. William B.	Westwood	MA	7 (1972-1974)	1972-1979
10322	Cooperman, Mr. and Mrs. Irwin	Westwood	MA	2 (1970)	1970
10376	Danforth, Mr. & Mrs.	Westwood	MA	0	1895
10270	Dilworth, Mr. and Mrs. Warden	Westwood	MA	0	1969
10602	Doorly, Mr.& Mrs. Paul	Westwood	MA	1 (1977)	1977-1979
10212	Frick, Mr. and Mrs. George	Westwood	MA	12 (1966-1967)	1966-1967
10304	Girling, Mr. and Mrs. C. Edwin	Westwood	MA	2 (1968-1969)	1969-1970
10658	Hayes, Mr. & Mrs. Samuel	Westwood	MA	0	
10337	Katler, Mr. and Mrs. Leonard B.	Westwood	MA	3 (1970-1971)	1970

Top: Tea house at the Stimson estate, March 1915. Job #3491 – C.D. Stimson (Seattle, WA).

Bottom: Italianate garden, "Boxwood," 1927. Job #7241 – A.F. Sanford (Knoxville, TN).

Job #	Job Name/Alternative Name	Job Location		Plans	Correspondence
10561	Monroe, Dr. & Mrs. Grier	Westwood	MA	0	
10718	Patten, Dr. & Mrs. James T.	Westwood	MA	0	N.D.
10648	Query, Mr. & Mrs. Alphonse W. Jr.	Westwood	MA	0	1978
10291	Regan, Mr. and Mrs. Herbert	Westwood	MA	0	
10354	Rice, Mr. George T.	Westwood	MA	0	1971
10494	Robinson, Mr. & Mrs. Edward	Westwood	MA	1 (1976)	1976
10307	Simon, Mr. and Mrs. Andrew I.	Westwood	MA	0	1969
10542	Vogel, Mrs. William	Westwood	MA	2 (1975)	1975
06978	Conren, Joseph W.	Weymouth Heights	MA	2 (1921)	1921
09686	Dowse, W. B. H. Estate	Wianno	MA	40 (1909-1911; 1920; 1944)	1944
07099	Cluett, George A.	Williamstown	MA	139 (1922-1923)	1894-1938; 1970
09969	Foehl, C. A.	Williamstown	MA	32 (1953-1956)	1953-1962
09531	Avery, Paul	Winchester	MA	0	1937-1938
02626	Clarke, Alfred	Winchester	MA	0	1903-1904
10347	Cowgill, Mr. and Mrs. F. Brooks	Winchester	MA	0	
09524	Farnsworth, Harold V.	Winchester	MA	50 (1937-1938)	1938-1939
10341	Fitzgerald, Dr. and Mrs. Paul	Winchester	MA	4 (1970-1974)	1970-1974
01725	Ginn, Edwin H.	Winchester	MA	30 (1896-1951)	1896-1908; 1945-1951
10156	Kennedy, J. P.	Winchester	MA	0	
10466	Kent, Mr. & Mrs. John E.	Winchester	MA	2 (1973)	1973-1976
10616	Lennon, Mr. & Mrs. John	Winchester	MA	0	1977
02385	McCall, Fernald/McCall - Fernald Property/Myopia Park	Winchester	MA	3 (1896)	1901-1903
06576	Crane, Frances R. Mrs./Leatherbee, R. W./Masaryk/Crow Hill	Woods Hole	MA	47 (1919-1939)	1917-1950
01014	Fay Estate/Fay, Henry H./Fay, Joseph S.	Woods Hole	MA	16 (1885-1886)	1886-1887; 1909
10241	Muellner, Mrs. Richard	Woods Hole	MA	1 (1968)	1968-1969
09050	Nims, Eugene D.	Woods Hole	MA	13 (1923-1930)	1929-1930
06694	Allen, Mrs. Robert	Worcester	MA	0	1919
09512	Douley, L. L.	Worcester	MA	0	1937
03296	Eaton, Thomas B. Mrs./Eaton, Thomas B.	Worcester	MA	1 (1907)	1907
12017	Elm Park	Worcester	MA	0	1880
05334	Forbes, William T.	Worcester	MA	0	1911
06507	Goddard, H. W.	Worcester	MA	0	1917
09699	Heald, Robert S.	Worcester	MA	28 (1944-1952)	1945-1952
09731	Higgins, Milton P.	Worcester	MA	57 (1941-1948)	1946-1948
07855	Holy Cross College	Worcester	MA	4 (1918-1927)	1927
10345	Salo, Mr. Richard	Worcester	MA	0	
01228	Smith, Frank B. and Charles W.	Worcester	MA	5 (1892)	1892
06900	Wright, George M.	Worcester	MA	2 (1920)	1920-1921
10669	Bowen, Mrs. Kenneth	Wrentham	MA	0	1978
09867	Young, Wilbur/Glen Arden Subdivision, in	Youngstown	MA	1 (1949)	1949-1950

Job #	Job Name/Alternative Name	Job Location		Plans	Correspondence
07395	Bowerman, W.	Annapolis	MD	0	1924-1925
03298	Giddings, Elizabeth Miss	Annapolis	MD	7 (1907-1910)	1907-1910
03993	Bowles, Thomas H./Estate in Green Spring Valley	Baltimore	MD	43 (1900-1911)	1910
06571	Brady, S. P.	Baltimore	MD	0	1917
05346	Brown, Alexander	Baltimore	MD	0	1911
03609	Campbell, J. Vernon	Baltimore	MD	0	1909
05066	Cotton, Mrs. Bruce/Tyson, Mrs. Jesse	Baltimore	MD	0	1910
03733	Dugan, Pierre C./Pierre C. Dugan & Nephew Inc.	Baltimore	MD	5 (1909-1910)	1909-1911
03674	Dukes, Herman H.	Baltimore	MD	0	1909-1911
06325	Frick, James Swan/Roland Park	Baltimore	MD	21 (1916)	1915-1916
05818	Garrett, Robert and Sons/Electric R. R.	Baltimore	MD	0	1913
03166	Garrett, T. Harrison Mrs./Evergreen	Baltimore	MD	11 (1906)	1876-1883; 1899; 1906; 1927
00438	Gittings, John M.	Baltimore	MD	0	1902
00068	Gordon, Douglas H./Normandie Heights/Springdale	Baltimore	MD	6 (1902)	1902
02381	Grasty, Charles H.//estate in Roland Park	Baltimore	MD	5 (1903-1905)	1902-1905
03534	Holton, Hart B. Mrs./Holton, Hart B.	Baltimore	MD	1 (1906)	1908
02377	Jenkins, Joseph/Windy Gates/Jenkins, Joseph W., Jr.	Baltimore	MD	24 (1902-1906)	1902-1907; 1916
09034	Newman, J. K./Stables	Baltimore	MD	6 (1928)	1928-1929
07028	Simonson, Otto G.	Baltimore	MD	0	1958
07374	Stein, Charles	Baltimore	MD	0	1924
00259	Stewart, C. Morton Jr.	Baltimore	MD	4 (1902)	
02429	Taylor Estate Property/Baltimore Parks	Baltimore	MD	0	
07064	Tinsley, T. G./Tisley, T. Garland	Baltimore	MD	3 (1922)	1922
05099	Williams, Henry	Baltimore	MD	0	1910-1911
01235	Ogden, W. B.	Brooklandville	MD	2 (1892)	1872-1873; 1892
05179	Lurman, Miss Katherine	Catonsville	MD	0	1911
09183	Phillips, T. W. Hon./Indian Town Farm/Phillips, T. W. Jr./Indian Town Farms	Chaptico	MD	2 (1930)	1929-1931
09875	Damon, G. Huntington Mr. & Mrs./Kenwood	Chevy Chase	MD	4 (1950)	1950
06533	Smith, Franklin H.	Chevy Chase	MD	1 (1917)	1917
09392	Strong, Gordon	Dickerson	MD	0	1935
02266	Murray, Mrs. Edward	Elk Ridge	MD	0	188-; 1903
03067	Norris, Miss Elizabeth Cromwell	Elk Ridge	MD	0	1905
03682	Olmsted, F. L. House at Elkton/Olmsted, Frederick Law Jr. & Robert Lee Gill, Jr. Estate	Elkton	MD	8 (1939-1940)	
03681	Gill, Robert Lee Jr./Woodknoll	Elkton	MD	3 (1940)	1940
05973	Baldwin, Frank G. Mrs./Baldwin, Katharine/Garrison Post Office	Green Spring Valley	MD	5 (1914)	1914
02378	Jenkins, George C.	Green Springs	MD	11 (1902)	

Job #	Job Name/Alternative Name	Job Location		Plans	Correspondence
07582	Warner, George	Loreley	MD	0	1925-1928
03363	Hambleton, F. S.	Lutherville	MD	2 (1907)	1907
10351	Gore, Mr. Coleman/Gore's Island	Montgomery County	MD	2 (1968)	1971
07887	Thorpe, Merle	Montgomery County	MD	97 (1926-1930)	1927-1929; 1939; 1946-1947
07030	Bernheim, Bertram M. Mrs./Bernheim, Bertram M.	Pikesville	MD	78 (1922-1925)	1922-1928
03326	Deford, Robert/Folly Farm	Towson	MD	18 (1894-1913)	1907-1913
09784	Pasarew, I. A.	Towson	MD	3 (1947)	1947
07450	Abbott, E. L.	Auburn	ME	0	1925
09317	Irish, S. O.	Auburn	ME	16 (1932-1933)	1932-1935
06836	Burleigh, Lewis A.	Augusta	ME	4 (1920)	1920-1923
06861	Gannet, Guy P.	Augusta	ME	7 (1920)	1920-1921
09695	Kinsley, M. E.	Augusta	ME	11 (1945-1947)	1945-1948
05521	Stubbs, Dr. Richard H.	Augusta	ME	0	1912
09202	Williamson, Joseph	Augusta	ME	6 (1926-1930)	1930
06896	Williamson, Joseph	Augusta	ME	4 (1920)	1920-1921
07554	Wyman, W. S. Farm	Augusta	ME	0	1925-1929
07375	Wyman, Walter S.	Augusta	ME	41 (1925-1929)	1924-1929
05831	Peters, William C. Dr.	Bangor	ME	4 (1913-1914)	1913-1916
03755	Dorr, George B.	Bar Harbor	ME	0	1902-1909
10336	Fenno, Mr. and Mrs. J. Brooks	Bar Harbor	ME	3 (1970)	1970-1977
01249	Fry, Charles	Bar Harbor	ME	8 (1892)	1892-1894
01892	Garland, J. A.	Bar Harbor	ME	6 (1882-1895)	1895-1896
01248	Gray, Mrs. George Z.	Bar Harbor	ME	4 (1892)	1892
01162	Joy, C. H.	Bar Harbor	ME	40 (1889-1891)	1889-1892
01241	McMillan, Hugh	Bar Harbor	ME	5 (1888-1893)	1892-1893
03751	Mitchell, John K./Mitchell, John K. 3rd	Bar Harbor	ME	8 (1903-1910)	1909-1910
07852	Ogden, David B.	Bar Harbor	ME	0	
01393	Pulitzer, Joseph	Bar Harbor	ME	11 (1894-1895)	1894-1895
01232	Vanderbilt, George W./Point D'Arcadie	Bar Harbor	ME	29 (1889-1893)	1889-1897
03153	Curtis, Benjamin/Starboard Acres	Blue Hills	ME	6 (1906)	1906
02972	Burtow, F. A.	Brunswick	ME	0	
09495	Bok, Mrs. Edward	Camden	ME	0	1937
03679	Earle, James M./High Pasture	Cape Neddick	ME	7 (1910-1926)	1910-1913; 1926
03424	Ballard, Ellis Ames	Chebeague Island	ME	0	1908
09896	Jette, E. M.	China Lake	ME	13 (1951)	1951
09143	Bisbee, Spaulding	Cumberland	ME	12 (1929-1930)	1929-1931
09203	Ireland, William D.	Cumberland	ME	8 (1930)	1930
01025	Felsted	Deer Isle	ME	133 (1894-1944)	1883-1899; 1933; 1940-1945; 1968-1977
05765	Derby, Dr. G. S.	Falmouth	ME	0	1912-1913
05656	Payson, Herbert	Falmouth	ME	3 (1912-1913)	1912-1913

Job #	Job Name/Alternative Name	Job Location		Plans	Correspondence
03159	Woodward, Dr./Woodward, George/ Heron House	Falmouth	ME	9 (1906-1966)	1906-1910; 1917; 1966-1968
03995	Randall, E. A.	Falmouth Foreside	ME	0	1910
06400	Tucker, R. P.	Flat Rock	ME	0	1916
09152	Randall, Ernest A.	Foreside	ME	3 (1929)	1929-1930
09828	Dennis, Henry R.	Gardiner	ME	16 (1948-1968)	1948-1955; 1968
06960	Thompson, J. H.	Gardiner	ME	0	1921-1922
09244	Bailly, Louis Madame	Hancock	ME	3 (1930)	1930-1931
03697	Parsons, L. Miss/Parsons, Llewellyn S./Crescent Surf	Kennebunk	ME	1 (1909)	1910-1911; 1929-1953
03407	Agnew, A. G.	Kennebunkport	ME	0	1907-1909
02960	Fay, Lucy A.	Kennebunkport	ME	1 (1904)	1904
05780	Robertson, E. W.	Kennebunkport	ME	0	1912
06569	Rogers, W. A. - Edgewater	Kennebunkport	ME	4 (1917)	1917; 1929
03162	Rogers, W. S./Rogers, WIlliam A./Campbell, William N./Fairfields	Kennebunkport	ME	27 (1906-1917)	1906-1938
10651	Hemingway, Mr. & Mrs. Booth	Kittery Point	ME	0	1978
06972	Dixon, F. L. Dr.	Lewiston	ME	5 (1921)	1921-1922
07553	Libby, W. S./Libbey, W. Scott	Lewiston	ME	10 (1925)	1925
01135	Brace, C. L.	Manset	ME	5 (N.D.)	1896
07859	Woolworth, F. M. Mrs.	Monmouth	ME	45 (1927-1928; 1933)	1927-1933
01297	Clark, Prof. S. F.	Mount Desert	ME	6 (1893)	1893-1895
06653	Lamont, Thomas W.	North Haven	ME	68 (1918-1921)	1918-1930; 1939; 1962
10618	Byrne, Mr. & Mrs. James	Northeast Harbor	ME	0	1977
10617	Hopkins, Mrs. D. Luke	Northeast Harbor	ME	1 (1978)	1977-1978
10619	Jenks, Mrs. M.M.	Northeast Harbor	ME	0	1977
09153	Kimball, L. E.	Northeast Harbor	ME	0	1929-1931
10161	Morison, Admiral and Mrs. Samuel Eliot/Good Hope	Northeast Harbor	ME	32 (1963-1966)	1963-1976
09711	Bok, Cary/Ducktrap Farm	Northport	ME	45 (1945-1947)	1945-1950
09498	Wales, Arvine Mrs.	Northport	ME	1 (1937)	1937
05061	Parsons, F. N./Parsons, Frances N.	Ogunquit	ME	2 (1910-1911)	1910-1911
07095	Whiting, F. A.	Ogunquit	ME	16 (1906-1958)	1922-1958
03398	Wright, C. H. C.	Paris Hill	ME	0	1907
09224	Belknap, William R. Mrs./Belknap, W. R.	Pemaquid	ME	10 (1930)	1930-1931
06240	Belknap, Mrs. William R.	Pemaquid Point	ME	0	1915
03414	Willis, P. L.	Portland	ME	8 (1907-1908)	1907-1908
06654	Norton, Charles D.	Pulpit Harbor	ME	1 (1919)	1918-1922
07848	Ginkel, Louis S./Gimbel, Louis S.	Raugeley	ME	0	1927
09327	Bok, Cary Mrs./Nimaha/Bok Zimbalist, Mrs.	Rockport	ME	22 (1932-1936; 1947)	1932-1937; 1947-1956
07998	Bok, Mary L. Mrs./Grianan & other info./ Guest House/Wee Hoose/Bok, Edward	Rockport	ME	39 (1928-1939)	1928-1940

Job #	Job Name/Alternative Name	Job Location		Plans	Correspondence
09609	Curtis Quartet Cottages	Rockport	ME	31 (1939-1941)	1937-1941
09788	Zimbalist, Mrs. E.	Rockport	ME	0	1947
03154	Dunham, E. K. Mrs./Dunham, Edward K./Hoe, Richard M./Keewaydin	Seal Harbor	ME	6 (1906)	1906-1911
03537	Hanna, Marcus Mrs.	Seal Harbor	ME	1 (1908)	1908-1914
03155	Hoe, Richard M./Eastholm	Seal Harbor	ME	4 (1906)	1906-1908
06923	Carter, C. B./Carter, Charles B.	Winthrop	ME	14 (1921)	1921-1922
06979	Francisco, L. A./Francisco, Leon	Wiscasset	ME	12 (1921-1922)	1921-1923
09171	Gardiner, William Tudor Hon.	Woolwich	ME	81 (1930-1946)	1929-1940; 1945-1947
09806	Thompson, Nathan/Thompson, N. W./Prince's Point	Yarmouth	ME	1 (1948)	1947-1948
01127	Hammond, G. W.	Yarmouthville	ME	14 (1888-1889)	1888-1890; 1898
03746	Gross, Alfred/Gross, Alfred H.	York	ME	1 (1912)	1909-1913
09115	Richard, Harold C.	York Harbor	ME	41 (1919; 1929)	1929-1930
00025	Stetson, F. L./Stetson, Francis Lynde	York Harbor	ME	9 (1901-1902)	1901-1904
07324	Bursley, J. A. and George W. Patterson	Ann Arbor	MI	0	1924
07066	Canfield, R. Bishop	Ann Arbor	MI	0	1922
05901	Carr, L. D./West Fair Oaks	Ann Arbor	MI	3 (1913-1914)	1913-1915
07715	Dow, Vivia Kinnersley Mrs./Barton Hills	Ann Arbor	MI	22 (1919-1929)	1926-1927
06409	Drake, R. E. Dr.	Ann Arbor	MI	7 (1916-1917)	1916-1917; 1927
06628	Earhart, H. B./Earhart, Harry B.	Ann Arbor	MI	141 (1918-1934)	1918-1919; 1925-1934
09354	Earhart, Richard	Ann Arbor	MI	98 (1934)	1934-1935
07604	Goss, Alfred	Ann Arbor	MI	1 (1926)	1926
03619	Huntington, George Mrs./Nichols Tract/Huntington, George E. B.	Ann Arbor	MI	19 (1911-1914)	1911-1914
06560	Whitney, H. K.	Battle Creek	MI	0	1917
05446	Sheldon, Henry D.	Detroit	MI	5 (1912-1916)	1911-1913
00638	Walker, F.H.	Detroit	MI	3 (1894)	
03610	Edison Farm/Geddes Power/Huron River/Geddes Farm/Edison Electric Company	Geddes	MI	49 (1908-1926)	1908-1913
07447	Blodgett, John	Grand Rapids	MI	201 (1909-1931)	1925-1938
06328	Grinnell, C. A.	Grosse Point	MI	0	1916
02225	Mather, W. G.	Ishpeming	MI	1 (1899)	1897-1899
05270	Atland, D. F.	Lake Saint Claire	MI	0	1911-1912
00059	Longyear, J. M.	Marquette	MI	13 (1891-1904)	1891-1899
06252	Leland, W. C.	Pontiac	MI	0	1915
05773	Dodge, John F.	Rochester	MI	0	1912-1916
00281	Hubel, F. A.	Saint Clair	MI	4 (1898-1903)	1898-1909; 1913; 1923
03612	Hemphill, Robert W. Jr./Huron River/Hemphill, Robert W.	Ypsilanti	MI	0	1908-1909
06068	Hartley, Cavour	Duluth	MN	25 (1908-1917)	1913-1917; 1926
03632	Hartley, G. G.	Duluth	MN	1 (1909-1910)	1909-1915
06186	Hartley, G. G. - New House	Duluth	MN	0	1915

Job #	Job Name/Alternative Name	Job Location		Plans	Correspondence
05878	Merrill, Thomas D.	Duluth	MN	1 (1913)	1913
09526	Boeckmann, Egil Dr.	Echo Hills	MN	60 (1937-1943)	1915; 1938-1944
05650	Burton, J. Hazen	Lake Minnetonka	MN	0	
00060	Peavey, F. H./Peavey, Frank H./Peavy, Frank H.	Minneapolis	MN	14 (1894-1895)	1894-1896
02996	Keeley, L. E./Keeley, Leslie E.	Saint Paul	MN	5 (1904)	1904-1906
06572	Heim, J. J.	Kansas City	MO	0	1917
01384	Davis, J. F.	Saint Louis	MO	10 (1893-1894; 1900)	1893-1894; 1900
00145	Francis, D. R.	Saint Louis	MO	11 (1895-1896)	1895-1897
01801	Pierce, H. C.	Saint Louis	MO	5 (1895)	1895-1899
06815	Culley, M. L.	Jackson	MS	0	
09941	Carrier, R. M.	Oxford	MS	25 (1952-1953)	1952-1953
10219	WIlliams, Dr J. D.	Oxford	MS	5 (1967)	1967-1968
01776	Ryerson, Hutchinson/Hutchinson, C. S./Ryerson, Martin A. and C. L. Hutchinson/Strawberry Hill	Asheville	NC	6 (1895-1896)	1895-1899; 1916
00170	Vanderbilt, George W./Biltmore	Asheville	NC	649 (1889-1909)	1886-1909
01240	McNamee, Charles	Biltmore	NC	8 (1891-1892)	1889-1892
06819	Strowd, R.L.	Chapel Hill	NC	0	1920
03052	Drayton-Grimke, Mrs. Emma	Flat Rock	NC	0	1901-1905
02971	Morton, Mary Miss	Flat Rock	NC	3 (1904)	1904
08231	Benjamin, Edward	Greensborough	NC	0	1929
00032	Norton, Misses/Norton, Lucie and Mattie	Hendersonville	NC	29 (1898-1900)	1898-1906
07349	Sargent, LeRoy	Hendersonville	NC	0	1924
07914	Boyd, Mrs. John Y.	Southern Pines	NC	0	1928
02228	Garrett, R. U.	Victoria	NC	3 (1899)	1899
00146	Graham, F. W. W.	Victoria	NC	7 (1899-1901)	1899-1905; 1922
02219	Perry, N. R.	Victoria	NC	5 (1899-1900)	1899-1900
02232	Van Bergen, Chas. Dr.	Victoria	NC	2 (1899-1900)	1899-1900
10125	Bottomley, Mrs. George T.		NH	2 (1930; 1960)	1960-1961
03790	Stearns, F. W.		NH	0	1909
02985	Whitwell, Miss	Asquam Lake	NH	0	1904; 1922
07756	Ansberry, T. T.	Bethlehem	NH	7 (1926-1927)	1927-1928
06438	Beck, E. L./St. Mary's School for Girls	Bethlehem	NH	220 (1916-1936)	1916-1938; 1958
07843	Guider, John W.	Bethlehem	NH	18 (1927-1931)	1927-1934
02983	Macbeth, George A.	Bethlehem	NH	6 (1904)	1904; 1914
05651	Lesh, Mrs. John H.	Canaan	NH	0	1912
10134	Churchill, Mrs. L W	Center Harbor	NH	34 (1961-1962)	1961-1963
09722	Amory, Copley	Charlestown	NH	12 (1945-1946)	1946-1947
02398	Maynard, F. P.	Claremont	NH	0	1902-1904
01236	Bishop, Niles/Niles, W. W.	Concord	NH	4 (1892-1911)	1880; 1892-1899; 1907-1911

The Heinz house and grounds, May 1901. Job #133 – H. J. Heinz (Pittsburgh, PA).

Job #	Job Name/Alternative Name	Job Location		Plans	Correspondence
00096	Thayer, William F.	Concord	NH	1 (1899)	1899
03560	Jencks, Francis M./Frothington, Frances E.	Dublin	NH	2 (1908)	1908
10409	Ober, Mr. & Mrs. Frederick C.	Durham	NH	1 (1972)	1972
09944	Morse, Milton	East Jaffrey	NH	0	1952
10459	Prokuski, Mr. & Mrs. Bronislaw P.	Goffstown	NH	2 (1973)	1973
10650	Stonie, Dr. & Mrs. Henry	Hampton	NH	0	1978
03037	Hitchcock, Emily H. (Mrs. Hiram)	Hanover	NH	5 (1900-1905)	1905
09993	Meck, John F.	Hanover	NH	3 (1954)	1954-1955
10530	Marino, Dr. & Mrs. Ernest	Hollis	NH	0	1975
03581	Mallet-Prevost, S./Mallet-Provost, S.	Intervale	NH	0	1908
03745	Zantzinger, C. C.	Intervale	NH	0	1909
09606	Marean, Endicott Mrs./Marean, Endicott	Jaffrey	NH	8 (1940)	1940-1941
09634	Elliot, John	Keene	NH	2 (1941)	1941
09528	Fuller, Honorable Alvah T./Union Chapel	Little Boar's Head	NH	70 (1938-1941)	1938-1941; 1967; 1978-1979
01128	Glessner, J. J./The Rocks	Littleton	NH	13 (1903-1939)	1888-1899; 1903-1917; 1935-1939

Job #	Job Name/Alternative Name	Job Location		Plans	Correspondence
09475	Kohler, Harry A.	Littleton	NH	0	1936
09604	Lee, Frances G. Mrs.	Littleton	NH	37 (1940)	1940-1941
06111	Morron, John R.	Littleton	NH	10 (1914)	1914-1915
06215	Morron, John R./Hill Acres	Littleton	NH	40 (1915)	1915-1916; 1938
10460	Corriveau, Mr. & Mrs. A.J.	Manchester	NH	0	
09938	Bingham, William J.	Marlboro	NH	0	1952
09874	Brigham, H. R.	Marlboro	NH	7 (1950)	1950
09715	Perry, D. P.	Mason	NH	20 (1945-1946)	1945-1946
09656	Lewis, Dr. Louis	Meredith	NH	0	1943; 1947
02997	Amory, Mrs. William	Monadnock	NH	0	1904-1905
02634	Anderson, George E.	Nashua	NH	0	1903-1904; 1939
10545	Babineau, Dr. & Mrs. Arthur	Nashua	NH	0	1975
10709	Humen, Dr. & Mrs. Donald	Nashua	NH	0	1979
02908	Hall, W. S.	Nelson	NH	0	
02910	Olmsted. F. L. - Cottage	Nelson	NH	8 (1932-1950)	
09655	Patek, A. J. Dr.	Nelson	NH	12 (1944-1945)	1943-1945
02909	Sharples	Nelson	NH	0	
03795	Whipple, J. Reed	New Boston	NH	6 (1909-1911)	1909-1911
07810	Tracy, J. A. Mrs./Tracy, J.J.	New London	NH	7 (1927)	1927
05926	Street Tree Planting/Harris, Mrs. N.W./ Newton, New Hampshire	Newton	NH	2 (1913)	1913
06433	Burnham, A. W.	North Conway	NH	0	1916
02920	Tyler, H. W.	North Woodstock	NH	2 (1904)	1904
09390	Booth, William Stone Mrs.	Peterboro	NH	18 (1935)	1935-1936
06437	Davis, Arthur E. - Son's Camp	Peterboro	NH	0	1916; 1923
09580	Keller, Carl Mrs.	Peterboro	NH	2 (1941)	1939-1941
10018	MacFarland, D.	Rye	NH	1 (1955)	1955-1956
06440	Drake, Francis E.	Rye Beach	NH	14 (1894-1916)	1916-1919
07904	Hobbs, Joseph	Rye Beach	NH	0	
10716	Foss, Mr. & Mrs. George	Sugar Hill	NH	0	1979
04012	Colgate, Richard M.	Sunapee	NH	9 (1910)	1910-1914
03227	Richard, D. W./Richards, Dickinson W.	Sunapee	NH	2 (1907)	1906-1910
09474	Tozzer, Alfred M.	Tamworth	NH	0	1936
09607	Lackey, Henry E. Mrs./Lackey, Henry E.	Temple	NH	5 (1940)	1940-1941
09121	Cooksey, G. B. Mrs./Cooksey, G. B.	Walpole	NH	8 (1929)	1929-1931
07130	Goodrich, Mrs. C. A.	Welsh Island	NH	0	1922-1924
06505	Mountain View House	Whitefield	NH	0	1917
02958	Rutherford, Winthrop	Allamuchy	NJ	12 (1904)	1904-1905
09365	Babbott, F. L. Dr.	Bernardsville	NJ	15 (1934-1935)	1934-1937
01723	Kunhardt, R. H./Kunhardt, H. R.	Bernardsville	NJ	2 (1896)	1896-1897
07723	Prentice, John H. Mrs.	Bernardsville	NJ	15 (1920-1929)	1926-1930; 1934
10094	Babbott, Dr and Mrs Frank L.	Bernardsville Borough	NJ	50 (1958-1960)	1959-1961

Job #	Job Name/Alternative Name	Job Location		Plans	Correspondence
09000	Bacheller, L. H.	Denville	NJ	0	1928-1929
06901	Fuld, Felix	East Orange	NJ	23 (1921-1924)	1920-1924
06119	Frelinghuysen, Frederick	Elberon	NJ	0	1897; 1915; 1923
02222	Murphy, Franklin	Elberon	NJ	1 (1899)	1899-1902
10350	Gund, Mr. and Mrs. Gordon	Kingston	NJ	6 (1970-1971)	1971
05438	Colgate, R. M./Colgate, Richard M.	Llewellyn	NJ	5 (1913-1914)	1911-1914
05439	Colgate, R. M./Subdivision/Llewellyn Park	Llewellyn	NJ	0	1871 (?); 1911-1914
07646	Dodge, M. Hartley	Madison	NJ	0	1926
01380	James, Mrs. D. Willis/James, D. Willis	Madison	NJ	23 (1892-1894)	1892-1896
01139	Twombly, H. McKay/Twombly, Hamilton McKay	Madison	NJ	215 (1890-1928)	1890-1895; 1903-1905; 1928; 1934; 1974-1978
03700	Murphy, Franklin/Elberon	Mendham	NJ	103 (1909-1916)	1899; 1909-1916
07940	Client of J. K. Powell/Powell, J.K./Sub-division	Metuchen	NJ	0	1928
03817	Earl, E. P.	Montclair	NJ	0	1909-1910
09041	Eshbaugh, William H.	Montclair	NJ	15 (1929-1930)	1929-1940
09056	Goodwillie, Frank	Montclair	NJ	2 (1929)	1929
06380	Harrison, Benjamin V.	Montclair	NJ	0	1916
07049	Johns, W. G.	Montclair	NJ	0	1922
03177	Osborne, Edmund B./Brookwood	Montclair	NJ	29 (1906-1911)	1906-1911
07542	Reynolds, A. M.	Montclair	NJ	2 (1925-1926)	
07987	Reynolds, G. W.	Montclair	NJ	0	
07527	Weston, Dr. Edward	Montclair	NJ	0	1925
03072	Wright, S. Jr.	Montclair	NJ	4 (1905-1906)	1905-1908
03559	Hawes, Margaret M. Miss	Morristown	NJ	6 (1908-1909)	1908-1910
12347	Lord, Mrs. James Cooper	Morristown	NJ	0	1874
06889	Marsters, Arthur A.	Morristown	NJ	17 (1920-1923)	1920-1934; 1939
00313	Mellon, Charles H.	Morristown	NJ	18 (1901-1904)	1903-1904
01038	Perkins, F.W.	Morristown	NJ	9 (1887)	
07212	Thomas, Seth	Morristown	NJ	5 (1923)	1923
00616	Page, H. A.	Mountain Station	NJ	23 (1879-1891)	1879; 1890-1898
07677	Rutgers, H. G. Jr.	New Brunswick	NJ	6 (1926)	1926
07511	Beinfield, Victor H.	Newark	NJ	0	1925
02990	Campbell, Peter	Newark	NJ	0	1904
05916	Church, Alonzo	Newark	NJ	0	1913
00619	Kearney, John Watts/Bellegrove	Newark	NJ	3 (1879)	1878-1879
02223	Murphy, Franklin	Newark	NJ	9 (1899-1908)	1899-1908; 1916
06924	Perkins, G. C.	Newark	NJ	0	1921-1922
06779	Tait, Frank M.	Newark	NJ	0	1919-1920
06317	Hay, James R.	Nutley	NJ	0	1896; 1915
00448	Page, Edward, D.	Oakland	NJ	0	1876; 1895-1896
06859	Delano, Moreau	Orange	NJ	42 (1920-1929)	1920-1929

Job #	Job Name/Alternative Name	Job Location		Plans	Correspondence
06456	Edison, Mrs. Thomas A.	Orange	NJ	0	1916
07875	Metcalf, Manton B. Mrs.	Orange	NJ	5 (1926-1928)	1927-1929
09076	Hobart, Garrett	Paterson	NJ	10 (1929-1931)	1929-1932; 1941
07007	Ard, Dr. F. C.	Plainfield	NJ	0	1922
07111	Irons, Henry C.	Plainfield	NJ	3 (1923-1924	1923-1924
03399	Bunn, H. C.	Princeton	NJ	0	1907
07630	Lambert, Gerard B.	Princeton	NJ	134 (1913-1930)	1926-1950
06348	Kinney, William B. Mrs.	Red Bank	NJ	25 (1916-1932)	1916-1934
09253	Denison, Charles L. Mrs.	Saddle River	NJ	28 (1929; 1931)	1931-1932
01245	Hoagland, J.C.	Seabright	NJ	50 (1891-1896)	1893-1897
00065	Strong, W. E.	Seabright	NJ	21 (1900-1906)	1900-1906
00169	McIntyre, Thomas A./Seabright	Shrewsbury	NJ	7 (1898)	1897-1899
06077	Sinclair, Robert S.	South Orange	NJ	7 (1914-1915)	1914-1916
03714	Bassett, Carroll	Summit	NJ	0	1909
07762	Bassett, Carroll P.	Summit	NJ	0	1927
07796	Bell, H. S.	Summit	NJ	3 (1927)	1927-1928
07101	Brown, Caxton	Summit	NJ	5 (1922-1930)	1922-1923; 1930
07521	Wendell, Arthur R.	Summit	NJ	2 (1925)	1925-1929
00442	Hill, E.C./Hamilton Terrace	Trenton	NJ	0	1900
06714	Slack, Walter C.	Trenton	NJ	2 (1919)	1919
06153	Hoff, Mr.	Upper Montclair	NJ	0	1915
07590	O'Brien, John F.	Verona	NJ	0	1925
06616	Hofheimer, Nathan Mrs./Hofheimer, N.	Warrenville	NJ	8 (1917-1918)	1917-1919
07679	Philippi, E. Martin	West Hill	NJ	0	1926
07260	Rule, A. R.	Westfield	NJ	26 (1924-1929)	1923-1929
05904	Smith, Frank W.	Westfield	NJ	4 (1913-1914)	1913-1914
12357	Hyde, H. B.		NY	0	1874-1875
12367	McNulty, Albert		NY	0	1877; 1890
06363	Schuyler Mansion	Albany	NY	1 (1917)	1916-1917
03384	Chalmers, Arthur A.	Amsterdam	NY	0	1907; 1913
05356	Gerry, Robert L.	Andes	NY	11 (1911-1934)	1911-1919; 1933-1934
09027	Noyes, Sydney W./Dobbs Ferry	Ardsley-on-the-Hudson	NY	15 (1928-1929)	1928-1932; 1951
05851	Agnew, C. R./Agnew, Cornelius R.	Armonk	NY	36 (1913-1927)	1913-1917; 1925-1927
00618	Letchworth, Mr. J.	Auburn	NY	50 (1879)	1878-1879
00644	Magoun, G. C.	Babylon	NY	3 (1882)	1882
09342	Williams, Harrison/Oak Pointe	Bayville	NY	1 (1929)	1933
05176	Fahnestock, William	Bedford	NY	16 (1909-1912)	1909-1912
03270	Low, Seth/Broad Brook Farm	Bedford	NY	12 (1907-1911)	1907-1908; 1911
06723	Tucker, Carll	Bedford	NY	491 (1919-1930)	1919-1939; 1977
07731	Dammaun, Milton	Bedford Hills	NY	0	1926
06710	White, Mrs. Harold T./Lakeover	Bedford Hills	NY	0	1919

Job #	Job Name/Alternative Name	Job Location		Plans	Correspondence
09544	Hochschild, Harold K./Eagle Nest	Blue Mountain Lake	NY	30 (1938)	1938-1939; 1946
00202	Law, Walter W.	Briarcliff	NY	4 (1900-1901)	1898-1901
02977	Collins, Newton M. Dr./Collins, Newton M. & Associates	Brighton	NY	8 (1904-1906)	1894; 1904-1909
04090	Stevens, H. S.	Bronxville	NY	0	1910
12177	Kennard, Charles E.	Brookline	NY	0	1890-1891
06326	Brokaw, Howard C.	Brookville	NY	78 (1915; 1928)	1915-1930; 1945
06262	Dows, David	Brookville	NY	38 (1913-1928)	1904; 1915-1928
06646	Harriman, Joseph W.	Brookville	NY	408 (1918-1928)	1918-1929; 1936
07465	Iselin, C. Oliver	Brookville	NY	46 (1925-1946)	1925-1934; 1944-1946
06567	Miller, W. W.	Brookville	NY	6 (1916-1917)	1917-1918; 1926
06939	Mitchell, S. Z.	Brookville	NY	231 (1920-1927)	1921-1934; 1954
00247	Albright, J. J.	Buffalo	NY	44 (1890-1913)	1890-1897; 1903-1907
00033	Fryer, Robert L./Fryer, Robert Livingston	Buffalo	NY	14 (1900)	1900-1904
09046	Goodyear, Frank/Rogers, E. P.	Buffalo	NY	137 (1928-1931)	1894; 1924-1932
01246	Hayes, Edmund	Buffalo	NY	7 (1891-1892)	1891-1917
02994	Kellogg, Spencer	Buffalo	NY	3 (1903-1904)	1904-1906
06302	Pomeroy, Robert W.	Buffalo	NY	0	1915
01779	Rogers, W. E./Rogers, William A.	Buffalo	NY	3 (1895)	1893-1897; 1915
05924	Allen, George W. H.	Cazenovia	NY	9 (1915)	1913-1916
05931	Chard, W. G.	Cazenovia	NY	15 (1913-1914)	1912-1914
09131	Barbour, Ella Wright/Whippoorwill Subdivision	Chappaqua	NY	10 (N.D.)	1929-1934
09186	Beach, G. C./Whippoorwill/Beach, George C.	Chappaqua	NY	6 (1930)	1930
09185	Benton, C. V./Whippoorwill	Chappaqua	NY	6 (1930)	1930
09245	Bird, S. Hinman/Whippoorwill	Chappaqua	NY	15 (1930)	1930
09018	Butler, Dr. Charles T.	Chappaqua	NY	0	1928
07999	Davidow, L. H.	Chappaqua	NY	0	1928-1930
09147	Higgins, Edward W./Whippoorwill	Chappaqua	NY	3 (1929)	1929-1930
09112	Kilborne, R. Stuart/Whippoorwill Subdivision/Kilborne, R. Stuart Jr.	Chappaqua	NY	9 (1929-1930)	1929-1933
09139	McHugh, John/Whippoorwill Subdivision	Chappaqua	NY	117 (1929-1931)	1929-1932; 1943
09212	Ruth, F. S. - Whippoorwill	Chappaqua	NY	6 (1930)	1930-1940
07568	Davenport, F. M./Davenport, Frederick M.	Clinton	NY	10 (1926)	1925-1926
03173	De Forest, Robert W.	Cold Spring	NY	0	1906; 1915-1916; 1924
03176	De Forest, Robert W. - West Hills Tract	Cold Spring	NY	0	1906-1907; 1916; 1924
03175	DeForest, Henry & Julia/DeForest, Henry W.	Cold Spring	NY	85 (1906-1927)	1906-1931
09097	Duer, Beverley/DeForest, Henry W.	Cold Spring	NY	4 (1929; 1931)	1929; 1931
03061	Healy, A. A.	Cold Spring	NY	0	1905

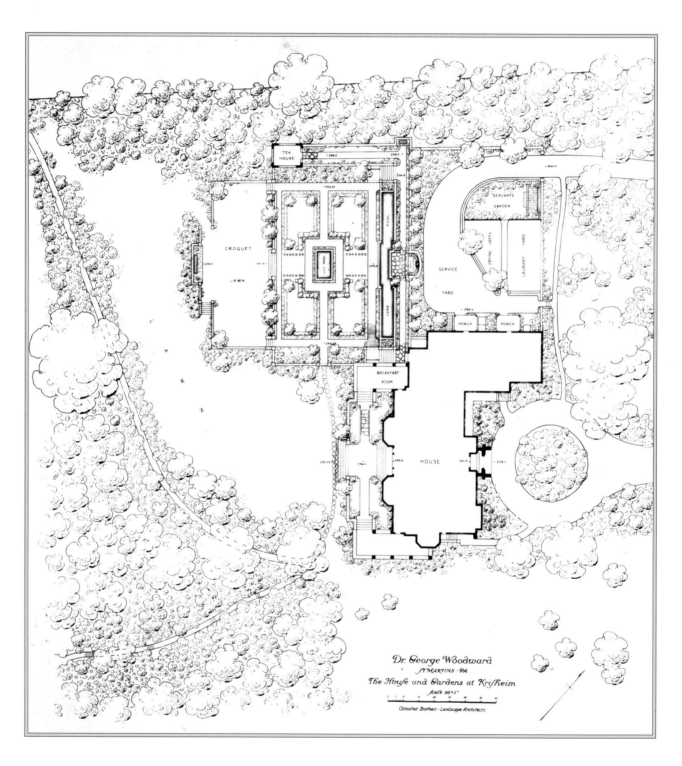

Plan of the house and gardens at "Krisheim," date unknown. Job #3223 – Dr. George Woodward (Saint Martin, PA).

View up the south axis of the Woodward garden, "Krisheim," November 1912. Job #3223 – Dr. George Woodward (Saint Martin, PA).

Job #	Job Name/Alternative Name	Job Location		Plans	Correspondence
04087	Stewart, W. A. W.	Cold Spring	NY	137 (1910-1912)	1910-1912; 1923
07502	Diebold, A. H.	Cold Spring Harbor	NY	14 (1925)	1925
07485	Draper, Mrs. George/Standard Oil/Draper, Dorothy	Cold Spring Harbor	NY	0	1925
07478	Franklin, Mrs. Walter P.	Cold Spring Harbor	NY	0	1925
05922	Henderson, Edward C.	Cold Spring Harbor	NY	10 (1906-1914)	1913-1914
06287	Jennings, Walter	Cold Spring Harbor	NY	125 (1916-1937)	1895; 1915-1921; 1930-1938
04088	Johnston, J. Herbert	Cold Spring Harbor	NY	0	1910
06499	Kahn, Otto H./Kahan, Otto	Cold Spring Harbor	NY	39 (1916-1917)	1916-1918; 1939; 1978
05436	Weld, Francis M.	Cold Spring Harbor	NY	0	1911
00452	Sinclair, H. P.	Corning	NY	0	1903
06492	Stillman, James	Cornwall	NY	48 (1915-1918)	1916-1917
05786	Gerry, Peter G.	Delhi	NY	4 (1916-1917)	1912-1917

Job #	Job Name/Alternative Name	Job Location		Plans	Correspondence
09504	Hochschild, Walter	Eagle Lake	NY	77 (1937-1947)	1937-1947
09104	Campbell, Mrs./Campbell, J. Hazard	East Aurora	NY	2 (1929)	1929
01722	Locke, F. D./Locke, Franklin D.	East Aurora	NY	1 (1896)	1895-1897
06265	Johnson, Bradis	East Islip	NY	1 (1915)	1915-1917
07134	Bermingham, John F.	East Norwich	NY	63 (1921-1923)	1922-1924
05925	Campbell, O.A.	East Norwich	NY	46 (1913-1964)	1921
10073	Campbell, O. A. Jr.	East Norwich	NY	3 (1914; 1964)	1958
07463	Munsey, Frank A.	Elizabethtown	NY	12 (1925)	1925
09280	Bagley, Henry Walker	Fishers Island	NY	4 (1931-1932)	1931-1937
07721	Benton, C. V.	Fishers Island	NY	31 (1926-1932)	1926-1932
07556	Bonbright, I. W./Bonbright, Irving W.	Fishers Island	NY	82 (1925-1927)	1925-1930; 1942
09126	Brown, Donaldson	Fishers Island	NY	0	1929-1930
07908	Buckingham, Charles V.	Fishers Island	NY	15 (1928-1929)	1928-1929
07890	Buckner, Mortimer N./Barley - Field House	Fishers Island	NY	43 (1927-1928)	1927-1929
07712	Buckner, Mortimer N./Island House	Fishers Island	NY	5 (1926)	1926-1928
07689	Bulkeley, R. B./Bulkeley, Richard B.	Fishers Island	NY	3 (1925-1926)	1926-1927
07850	Carpenter, W. S.	Fishers Island	NY	1 (1927)	1927-1931
07896	Carpenter, W. S. Jr./Buckner, Mortimer N./Brick Yard House/Carpenter, W.W., Jr.	Fishers Island	NY	14 (1928-1932)	1928-1933
07558	Dater, Alfred/Dater, Alfred W.	Fishers Island	NY	8 (1925-129)	1925-1930
07557	Ferguson, Helen	Fishers Island	NY	4 (1926)	1926-1927
07983	Ferguson, John M.	Fishers Island	NY	3 (1928)	1928-1929
09023	Ferguson, John S.	Fishers Island	NY	7 (1928-1929)	1928-1930
07540	Fuller, Henry J./Wendall, A. B.	Fishers Island	NY	0	1925-1930
07701	Hardy, George E.	Fishers Island	NY	10 (1926-1930)	1926-1930
07732	Hawkins, Beatrice Miss	Fishers Island	NY	5 (1926)	1926; 1931
07720	Hutchinson, Guy	Fishers Island	NY	24 (1926-1928)	1926-1928
07741	Hutchinson, W. J.	Fishers Island	NY	0	1926-1929
07545	Jackson, H. A.	Fishers Island	NY	11 (1925)	1925
07984	Kent, Fred I.	Fishers Island	NY	7 (1928)	1928-1929
07836	Maxwell, Henry L.	Fishers Island	NY	3 (1927)	1927-1928
07981	McDonell, A. A.	Fishers Island	NY	9 (1927-1929)	1928-1930
09133	Meeds, H. S. Jr.	Fishers Island	NY	8 (1929)	1929-1934
07722	Nichols, W. H.	Fishers Island	NY	54 (1925-1928)	1926-1930
07740	Noyes, Janssen	Fishers Island	NY	6 (1926-1927)	1926-1928
07709	Parsons, C. B.	Fishers Island	NY	0	1927
07860	Percy, Ralph H.	Fishers Island	NY	0	1927
07994	Reed, W. T.	Fishers Island	NY	2 (1928)	
07552	Ruth, F. S.	Fishers Island	NY	30 (1925-1926)	1925-1928
07891	Ruth, F. S./House #1 Chocomount	Fishers Island	NY	6 (1928)	1927-1929
07695	Ruth, W. N./Ruth, Walter	Fishers Island	NY	0	1926-1932; 1940-1942
07982	Schultz, A. E. Mrs.	Fishers Island	NY	10 (1927-1929)	1928-1930

Job #	Job Name/Alternative Name	Job Location		Plans	Correspondence
07636	VanDyke, Douglass	Fishers Island	NY	27 (1926)	1926-1927
07824	Walker, Henry P.	Fishers Island	NY	6 (1926-1927)	1927
09054	Wallace, A. B. Sr.	Fishers Island	NY	8 (1926-1929)	1929-1930
09266	Wells, J. Cheney	Fishers Island	NY	9 (1931)	1931
07910	White, Charles	Fishers Island	NY	12 (1927-1928)	1928
07840	Williams, H. D.	Fishers Island	NY	2 (1927)	1927
09051	Wright, Edward A.	Fishers Island	NY	3 (1929)	1929
09222	Yates, Eugene A.	Fishers Island	NY	1 (N.D.)	1930
07194	Wilkes, N. R./Sage/Wilkes, Nathaniel R.	Forest Hills	NY	21 (1921-1923)	1922-1923
03169	Osborn, William Church	Garrison	NY	10 (1906-1907)	1906-1907
01778	Rogers, W. S.	Garrison	NY	1 (1895)	1892-1897
12527	Wadsworth, W. A.	Geneseo	NY	0	1874-1875; 1878
02620	King, W. J.	Geneva	NY	5 (1903)	1902-1903
05578	Aldred, J. E./Baker, George	Glen Cove	NY	233 (1905-1937)	1912-1941
03799	Babbott, Frank L.	Glen Cove	NY	0	1909-1912
05826	Baker, George F. Jr./Baker, George F.	Glen Cove	NY	70 (1913-1933)	1913-1933
06266	Davison, K. T. Mrs./Davison, Henry P.	Glen Cove	NY	89 (1913-1923)	1915-1924; 1934
06795	Hine, F. Worthington	Glen Cove	NY	5 (1920)	1920
06307	Hine, Francis L./Locust Valley	Glen Cove	NY	110 (1915-1919)	1915-1924
06293	Porter, W. H./Porter, William H.	Glen Cove	NY	1 (1917)	1917
03120	Pratt Estate/Pratt, George and Harold	Glen Cove	NY	282 (1903-1936)	1873; 1906-1911; 1919; 1934-1938
09468	Pratt, Richardson	Glen Cove	NY	1 (1936)	1936
06647	Runyon, Clarkson Mrs./Runyon, Clarkson Jr.	Glen Cove	NY	3 (1919)	1917-1920
06351	Aldrich, Sherwood/Sloane, Alfred P./Sloan, Alfred P. Jr.	Great Neck	NY	28 (1916-1921)	1916-1917; 1926-1929
07140	Burnham, Lee S./Great Neck Estates	Great Neck	NY	34 (1920-1923)	1922-1924
03807	Davis, L. Shannon/Great Neck Long Island	Great Neck	NY	0	1909
01177	Eldridge, Roswell	Great Neck	NY	0	1900
07116	Grace, Morgan H.	Great Neck	NY	11 (1923)	1923-1926; 1940
06261	Phipps, Henry Mrs./Phipps, Henry C.	Great Neck	NY	26 (1915-1916)	1915-1916
06312	Satterwhite, P. P. Dr./Satterwhite, Preston P.	Great Neck	NY	25 (1915-1916)	1915-1917
07656	Stutzer, H.	Great Neck	NY	0	1926
09231	Eagle Nest Country Club/Hochschild, Harold/Eagle Nest Corporation/Eagle Nest	Hamilton County	NY	149 (1928-1948)	1930-1950
07804	Allen, George	Hartsdale	NY	0	
00189	Butler, Charles/Fox Meadow	Hartsdale	NY	5 (1895-1900)	1895-1900; 1913; 1920-1924
02888	Noll, Charles	Hartsdale	NY	0	
00312	Shaw, Albert/Shaw, Albertnos	Hastings-on-Hudson	NY	2 (1903)	1903

Job #	Job Name/Alternative Name	Job Location		Plans	Correspondence
05827	Wood, Walter A. Jr./Wood, Walter A.	Hoosic Falls	NY	12 (1912-1914)	1913-1915
03111	Gould, Miss Helen M.	Hudson	NY	0	1906-1907
05526	Conklin, Roland Ray/Rosemary Farm	Huntington	NY	23 (1912-1913)	1912-1916
05100	DeForest, Robert W./Dunn Property	Huntington	NY	1 (1910-1911)	1910-1912; 1921; 1978
04018	DeForest, Robert W./Williamson Property	Huntington	NY	10 (1910-1911)	1910-1916; 1978
05051	Gould, C. A.	Huntington	NY	0	1910
03997	Dows, David	Irvington	NY	0	1910
02624	Dows, David Mrs./Dows, David	Irvington	NY	5 (1904)	1903-1909
06366	Dunham, Dr. Carroll and others	Irvington	NY	0	1916
03200	Reid, D. G./Bennett School/Reid, Daniel G.	Irvington	NY	14 (1906-1907)	1906-1909
07736	Scott, Harold B.	Irvington	NY	3 (1926-1927)	1926-1929
06743	Havemeyer, Horace	Islip	NY	3 (1916-1919)	1919-1924
00054	Hollins, H. B.	Islip	NY	0	1890-1900
03917	Hollins, H. B./Hollins, H. B. Jr.	Islip	NY	10 (1890-1900)	1910
03042	Fleming, Bryant	Ithaca	NY	0	1905-1908
06482	Kent, George E./Kent, George Edward	Jericho	NY	20 (1917-1927)	1916-1927
07464	Livermore, Jesse	Kings Point	NY	7 (1925-1926)	1925-1926
06256	Evans, Henry/Knollwood	Knollwood	NY	3 (1915)	1915
06402	Gerry, Angelica	Lake Delaware	NY	1 (1916)	1917
06053	Stevens, Mrs. Richard T.	Lake Waccabuc	NY	0	1914
07153	Gillette, Leon	Larchmont	NY	3 (1923)	1923
07255	Hasbrouck, James F. Dr.	Larchmont	NY	24 (1923-1924)	1923-1924
09942	Reed, W. P. Dr.	Larchmont	NY	4 (1952)	1953
09870	Reed, William Page Dr.	Larchmont	NY	2 (1949-1950)	1949-1950
05444	Miller, George C. Mrs./Miller, George Clinton	Lawrence	NY	2 (1911)	1911-1912
01034	Schenck, J.F.	Lawrence	NY	2 (N.D.)	1886
05933	Agnew, George B./Westchester County/Katonah	Lewisboro	NY	19 (1913-1914)	1913-1915; 1938
09961	Campbell, W. C.	Lloyd Neck	NY	0	1953
07359	Field, Marshall	Lloyd Neck	NY	9 (1925-1926)	1924-1927
06948	Baker, G. F. Jr./Cravath Subdiv. (in)/Baker, George Jr.	Locust Valley	NY	5 (1921)	1921-1922
07581	Battershall, F. S.	Locust Valley	NY	10 (1919-1926)	1925-1928
09452	Dickinson, Hunt T.	Locust Valley	NY	23 (1933-1937)	1936-1937
07742	Franklin, P.A.L./Franklin, P.A.S.	Locust Valley	NY	0	1926
09119	Gates, Artemus L.	Locust Valley	NY	15 (1929)	1929-1930
06893	Gibson, Harvey D./Bourne, G.G./Bourne, George F./Gibson, Harvey D.	Locust Valley	NY	32 (1926-1928)	1920-1929
09282	Gray, Henry G. Mrs.	Locust Valley	NY	3 (1931)	1931-1933
02945	Guthrie, W. D./Meudon	Locust Valley	NY	5 (1905-1907)	1903-1907
06892	Lamont, Thomas W./Gibson, Harvey/Gibson, Harvey D./Portion of Cravath Subdivision	Locust Valley	NY	30 (1920-1922)	1922-1929

Job #	Job Name/Alternative Name	Job Location		Plans	Correspondence
06757	Lyon, J. D./Franklin, Philip/Lyon, J.D./Franklin, Philip A.S.	Locust Valley	NY	31 (1919-1927)	1919-1921; 1927
07673	Pennoyer, Paul D.	Locust Valley	NY	3 (1926)	1926
06786	Saint John's Lattingtown Rectory	Locust Valley	NY	12 (1919-1928)	1920-1931
03791	Simpson, Robert H.	Locust Valley	NY	0	1909
07322	Steitinius, Edward Q./Stettinius, Edward R.	Locust Valley	NY	0	1924; 1939
07313	Taylor, Myron/Wayside Cottage	Locust Valley	NY	3 (1924)	1924-1926
06175	Lawson, C. M./Hempstead Gardens	Long Beach	NY	0	1915-1916
06531	Aldred, J. E./Mrs. Remick/J.E. Aldred's Mother	Long Island	NY	3 (1917)	1917
07503	Aron, Jacob	Long Island	NY	25 (1925-1930)	1925-1934
06241	Ball, Mr.	Long Island	NY	0	1915
06297	Brokaw, Irving	Long Island	NY	40 (1926)	1915; 1926-1928
02891	Gould, C. A.	Long Island	NY	0	1904
07623	Nassau Shores/Harmon National Real Estate Corporation	Long Island	NY	1 (N.D.)	1926
07700	Ricks, Jesse	Long Island	NY	0	1926
06488	Ripley, J. A.	Long Island	NY	0	1916
03738	Van du Zee, Harold	Long Island	NY	0	1909
12227	Lincoln, W. H,	Longwood	NY	0	1891
05885	DeWitt, Mrs. W. E.	Madison County	NY	0	1913
00040	Constable, John M. & Fred. A.	Mamaroneck	NY	107 (1900-1920)	1898-1928
06611	Littwitz, Max	Mamaroneck	NY	25 (1917-1918)	1917-1919
07190	Grace, Joseph P.	Manhasset	NY	46 (1920-1924)	1923-1925
09389	McConnell, M. E. Mrs.	Manhasset	NY	5 (1935)	1935-1936
07348	Munsey, F. A./Munsey, Frank A.	Manhasset	NY	43 (1924-1925)	1924-1926; 1937; 1943
09140	Groesbeck, C. E.	Matinecock	NY	55 (1929-1931)	1929-1934
09137	Rentschler, Gordon S./Cravath Property	Matinecock	NY	9 (1925-1929)	1929-1934
07691	Batterman, H. L.	Mill Neck	NY	2 (1926)	1926-1927
12377	Brown, George H.	Millbrook	NY	0	1867
06282	Burton, R. L.	Millbrook	NY	0	
06284	Edwards, Laura J.	Millbrook	NY	0	
06246	Flagler, Henry Harkness	Millbrook	NY	0	1915
06283	MacLane, H. R.	Millbrook	NY	0	1915-1916
06285	Miller, Roswell Mrs.	Millbrook	NY	1 (1915)	1915-1916
03810	Moore, Leah Miss	Millbrook	NY	6 (1910-1911)	1909-1911
06084	Tower, J. T./Tower, Joseph T.	Millbrook	NY	16 (1914-1916)	1914-1929; 1937
06243	Wing, J. Norman Mrs./Wing, J. Morgan	Millbrook	NY	2 (1915-1916)	1915-1916
02636	Hither Hills/Benson, F. S	Montauk	NY	1 (1904)	
09079	Bragg, Caleb S.	Montauk Point	NY	4 (1929-1930)	1929-1930
06484	Clayburgh, Albert	Mount Kisco	NY	39 (1917-1921)	1916-1922
06763	Welch, Francis W,	Mount Kisco	NY	0	1919

Job #	Job Name/Alternative Name	Job Location		Plans	Correspondence
00688	Neilson, James	New Brunswick	NY	3 (1889)	1889-1891
09031	Gorman, P. H.	New Castle	NY	1 (1928)	1928
09111	Watt, W. C.	New Castle	NY	36 (1929-1930)	1929-1931; 1978
09029	Willingham, W. A./Whippoorwill Subdiv.	New Castle	NY	1 (1928)	1928
09032	Youville, Thomas B./Yuille, Thomas B.	New Castle	NY	2 (1928)	1928
09098	Jeffreys, Lee	New Hartford	NY	24 (1928-1929)	1929-1931
12387	Collins, E. K.	New Rochelle	NY	0	1860-1861
01165	Iselin, Adrian	New Rochelle	NY	8 (1892-1893)	1890-1894
01164	Iselin, C. Oliver/Premium Point	New Rochelle	NY	69 (1889-1893)	1889-1893
07017	Martin, Robert W.	New Rochelle	NY	0	1922
03695	Robinson, C. W.	New Rochelle	NY	0	1909
09467	Babbott, F. L. Jr. Mrs.	New York City	NY	1 (1936)	1936-1937
07858	Baker, George F. J./Baker, George F. Jr.	New York City	NY	0	1927
05098	Born, Mrs. P. H.	New York City	NY	0	1910
05576	de Forest, Henry W./California Project	New York City	NY	0	1912
02915	Glaenger, Eugene/Glazner, Eugene	New York City	NY	0	1903-1904
07841	Harmon, William E./Tree Planting	New York City	NY	0	1927
09016	Hatch, Harold A. Mrs./Hatch, Harold A.	New York City	NY	3 (1928-1934)	1928;1934
09301	Heydt, Fred G.	New York City	NY	0	1931-1932
06230	Libbey, E. D.	New York City	NY	0	1915
06875	Mayer, Lucius W.	New York City	NY	0	1920-1921
03710	Meyer, Charles G.	New York City	NY	0	1909
02926	Olmsted. F. L. Jr.	New York City	NY	0	1936
05441	Perkins, Frank E. - Arc.	New York City	NY	0	1911
07282	Slater, Mrs. Edwin	New York City	NY	0	1924
02940	Wokoun, F./A. B. Cure Co.	New York City	NY	0	1904
09030	Taylor, W.R.K.	Newcastle	NY	5 (1928-1929)	1928-1930
00066	Perky, Henry D.	Niagara Falls	NY	0	1901
07995	Garvan, Francis P.	North Hempstead	NY	75 (1928-1930)	1928-1934
09173	Rogers, H. H.	North Sea	NY	2 (1925-1930)	1929-1930
01047	Cutting, Bayard/Westbrook	Oakdale	NY	40 (1887-1894)	N.D.; 1886-1894; 1920; 1940; 1946-1947
07682	James, Henry C./Cutting, W. B./Part of Cutting Estate, Westbrook	Oakdale	NY	2 (1927-1928)	1926-1928
09019	Suffolk Improvement Company/Melville, Frank/Old Field South Subdivision	Old Field	NY	51 (1928-1929)	1928-1934
05997	Loew, W. George Mrs./Loewmoor/Loew, William G./	Old Westbury	NY	144 (1910-1934)	1914-1935; 1942
12397	Brown, John Crosby	Orange Mountain	NY	0	1873-1874
07372	Hilton, Frederick/Hilton, Frederick M.	Ossining	NY	13 (1917-1925)	1924-1925
05857	Bullock, George/Moses Point	Oyster Bay	NY	0	1913
06645	Coe, William R./Planting Fields	Oyster Bay	NY	395 (1917-1936)	1917-1940; 1947; 1955; 1972-1979

The Ames estate gate lodge, North Easton, date unknown. Job #649 – Memorial Hall (North Easton, MA). Listed in Grounds of Public Buildings.

Job #	Job Name/Alternative Name	Job Location		Plans	Correspondence
06642	Davison, H. P./Pomeroy, D. E./Pomeroy, Daniel E.	Oyster Bay	NY	19 (1917-1927)	1918-1927; 1951-1957
06689	Doubleday, Nelson	Oyster Bay	NY	109 (1916-1935)	1919-1925; 1935-1936
07311	Garver, John A.	Oyster Bay	NY	16 (1924)	1923-1924
09175	Kerrigan, J. J./Kerrigan, Joseph J.	Oyster Bay	NY	6 (1928-1929)	1929-1930
09760	LaMontagne/LaMontagne, Harry	Oyster Bay	NY	6 (1946-1947)	1946-1947
07653	McCann, Charles	Oyster Bay	NY	0	1926
06458	McKelvey, Charles W. Mrs.	Oyster Bay	NY	7 (1908-1917)	1916-1922
06218	Sanderson, Mrs. Henry/Mrs. Frederick Wheeler/Sanderson, Henry/Wheeler, F.S.	Oyster Bay	NY	640 (1905-1937)	1915-1928; 1937; 1950
00628	Tuckerman, W. C.	Oyster Bay	NY	2 (1882)	1882
06993	Works, Bertram/Work, Bertran	Oyster Bay	NY	0	1921-1922
07866	Lamont, Thomas W.	Palisades	NY	105 (1927-1932)	1927-1937; 1948-1979
09565	Webster, Donald B.	Palmyra	NY	15 (1938-1939)	1939
06612	Leonard, S. J.	Piping Rock	NY	0	1917-1919

Job #	Job Name/Alternative Name	Job Location		Plans	Correspondence
00243	Rockefeller, J. D./Rockefeller, John D., Jr./Pocantico Hills	Pocantico Hills	NY	265 (1895-1934)	1894-1943
03739	Harris, John McArthur	Pocono Mountains	NY	0	1909
06731	Meurer, Mrs. Jacob	Port Jefferson	NY	0	1919
02224	Morch, Thomas/March, Thomas	Port Jefferson	NY	24 (1899)	1899; 1904-1905
09333	MacNutt, F. A.	Port Washington	NY	0	1933
07446	Platt, C. A./Rumsey, C. C.	Port Washington	NY	0	1925-1926
03387	Dunham, Carroll Dr.	Pottersville	NY	2 (1905-1907)	1907-1908
06052	Atwater, Lucy J./Woodside	Poughkeepsie	NY	0	1914
03077	Dows, Tracy	Rhinebeck	NY	27 (1906-1908; 1927)	1905-1917; 1922
03081	Olin, S. H./Olin, Stephen H.	Rhinebeck	NY	35 (1905-1907)	1905-1907
09967	Kerlin, Gilbert Mrs.	Riverdale	NY	6 (1953-1954)	1953-1954
06638	Aubin, Miss/Aubin, R.E.	Rochelle Heights	NY	2 (1917-1918)	1917-1919
09230	Hutchinson, Charles F.	Rochester	NY	6 (1930-1931)	1930-1931
06670	Brady, Nicholas F. Mrs./Brady Estate	Roslyn	NY	20 (1919)	1919-1920
02989	Canfield, A. Cass Mrs.	Roslyn	NY	13 (1902-1906)	1904-1906
06751	Demarest, J. M./Demarest, John M.	Roslyn	NY	59 (1919-1922)	1919-1927
06319	Phipps, H. C./Phipps, Henry C.	Roslyn	NY	4 (1915-1916)	1915-1916
03071	Fisk, Pliny	Rye	NY	0	1905
06263	Lufkin, E. C.	Rye	NY	26 (1915-1916)	1915-1917
05387	Park, Hobart J.	Rye	NY	3 (1910-1918)	1911
06640	Park, Hobart J.	Rye	NY	0	1918-1919
07753	Smith, R. M.	Rye	NY	46 (1927-1928)	1926-1929
07220	Walworth, Joseph	Rye	NY	5 (1923)	1923
09004	Walworth, Joseph	Rye	NY	27 (1928-1930)	1928-1932
03062	Sanger, William C./Sanger, WIlliam Carey/Sangerfield Farm	Sangerfield	NY	47 (1905-1918)	1904-1922
04003	Cluett, Walter H./Rockledge Pk/Rockledge	Saranac Lake	NY	3 (1910)	1910-1912; 1950; 1963-1965
06398	Bemis, H. A.	Scarborough	NY	4 (1916)	1916-1917
07307	Harden, E. W./Ullman Property	Scarborough	NY	40 (1924)	1923-1925
06406	Henry, Philip W. Mrs.	Scarborough	NY	3 (1916-1917)	1916-1917
06390	Kies, W. S./Kies, William S.	Scarborough	NY	2 (1916)	1916
05277	Mather, Mr. Robert/Elliott Shepard Estate	Scarborough	NY	0	1911
00042	Shepard, Eliott F.	Scarborough	NY	29 (1895-1921)	1892-1899
02988	Speyer, James/Waldheim	Scarborough	NY	17 (1904-1906)	1904-1927; 1934
06443	Vanderlip, F. A./Beechwood Subdiv.	Scarborough	NY	75 (1916-1920)	1917-1920; 1935-1936
07902	Young, John Orr	Scarsdale	NY	2 (1928)	1928
09219	Hanson, Willis T.	Schenectady	NY	41 (1930)	1930-1933
03344	Beebe, C. D./Loneoak/Lone Oak	Skaneateles	NY	7 (1907-1908)	1907-1908
07643	Smith, Flora Miss	Skaneateles	NY	7 (1926)	1926
07549	Dahl, Gerhard M.	Smithtown	NY	39 (1925-1926)	1925-1927

Job #	Job Name/Alternative Name	Job Location		Plans	Correspondence
07292	Hedstrom, A. E./Hedstrom, Arthur E.	Snyder	NY	32 (1924)	1924
00634	Barber, T. H.	Southampton	NY	6 (1893-1894)	1893-1897
06577	Clark, J. S.	Southampton	NY	7 (1917)	1917
05654	Clark, J. S./Clark, Joseph S.	Southampton	NY	5 (1912)	1912-1914
10678	Jacobs, Mr. & Mrs. Arthur	Southampton	NY	3 (1973-1978)	1978
06754	Patterson, Rufus/Lenoir	Southampton	NY	4 (1919-1920)	1919-1920
06042	Rogers, H. H.	Southampton	NY	29 (1913-1924)	1914-1915; 1925-1934
01390	Sands, B.A. Esq./Sands, B. Aymar	Southampton	NY	7 (1894-1895)	1894-1895
06329	Hemphill, Alexander J.	Spring Lake	NY	14 (1916-1920)	1916-1920
05993	Ball, E. A.	Springville	NY	0	1914
01013	Ford, R. T.	Staatsburgh	NY	8 (1884-1885)	1884-1885
07040	Burden, James A.	Syosset	NY	109 (1922-1924)	1922-1927; 1933; 1942-1948
06340	Fowler, Dr. R. H.	Syosset	NY	0	1916
07661	Chase, Arthur G.	Syracuse	NY	66 (1926-1939)	1926-1939
00122	Hamilton, W.T.	Syracuse	NY	18 (1882)	1871; 1882
00443	Hazard, John G.	Syracuse	NY	0	1901
01431	Holden, H. R.	Syracuse	NY	0	1901
03349	Nottingham, William	Syracuse	NY	0	1907
00164	Pierce, E. L.	Syracuse	NY	10 (1901)	1901
05434	Smith, Burns Lyman	Syracuse	NY	0	1911
12407	White, H.S.	Syracuse	NY	1 (1891)	1891
00248	Rockefeller, J. D. 3rd - The Ruins/Rockefeller, John D., Jr.	Tarrytown	NY	7 (1924-1939)	1891-1895; 1939-1941
00244	Rockefeller, John D. Jr. - Buttermilk Hill	Tarrytown	NY	91 (1930-1939)	1939
01121	Rockefeller, William/Rockwood Hall	Tarrytown	NY	89 (1887-1895)	1887-1897
03716	Aldrich, Richard	Tarrytown-on-Hudson	NY	8 (1910-1911)	1909-1916; 1958; 1970
00158	Mitchell, J. Murray/Mitchell, John Murray	Tuxedo	NY	19 (1900-1903)	1899-1907
06614	Blair, J. Insley/Blair, J. Insle	Tuxedo Park	NY	114 (1915-1922)	1917-1923; 1928; 1934
02268	Collier, Price	Tuxedo Park	NY	2 (1902)	1900-1903
06596	Keech, Mrs. Frank B./Keech, Clara Jay	Tuxedo Park	NY	0	1917
09047	Lorillard, Pierre Mrs./Beard, A. M./Beard, Anson McCook	Tuxedo Park	NY	98 (1929-1931)	1929-1935
07201	Mitchell, Charles E.	Tuxedo Park	NY	20 (1923-1925)	1923-1925; 1935
05519	Blakie, Miss/Blaikie, Helen G.	Utica	NY	0	1912
07240	Childs, W. J.	Utica	NY	0	1923
07245	Dibble, E. W./Dibble, Everett W.	Utica	NY	16 (1923-1924)	1923-1924
06737	Hamman, Louis H.	Utica	NY	0	1919
07107	Roberts, Harry W./Lot in Tilden Subdivision	Utica	NY	26 (1922-1925)	1922-1926; 1946
05835	Roberts, Harry W./Tilden Realty Co.	Utica	NY	10 (1913)	1913-1914
05948	Sherman, R. U.	Utica	NY	0	1913

Job #	Job Name/Alternative Name	Job Location		Plans	Correspondence
07141	Smith, Pratt G. Subdivision/Elmhurst	Utica	NY	23 (1922-1923)	1922-1924
09247	Soper, J. P.	Utica	NY	9 (1930-1931)	1930-1932; 1959
07443	Watson, F. B./Watson, Frank B.	Utica	NY	7 (1925)	1925
07105	Wicks, C. W. Senator/Wicks, Charles W.	Utica	NY	12 (1922-1923)	1922-1923
03065	Mitchell, Roland/Mitchell, Roland G.	Wading River	NY	2 (1905)	1905; 1916-1926
00037	Flower, Anson R.	Watertown	NY	13 (1902)	1901-1907
07010	Minnier, B. J./New York Air Brake Company	Watertown	NY	5 (1923)	1922-1923
04091	Taylor, J. B./Taylor, John B.	Watertown	NY	10 (1910-1912)	1910-1914
00073	Jones, Stanley	West Hampton	NY	4 (1929-1931)	
06613	Bingham, H. P.	West Park	NY	22 (1918-1919)	1917-1919
06316	Phipps, John S.	Westbury	NY	23 (1915-1916)	1915-1916; 1959
07094	Reybwin, Samuel W./Reyburn, Samuel W.	Westchester County	NY	0	1922
06502	Auchincloss, Charles C.	Wheatley	NY	0	1917
09088	Gavin, Michael Mrs./Gavin, Michael	Wheatley	NY	12 (1929-1930)	1929-1930
06393	Hill, James N./Hill, James Norman	Wheatley	NY	14 (1916-1919)	1916-1919; 1931
00088	Whitney, W. C.	Wheatley	NY	144 (1895-1925)	1895-1897; 1924-1925; 1941
09271	Widener, George D.	Wheatley	NY	7 (1930-1931)	1931
09135	Taylor, W. R. K.	Whippoorwill	NY	0	N.D.
03172	Harriman, Oliver	White Plains	NY	0	1906-1908
01058	Reid, Whitelaw/Ophir Farm	White Plains	NY	246 (1888-1893)	1888-1895
07704	Dunham, George E. Mrs./Dunham, George E.	Whitestown	NY	3 (1925-1926)	1926-1927
02238	Townsend, Howard	Wickapogue	NY	12 (1900-1912)	1900-1901; 1912-1915
03366	Ward, Mrs. L. A. Crowley/Ward, L. A. Coonley	Wyoming	NY	0	1907
01148	Mitchell, William Estate	Yonkers	NY	14 (1889-1890)	1889-1893; 1917-1919
05909	Thompson, W. R.	Yonkers	NY	0	1913-1914
09052	Fox, Mortimer J.	Yorktown	NY	8 (1920; 1926; 1929)	1929
06778	Fording Estate/Fording, Arthur O.	Alliance	OH	4 (1920)	1919-1920
06260	Myers, P. A.	Ashland	OH	0	1915
07097	Sheffield, Henry E.	Bratenahl	OH	5 (1911-1922)	1922-1923
07257	Freidlauder, Mrs. Alfred/Friedlander, Alfred	Cincinnati	OH	0	1923
07113	Rauh, Julian S.	Cincinnati	OH	26 (1922-1924)	1923-1925
07191	Roth, Robert S./Roth, Albert S.	Cincinnati	OH	0	1923
06368	Skinner, S.W. Mrs.	Cincinnati	OH	15 (1916)	1916-1920
06412	Bicknell, Warren	Cleveland	OH	41 (1916-1921)	1916-1927; 1944-1947
06405	Bingham, H. P./City Lot/Bingham, Henry P./Hanna, L.C.	Cleveland	OH	13 (1916-1918)	1916-1921
06347	Bingham, Harry P.	Cleveland	OH	7 (1916)	1916-1917
06281	Prescott, Orville/Prescott, Orville W.	Cleveland	OH	0	1915-1916

Job #	Job Name/Alternative Name	Job Location		Plans	Correspondence
06854	Hall, Samuel P./Dodd, J. F./Stratford Housing Project	Columbus	OH	0	1920
05936	Leonard, William V.	Columbus	OH	1 (1913)	1913-1914
06917	Barringer, John H./Barringer, J. H./Hills and Dales	Dayton	OH	0	1921
05855	Canby, H. B./Dayton View	Dayton	OH	0	1913
06327	Carnell, R. G. Mrs./Carnell, H.G.	Dayton	OH	28 (1915-1921)	1915-1917
05778	Carr, Henry M.	Dayton	OH	0	1912
06177	Carr, S. H.	Dayton	OH	10 (1915)	1915
03388	Carr, S. H.	Dayton	OH	0	1903-1909
03127	Chalmers, Hugh	Dayton	OH	11 (1905-1906)	1906-1908
06399	Clegg, Harrie P.	Dayton	OH	2 (1916-1917)	1916-1917
06004	Clegg, Harrie P.	Dayton	OH	10 (1913-1915)	1914-1917
07112	Client of E. F. Simpson/Simpson, E. F.	Dayton	OH	0	1923
07056	Coolidge, J. B.	Dayton	OH	1 (1922)	
05480	Cox, James M.	Dayton	OH	13 (1912-1918)	1912-1922
06009	Crane, J. H. Mrs./Oakwood	Dayton	OH	1 (1914)	1914; 1917; 1923
06698	Crane, Joseph H. Mrs./Rubicon Rd. Sub-div./Crane, Joseph H.	Dayton	OH	18 (1919-1927)	1919-1927
05506	Deeds, E. A. - Moraine Farm	Dayton	OH	94 (1912-1924)	1904; 1912-1925; 1947; 1952
02980	Deeds, Edward A.	Dayton	OH	5 (1904)	1904-1906
06179	Dees, E. A./Miscellaneous	Dayton	OH	0	1915-1921
06070	Dees, E. A./Waldon Farm	Dayton	OH	0	1914-1915
05966	Dickey, Mrs. Robert R.	Dayton	OH	0	1914; 1917
05509	Eby Farm/Patterson, J. H./Patterson, John H.	Dayton	OH	16 (1912-1914)	1912-1915
05968	Edwards, Margaret Nathan/Edwards, Mrs. James P.	Dayton	OH	0	1914
06945	Glenbeck, M. Z. Beck - Subdivision/Beck, M. Z.	Dayton	OH	0	1921-1922
05960	Goodhue, D.	Dayton	OH	0	1914-1915
06455	Gorman, G. H. Mrs./Gorman, G. Harry	Dayton	OH	3 (1916)	1916-1917; 1921
06374	Gorman, G. H./Oakwood/Gorman, G. Harries	Dayton	OH	21 (1916-117)	1916-1917
07100	Gunckel, E. L. Mrs./Gunckel, E. L.	Dayton	OH	5 (1922)	1922-1923
07057	Harley, E. C./Lot B in Ridgeview	Dayton	OH	8 (1922)	1922
06691	Harrison, O. L.	Dayton	OH	8 (1919-1920)	1919-1921
04013	Houk, R. T.	Dayton	OH	0	1910-1911; 1919
06862	Houk, Robert T.	Dayton	OH	0	
07055	Huffman, Horace M. - Home Place	Dayton	OH	1 (1922)	
05978	Kettering, C. F./Kettering, Charles F.	Dayton	OH	66 (1914-1919)	1914-1919; 1962
06952	Keyes, W. A./Keyes, William A.	Dayton	OH	20 (1921)	1921-1922
06211	Kidder, W. S./City House/Private Place/Greenhouse/Kidder, Walter S.	Dayton	OH	44 (1915-1919)	1915-1920

View of the McDuffie garden looking toward the house, August 1927. Job #5883 – Duncan McDuffie (Berkeley, CA).

Job #	Job Name/Alternative Name	Job Location		Plans	Correspondence
06732	King, Mrs. S. S.	Dayton	OH	0	1919
06986	Lapp, J. A./Hills & Dales	Dayton	OH	6 (1921)	1921
05777	Legler, B. T.	Dayton	OH	0	1912
06198	Legler, T. B.	Dayton	OH	0	1915
05908	Lowe, Houston	Dayton	OH	9 (1912-1914)	1913-1914
06715	Loy, Harry	Dayton	OH	0	1919
06633	Markham, J. M.	Dayton	OH	2 (1918)	1918-1919
06214	McCann, J. B.	Dayton	OH	0	1914-1917
06249	McCann, Judge	Dayton	OH	0	1915
06233	Mead, Georg/Mead, George H./Oakwoode	Dayton	OH	37 (1915-1920)	1915-1921
05965	Ohmer, Dr. William	Dayton	OH	0	1914; 1920
06808	Ohmer, William	Dayton	OH	0	1920
05959	Ohmer, William	Dayton	OH	0	1914
07456	Parrott, Miss Frances/Elizabeth Garden	Dayton	OH	0	1925-1926
06483	Patterson, Frederick/Sprigg, Judge Carroll	Dayton	OH	8 (1916-1920)	1916-1923
01721	Patterson, J.	Dayton	OH	3 (1896)	1895-1899
02273	Patterson, J. H./Far Hills	Dayton	OH	45 (1902-1921)	1895-1896; 1901-1922
05807	Patterson, J. H./Sugar Camp Property	Dayton	OH	0	

Job #	Job Name/Alternative Name	Job Location		Plans	Correspondence
06872	Patterson, Jefferson	Dayton	OH	4 (1920-1921)	1920-1921
06384	Patterson, Miss Dorothy - House	Dayton	OH	0	1916-1917
02220	Patterson, R. Sr.	Dayton	OH	1 (1899)	1899
06441	Patterson, Robert D./Schiebensuber Farm	Dayton	OH	11 (1917-1921)	1916-1925
07213	Patterson, Robert Dunn	Dayton	OH	68 (1923-1924)	1923-1927
06382	Perrine, M. Miss/Perrine, Martha	Dayton	OH	1 (1917)	1916-1917
06624	Rike, Fred H./Hills and Dales	Dayton	OH	4 (1918-1919)	1918-1919
03087	Schantz, Adam, Jr.	Dayton	OH	2 (1905-1909)	1905-1906
06117	Schantz, Adam/Cincinnati Pike Farm	Dayton	OH	0	1915
06183	Schantz, Adam/Cincinnati Pike Farm/Schumacher Tract	Dayton	OH	0	1915
06250	Schantz, Adam/Coy Tract	Dayton	OH	0	1915
06184	Schantz, Adam/Mitchell Property	Dayton	OH	0	1915-1916
05655	Shaw, George G.	Dayton	OH	7 (1913-1915)	1912-1915
05763	Smith, F. H./Smith, Frank Hill	Dayton	OH	1 (1907)	1912-1915
05961	Smith, Frank Hill	Dayton	OH	0	
06897	Steffey, C. E./Hills & Dales	Dayton	OH	38 (1920-1924)	1920-1924
04058	Stoddard, C.G.	Dayton	OH	0	1910
03228	Talbott, H. E. Col./Hilton, A. B./Runnymede/in Oakwood subdivision	Dayton	OH	15 (1907-1920)	1907; 1912-1923
06404	Triangle Park/Delco Athletic Park/Idylwild	Dayton	OH	7 (1916-1917)	1916-1919
00327	Winters, Valentine	Dayton	OH	4 (1901-1914)	1901-1903; 1914-1917
05915	Deeds, E. A. - Homestead/Old Homestead	Granville	OH	3 (1913)	1913
06254	Jones, J. S./Bryn Du Farm	Granville	OH	0	1915
03693	McClain, Mr. E. L.	Greenfield	OH	0	1909-1918
01204	Ellsworth, J. W.	Hudson	OH	3 (1891)	1891-1899
09015	Bicknell, Warren	Kirtland	OH	36 (1928-1929)	1928-1932
00305	Sherwin, Henry/Sherwin, Henry A./Windon	Kirtland	OH	144 (1903; 1914-1920)	1903-1906; 1914-1932; 1978
09174	King, Charles	Mentor	OH	0	1929
09089	King, Ralph T.	Mentor	OH	24 (1929-1930)	1929-1931
03051	Moore, Edward W.	Mentor	OH	2 (1899; 1905)	1905-1906
07058	Scott, Frank A. and others	Mentor Township	OH	0	1922
06697	Cox, J. M./Cox, James M.	Middletown	OH	7 (1919)	1919-1920
06937	Allyn, S. C./Hills & Dales	Montgomery County	OH	4 (1921)	1921
06938	Beust, Carl W./Hills & Dales	Montgomery County	OH	21 (1921-1922)	1921-1922
03343	Stroop, William S./Grand View Hill	Montgomery County	OH	12 (1916-1919)	1907; 1912-1919
06755	Grant, R. H./Grant, Richard H.	Montgomery Township	OH	4 (1919-1920)	1919
02264	Lane, S. B. Mrs./Lane, H. M.	Norwood	OH	3 (1900-1901)	1897-1901

Job #	Job Name/Alternative Name	Job Location		Plans	Correspondence
07288	Barringer, J. H.	Oakwood	OH	6 (1924)	1924
07907	Knight, W. W.	Perrysburg	OH	19 (1928)	1928-1929
07156	Lewis, Charles T. Mrs./Lewis, C. T.	Perrysburg	OH	9 (1923)	1923-1924
09090	Lewis, Frank S.	Perrysburg	OH	1 (1929)	1929
07155	Lewis, Howard	Perrysburg	OH	17 (1923-1924)	1923-1924
07516	Secor, J.K. Mrs./Secor, J. K.	Perrysburg	OH	7 (1918-1929)	1925-1931
07692	Halle, Salmon P.	Shaker Heights	OH	1 (1920-1926)	1926-1928
10046	Perry, A. Dean	Shaker Heights	OH	17 (1956-1957)	1955-1957
06493	Buchwalter, L. L.	Springfield	OH	11 (1916-1917)	1916-1917
05870	Harries, J. and R./Harries Station	Springfield Pike	OH	0	1913
06973	Wehrle Farm, The/Wehrle, W. W. and A. T.	Thornville	OH	27 (1915-1922)	1921-1922; 1934
07763	Troxel, Lynn	Tiffin	OH	125 (1927-1944)	1927-1934; 1940-1945; 1952
06426	Clients of Edward O. Fallis	Toledo	OH	0	1916
07150	Cullen, Marion C./Lewis, Mrs. C. T.	Toledo	OH	0	1922-1924
06369	Dunn, H. T.	Toledo	OH	1 (1916)	1916
07319	Ford, Edward Mrs./Ford, Edward	Toledo	OH	92 (1924-1931)	1924-1931
07883	Ford, George R./Perrysburg	Toledo	OH	74 (1922-1931)	1927-1932
07320	France, G. A. Stove Company/France, George	Toledo	OH	18 (1906-1924)	1924
07323	MacNichol, G. P. Dr.	Toledo	OH	1 (1924)	1924-1925
07913	Reynolds, H. S.	Toledo	OH	0	
07401	Stranahan, Frank	Toledo	OH	326 (1925-1930)	1925-1930; 1940; 1956-1969
06592	Willys, J. N. Estate	Toledo	OH	0	1917
06372	Hayner, Mary J. Mrs.	Troy	OH	9 (1914-1916)	1916-1917
06746	Johnston, H. L.	Troy	OH	14 (1919-1921)	1919-1922
06618	Kidder, Walter S./Resthaven/Miami County Farm	Troy	OH	13 (1918-1919)	1918-1920
05907	Johnson, Isaac T.	Urbana	OH	0	1913
06174	Campbell & Garlick/Campbell, J.A./Garlick, Richard	Youngstown	OH	245 (1915-1920)	1915-1918; 1932
06448	Campbell, James/Campbell, J.A.	Youngstown	OH	96 (1916-1920)	1916-1920
06446	Garlick, H. M.	Youngstown	OH	3 (1916)	1916
06447	Garlick, Richard	Youngstown	OH	62 (1916-1920)	1916-1922
06191	Logan, John A.	Youngstown	OH	0	
06192	Logan, John A. - Home	Youngstown	OH	0	1915-1916
06190	Logan, Mrs. John A.	Youngstown	OH	0	
06852	Manning, W. E.	Youngstown	OH	31 (1919-1921)	1920-1921
06339	Meyer, Mrs. I. Harry	Youngstown	OH	0	1916
06193	Thomas, W. A.	Youngstown	OH	0	1915
08228	Bennett, Dr. Kenney G.	Stillwater	OK	0	
03642	Page, J. F.	Chatsop Beach	OR	0	1909
03721	Palmer, George	La Grande	OR	0	1909

Job #	Job Name/Alternative Name	Job Location		Plans	Correspondence
05090	Simpson, L. J.	North Bend	OR	0	1910
03634	Adkins, Miss Ora L.	Portland	OR	0	1909
03418	Ainsworth, J. C.	Portland	OR	0	1907; 1915
03439	Ainsworth, Misses Maud and Bell/Estate in Portland Heights subdivision	Portland	OR	0	1907
08073	Autzen, Thomas	Portland	OR	0	1926-1930
02632	Ayer, W. B./Ayer, Winslow B.	Portland	OR	1 (1903)	1903-1914
03992	Biddle, Mrs. (Captain) William S./Estate in Waverly Heights subdivision	Portland	OR	0	1909
01050	Brewster, W. L.	Portland	OR	2 (1903)	1889
02627	Brewster, W. L.	Portland	OR	0	1903
00453	Cary, Judge Charles	Portland	OR	0	1903
08090	Corbett, Hamilton	Portland	OR	59 (1927-1928)	1927-1929
03719	Corbett, Harry L.	Portland	OR	0	1909
03219	Failing, Henrietta Miss/Failing, Henrietta and Mary F./Ardmore	Portland	OR	12 (1906-1908)	1906-1908
03412	Failing, J. F. Mrs./Failing, J. F.	Portland	OR	9 (1907-1908)	1907-1908
03756	Giesy, Dr. A. J./Giesey, A. J.	Portland	OR	0	1909
03747	Gilbert, Wells/Walker, Cyrus	Portland	OR	9 (1910-1914)	1909-1915; 1952
03593	Hamblet, H. L.	Portland	OR	0	1908-1909
03220	Hewett, Henry	Portland	OR	6 (1908-1909)	1906-1917
03991	Hogne, Harry Wildey/Hogue, Harry Wildey	Portland	OR	0	1909
03722	Kerr, Peter/Elk Rock in Abernathy Heights Subdivision	Portland	OR	13 (1909-1929)	1909-1910; 1929
03915	Kerr, Thomas/Estate in Waverly Heights subdivision	Portland	OR	0	1909
03224	Ladd, C. E.	Portland	OR	0	1903
03125	Ladd, Mrs. W. Love	Portland	OR	15 (1906-1926)	1906
03226	Ladd, W. M./Ladd, William H./Hazel Fern Farm	Portland	OR	1 (1902)	1906-1908
04015	Lewis, C. H./Lewis, C. Hunt	Portland	OR	8 (1910-1911)	1910-1911
05653	Lewis, David C.	Portland	OR	7 (1912-1913)	1912-1914
03221	Lewis, Francis Mrs./Lewis, Frances	Portland	OR	3 (1907-1908)	1906-1909
05515	Lewis, R. W.	Portland	OR	29 (1912)	1912-1913
03594	Lombard, B. M.	Portland	OR	0	1908
03633	Mills, A. L.	Portland	OR	0	1909
08074	Squires, Cameron	Portland	OR	1 (1926)	1926-1927
03916	Voorhies, Gordon/Estate in Waverly Heights subdivision	Portland	OR	0	1909
07504	Dorrance, Ethel M. Mrs.	Radnor	OR	20 (1900-1928)	1925-1928
03218	Corbett, Henry F./Corbett, Helen Ladd/ Corbett, Mrs. Henry S./Corbett, Hamilton F./estate in Abernathy Heights subdivision	Rivera	OR	0	1906-1909; 1924
03919	Kerr, Peter/Waverly Heights	Waverly Heights	OR	0	1909-1910

Job #	Job Name/Alternative Name	Job Location		Plans	Correspondence
07847	Stevens, Walter P.	Abington	PA	2 (1927-1928)	1927-1928
03580	Stewardson, E. L.; Abington	Abington	PA	0	1908-1911
09469	Bok, Cary W.	Ardmore	PA	48 (1935-1940)	1936-1947; 1954-1966
09456	Pew, J. Howard	Ardmore	PA	101 (1908; 1936-1938)	1936-1939
01234	Pitcairn, John	Bethayres	PA	17 (1892-1895)	1893-1897
06353	Caldwell, J. E./Caldwell, James E.	Bryn Mawr	PA	80 (1916-1919)	1916; 1919
03365	Colton, Sabin W. Jr./Colton, Sabin/Miller, John R.	Bryn Mawr	PA	28 (1908-1910)	1907-1911
02894	Drexel, Mrs. G. W. C./Wootton	Bryn Mawr	PA	0	1901-1902
07826	Kuhn, C. Hartman	Bryn Mawr	PA	0	1927
00136	Miller, J. Rulon/Rulon-Miller, John	Bryn Mawr	PA	4 (1895-1896)	1895-1897
06005	Potto, Francis L./Mrs. Wycoff Smith	Bryn Mawr	PA	0	1914
03250	Smith, W. Hinckle	Bryn Mawr	PA	31 (1907-1925)	1907-1915; 1922-1929
07665	Garbisch, Norbert S. Dr.	Butler	PA	20 (1925-1927)	1926-1927
07869	Phillips, Benjamin	Butler	PA	0	1927
07386	Phillips, T. W.	Butler	PA	78 (1924-1930)	1924-1931
03806	Lewis, John F.	Chester County	PA	0	1909
07727	Austin, R. L.	Chestnut Hill	PA	1 (1927)	1926-1928
03292	Austin, Richard L.	Chestnut Hill	PA	13 (1907-1917)	1907-1910; 1916-1918; 1927
03137	Ballard, E. A./Ballard, Ellis Ames/estate in St. Martins Subdivision	Chestnut Hill	PA	8 (1906-1907)	1906-1908
07773	Ballard, Ellis Ames	Chestnut Hill	PA	1 (1925-1927)	1927
00166	Clark, Joseph S./Clark & Taylor	Chestnut Hill	PA	45 (1902-1926)	1902-1912; 1916-1921
03990	Clark, Mrs. E. W./Keewaydin	Chestnut Hill	PA	0	1910
05267	Dixon, T. H.	Chestnut Hill	PA	7 (1906; 1911)	1906-1911
12510	Fielding, Mantle	Chestnut Hill	PA	1 (1897)	
06777	Gillmore, Quincy A./Baird Property Seminole & Rex Ave./Gates, Thomas	Chestnut Hill	PA	20 (1905-1927)	1919-1920; 1926-1927
03732	Gowen, F. I./Harrison, A.C. estate/Gowen, Francis I.	Chestnut Hill	PA	4 (1909)	1909
00309	Gowen, Francis I.	Chestnut Hill	PA	25 (1903-1911)	1903-1918
03630	Harris, Henry Frazer	Chestnut Hill	PA	0	1909
03160	Harris, J. A. Jr.	Chestnut Hill	PA	0	1906
04095	Henry, Mrs. C. W./Mermaid Lane	Chestnut Hill	PA	0	1910
03562	Jenks, W. S.	Chestnut Hill	PA	0	
00046	Jones, J. Levering/Wissahickon Heights	Chestnut Hill	PA	9 (1900-1901)	1900-1901
05555	Lea, Arthur H.	Chestnut Hill	PA	100 (1945-1957)	1912-1914
09567	McDougle, James A.	Chestnut Hill	PA	0	1939
00168	Taylor, F. W. (& Clark, J.S.)	Chestnut Hill	PA	37 (1902-1904)	1902-1912; 1916-1919; 1928-1931
03369	Welsh, Edward T.	Chestnut Hill	PA	0	1906-1911
07378	Widener, George D.	Chestnut Hill	PA	112 (1918-1927)	1924-1934

Job #	Job Name/Alternative Name	Job Location		Plans	Correspondence
05829	Woodward, Dr. George/vicinity Gravers Lane and Willow Grove	Chestnut Hill	PA	0	1913-1917
03530	Woodward, George Dr.	Chestnut Hill	PA	4 (1913)	1913-1915
03178	Woodward, George Dr./Cogslea/ Kresheim/St. Martins Station Grounds/	Chestnut Hill	PA	6 (1906-1909)	1906-1907
03497	Zantzinger, C. C.	Chestnut Hill	PA	5 (1908-1911)	1908-1911; 1917
03396	Zantzinger, C. C./Newhall	Chestnut Hill	PA	0	
03146	Clark, Percy H.	Cynwyd	PA	35 (1906-1911)	1906-1911; 1931
05062	Cassatt, J. G.	Daylesford	PA	0	1910-1911
03737	Kuhn, C. Hartman	Devon	PA	0	1909-1910
05785	Lea, Charles M.	Devon	PA	4 (1912)	1912-1913
09048	Lohmann, Alfred P.	Easttown	PA	4 (1929)	1929
06848	Dixon, F. Eugene	Elkins Park	PA	209 (1916-1930)	1920-1935; 1973-1974
03672	Steele, John L./Steele, Mrs. William, estate of	Elkins Park	PA	5 (1909)	1909
06579	Behrend, Ernst/Behrend, Ernest R.	Erie	PA	7 (1914-1919)	1917-1919
07137	Strong, C. H./Harbor Creek Farm	Erie	PA	9 (1922-1923)	1894-1899; 1922-1923
01345	Strong, Mrs. Charles	Erie	PA	8 (1892-1893; 1922-1923)	1893-1898; 1922-1925
01226	Watson, H. F.	Erie	PA	9 (1892-1894)	1893-1899
03368	Baker, Alfred E. Dr.	Germantown	PA	2 (1907)	1907-1908
03566	Brown, Henry W.	Germantown	PA	6 (1908)	1908-1909
03144	Clark, C. M./Clark, Clarence M./Cedron	Germantown	PA	49 (1905-1910)	1906-1909
06334	Strawbridge, Frederick H./Torworth	Germantown	PA	4 (1915-1916)	1916
06224	Warden, W. G.	Germantown	PA	0	1915-1916
05347	Wister Estate	Germantown	PA	0	1911
05557	Coulter, Emma Mrs./Coulter Estate	Greensburg	PA	2 (1906-1912)	1912
07861	Smith, John Story	Gwynned	PA	18 (1927-1928)	1927-1928
01422	Griscom, C. A./Griscom, Clement A./ Dolobran	Haverford	PA	16 (1894-1896)	1894-1896; 1922-1923
03157	Griscom, Rodman E./Griscom, Clement A.	Haverford	PA	2 (1906)	1894-1896; 1906
06146	Lloyd, Horatio G.	Haverford	PA	2 (1911-1915)	1915
02967	Pierce, Charlotte C.	Haverford	PA	5 (1905-1909)	1904-1909
06308	Thomson, Dr. A.G./Thomson, Archibald G.	Haverford	PA	16 (1913-1916)	1915-1916
06358	Warden, Clarence A.	Haverford	PA	4 (1916)	1916-1917
10528	O'Brien, Mr. Thomas & Mr. George Griffith	Johnstown	PA	0	
09114	Kent, Edward H.	Lehman Township	PA	6 (1926; 1929)	1929
09226	Laughlin, Mrs. George M.	Ligonier	PA	0	1930
07903	Herkness, J. Smiley	Meadowbrook	PA	0	1928
07158	Furness, Fairman R.	Media	PA	0	1923-1925
06716	Jeffords, Walter M.	Media	PA	11 (1919-1927)	1919-1928; 1969; 1978

Job #	Job Name/Alternative Name	Job Location		Plans	Correspondence
09276	Bok, Edward W. Mrs./Swastika	Merion	PA	21 (1931-1932)	1931-1932
07835	Corson, Newton W.	Merion	PA	3 (1927-1929)	1927-1929
03637	Wanamaker, William H. Jr./Kuhn, C. Hartman	Merion	PA	1 (1910)	1909-1911
03164	Pinchot, J. W./Pinchot, James W./Grey Towers	Milford	PA	0	1893-1895; 1906-1907; 1977
09095	Elkins, William M.	Montgomery County	PA	52 (1929-1931)	1929-1933
03477	Stewardson Montgomery Company/Harte-Stewardson/Harte, Dr. R. H./Stewardson Place	Montgomery County	PA	22 (1907-1910)	1906-1916; 1951
06880	Roush, J. C./Roush, Stanley	Mount Lebanon	PA	53 (1919-1921)	1920-1923
00101	Roberts, Percival	Narberth	PA	67 (1902-1904)	1899-1904; 1916
01437	Morris, Wistar//Morris, Mrs. Wistar	Overbrook	PA	9 (1896-1897)	1895-1898
02999	Simpson, W. P.	Overbrook	PA	1 (1904)	1904
06408	Story, Edward	Overbrook	PA	0	1916
03432	Townsend, J. Barton	Overbrook	PA	18 (1905-1906)	
06045	Roberts, Edward/Roberts, Edward, Jr.	Paoli	PA	1 (1914)	1914
03170	Bond, Francis/Bond, Francis E.	Penllyn	PA	10 (1905-1906)	1906
07889	Smith, Albert C./Smith, Albert L.	Penllyn	PA	0	1927-1930
07507	White, Thomas R.	Penllyn	PA	8 (1925-1926)	1925-1927
00186	Bertram, Mr.	Philadelphia	PA	0	
05268	Biddle, J. W./Biddle, J. Wilmer	Philadelphia	PA	40 (1911-1912)	1911-1916; 1930
06076	Carson, Hampton L./Rydal estate	Philadelphia	PA	9 (1914-1915)	1914-1916
05272	Clark, Herbert L.	Philadelphia	PA	14 (1911)	1911-1913
05990	Clark, J. S. et al./Chestnut Hill Improvements	Philadelphia	PA	10 (1913-1914)	1914; 1916
05572	Cooke, Jay 3rd/Cooke, Joy III	Philadelphia	PA	51 (1912-1929)	1912-1917; 1929-1930
07575	Cooke, M. L./Cooke, Morris L./St. George's Road	Philadelphia	PA	5 (1909; 1926)	1925-1926
05657	Earle, James M. Mrs./Earl, James M.	Philadelphia	PA	3 (1912-1916)	1910-1916
03646	Fairchild, Samuel E. Jr.	Philadelphia	PA	2 (1909)	1909
03420	Fearm, Charles/Fearon, Charles	Philadelphia	PA	0	1908
05517	Harper, William Warner	Philadelphia	PA	5 (1912)	1912-1913; 1929
02623	Harte-Spalding/Harte, R.H. and Philip L. Spalding	Philadelphia	PA	44 (1900-1906)	1903-1908
03386	Horstmann, Walter/Horstman, Walter	Philadelphia	PA	0	1907
05969	Houston, H. H. Estate	Philadelphia	PA	13 (1910-1914)	1914-1919
06674	Houston, Samuel F./Houston, Sam F.	Philadelphia	PA	14 (1919)	1919-1920
05977	Houston, Samuel J.	Philadelphia	PA	0	1914
03479	Jenks, John Story Jr.	Philadelphia	PA	24 (1908-1913)	1908-1914; 1926-1929; 1934
06242	Kemble, Mrs. Isaac/Phillips Hill	Philadelphia	PA	0	1915
06678	Pastorius Park/Woodward, George/Pastorino Park	Philadelphia	PA	20 (1915-1931)	1919-1921; 1931-1935
06181	Stotesbury, E. T.	Philadelphia	PA	58 (1915-1917)	1915-1917

Job #	Job Name/Alternative Name	Job Location		Plans	Correspondence
05522	Thomas, Churchman &. Molitor	Philadelphia	PA	0	1912
07842	Trumbauer, Horace	Philadelphia	PA	0	1927
00456	Windrim, John T.	Philadelphia	PA	0	
06413	Clothier, William J.	Phoenixville	PA	5 (1912-1916)	1916
00049	Guffey, J. M./Guffy, J. W.	Pittsburgh	PA	16 (1901-1902)	1901-1902
00133	Heinz, H. J.	Pittsburgh	PA	6 (1902)	1901-1908
04078	Heinz, Howard	Pittsburgh	PA	2 (1910)	1910
07662	Hunt, Mrs. Ray Arthur	Pittsburgh	PA	0	1926-1927
00311	Lovejoy, F.T.F.	Pittsburgh	PA	9 (1902-1903)	1902-1903
06759	Mellon, A. W./Chatham College	Pittsburgh	PA	8 (1916-1920)	1919-1920
06752	Mellon, R. B.	Pittsburgh	PA	15 (1911; 1919-1921)	1919; 1931-1932
00271	Mellon, W. L.	Pittsburgh	PA	9 (1901-1903)	1901-1902
06933	Merrick, Frederick I.	Pittsburgh	PA	5 (1921-1922)	1921-1922
03055	Oliver, J. B./Oliver, James B. - Sewickley	Pittsburgh	PA	8 (1905)	1905-1906
09265	Scaife, Alan M.	Pittsburgh	PA	20 (1931)	1931
01770	Vandergrift, J. J./Vandergrift, J. J. and C. J. Lockhart/Homewood Driving Park	Pittsburgh	PA	0	1895-1918; 1976-1980
03145	Shaefer, Arthur W.	Pottsville	PA	14 (1906-1907)	1906-1908
03456	Sheafer, Paul	Pottsville	PA	3 (1908)	1908-1911
05652	Clark, H. L./Brooke Farm/Clark, Herbert L.	Radnor	PA	69 (1912-1916)	1912-1917; 1927-1929; 1948-1949; 1954
06442	Clothier, Isaac H. Jr.	Radnor	PA	4 (1916)	1916-1918
03050	Hemsley, Frederick	Radnor	PA	21 (1900; 1905-1906)	1905-1906
06377	Kuhn, C. Hartman	Radnor	PA	11 (1915-1916)	1916-1918
03140	McFadden, J. Franklin	Radnor	PA	28 (1906-1925)	1906-1919
01421	Paul, James Jr.	Radnor	PA	0	1900
06741	Strawbridge, Robert E.	Radnor	PA	39 (1919-1920)	1919-1920
06881	Thomson, Walter S.	Radnor	PA	23 (1920-1921)	1920-1922
07655	Wheeler, Charles	Radnor	PA	19 (1925-1926)	1926
05452	Derr, Cyrus D.	Reading	PA	0	1911
07038	Horst, George D./Host, George D.	Reading	PA	0	1922
05330	Horst, John	Reading	PA	13 (1911-1913)	1911-1913; 1919
09195	Livingood, Dr. John E.	Reading	PA	0	1930
05331	Nolde, Jacob	Reading	PA	8 (1911-1912)	1911-1913; 1926-1927
05433	Austin, William L.	Rosemont	PA	3 (1905-1911)	1911-1912
00326	Converse, John H.	Rosemont	PA	16 (1903-1904)	1903-1904
03564	Gilbert, John W./Red Top	Rydal	PA	5 (1908-1911)	1908-1911
07267	Putt, Frank B.	Rydal	PA	18 (1924)	1923-1927
05884	Harrison, Harry W.	Saint Davids	PA	7 (1915)	1913-1915
03152	Woodward, Dr./Woodward, George/Fairmont Park/Kresheim Valley Drive and Estate	Saint Martin	PA	7 (1906)	1906-1907

Job #	Job Name/Alternative Name	Job Location		Plans	Correspondence
03223	Woodward, George Dr./Krisheim	Saint Martin	PA	416 (1906-1931)	1903-1935; 1966-1968
00317	Fuller, Mortimer B./Fuller, E. L.	Scranton	PA	98 (1903-1917)	1903-1921; 1926-1930
04002	Billquist, T. E.	Sewickley	PA	4 (1910)	1910
09558	Crutchfield, J. S.	Sewickley	PA	0	1938
03124	Lockhart, J. H.	Sewickley	PA	0	
06977	Nicola, George	Sewickley	PA	0	1921
06949	Painter, Charles A./Painter, Charles A. Jr.	Sewickley	PA	34 (1921)	1921;1928
06820	Park, James H.	Sewickley	PA	90 (1906; 1920-1921)	1920-1922
00143	Thaw, William Jr. Mrs.	Sewickley	PA	13 (1901-1916)	1901-1906; 1914-1916
05054	Willock, F. S.	Sewickley	PA	8 (1910-1911)	1910-1911
09339	Wetzel, R. C./Wyomissing	Spring Township	PA	20 (1933)	1933-1934
06855	Holcombe, Annie P.	Troy	PA	0	1920
03577	Bodine, Samuel T./Haas, Otto/Stoneleigh	Villa Nova	PA	175 (1906-1958)	1908-1928; 1937-1940; 1958-1959
06736	Bodine, William W.	Villa Nova	PA	34 (1919-1921; 1928-1929)	1919-1922; 1927-1928
06335	Clothier, Morris L.	Villa Nova	PA	165 (1911; 1916-1920)	1915-1920
01291	DaCosta, Dr. J.M.	Villa Nova	PA	8 (1890-1893)	1893-1894
06708	Harrison, Mrs. Charles C. Jr.	Villa Nova	PA	0	1919-1921
03251	McFadden, George	Villa Nova	PA	66 (1915-1926)	1915-1928
03321	McFadden, George H.	Villa Nova	PA	44 (1912-1919)	1907; 1918-1927
05273	Montgomery, Robert L.	Villa Nova	PA	3 (1911)	1911-1912
00030	Biddle, E. Craig	Wayne	PA	39 (1901-1902)	1900-1916
00286	Biddle, E. Craig	Wayne	PA	0	
03171	Wright, William Townsend	Wayne	PA	5 (1905-1906)	1906
06112	Pyle, Robert	West Grove	PA	2 (1920-1922)	1915-1917; 1922
09377	Huber, C. F.	Wilkes-Barre	PA	13 (1934-1936)	1935-1936
07127	McClintock, G. S./McClintock, Gilbert S.	Wilkes-Barre	PA	3 (1923)	1923-1924; 1951
02895	Henry, Charles W. Mrs./Stonehurst	Wissahickon Heights	PA	35 (1904-1914)	1902-1916
03158	Porter, Charles A.	Wissahickon Heights	PA	0	1906
07791	Martin, J. C.	Wyncastle	PA	8 (1927)	1927-1930
02040	Morgan, Randall/Morgan, Randal	Wyndmeer	PA	3 (1897)	1897; 1916; 1930
07586	Gross, Joseph W.	Wynnewood	PA	29 (1925-1927)	1925-1926
05875	Farr, Bertram H.	Wyomissing	PA	0	1913-1914
07124	Fencel, G. V./Fencil C. V.	Wyomissing	PA	0	1923
06930	Gerry, A. A.	Wyomissing	PA	0	1921
06905	Janssen, Henry	Wyomissing	PA	47 (1919-1926)	1921-1934
06864	Meinig, E. Richard	Wyomissing	PA	116 (1917-1924)	1920-1926; 1931
07252	Mills, Charles A.	Wyomissing	PA	15 (1923-1924)	1923-1925
07109	Moyer, George	Wyomissing	PA	0	1922

Job #	Job Name/Alternative Name	Job Location		Plans	Correspondence
07254	Oberlaender, Gustav	Wyomissing	PA	11 (1923-1924)	1923-1924
06916	Palmer, T. D.	Wyomissing	PA	11 (1921)	1921
06865	Thun, Ferdinand	Wyomissing	PA	1 (1924)	1920; 1924
07668	Client (Unnamed)/Wyomissing Hills Subdivision	Wyomissing Hills	PA	0	1926-1931
06599	Emerton, R. W.	York	PA	13 (1916-1917)	1917-1918
09075	Etnier, C. E./Wyndham Hills	York	PA	33 (1929-931)	1929-1932
03299	Farquhar, A. B.	York	PA	0	1907
02970	Frick, C. C.	York	PA	1 (1904)	1904-1905
05091	Glatfelter, W. L./Glatfelter, William L.	York	PA	44 (1911-1924)	1910-1926; 1932-1944
07244	Hoober, John A./Hoober, John Aaron	York	PA	1 (1923)	1923-1926
03143	Schmidt, George S.	York	PA	6 (1905-1907)	1905-1907
09261	Shipley, W. S	York	PA	54 (1931)	1931-1932
06292	Small, C. M. Miss/Small, Casandra M.	York	PA	13 (1916)	1915-1916
02965	Small, Samuel	York	PA	5 (1900-1909)	1904-1909; 1959
03295	Smith, C. Elmer	York	PA	0	1905-1908

Fairsted, date unknown. Job #673 – F.L. Olmsted Estate/Fairsted (Brookline, MA).

Job #	Job Name/Alternative Name	Job Location		Plans	Correspondence
05967	Field, Frank O.	Barrington	RI	3 (1914)	1914
03151	Hoffman, H. A./Hoffman, Henry A.	Barrington	RI	26 (1906-1919)	1906-1919
00411	Hoffman, William H. - Home	Barrington	RI	130 (1900-1932)	1900-1932
06428	Hoffman, William H./Hoffman, Arnold/ House for son Arnold	Barrington	RI	45 (1911-1921)	1916-1921
10521	Lesselbaum, Dr. & Mrs. Harvey	Barrington	RI	0	1975
07265	Merriman, Isaac B.	Barrington	RI	20 (1923-1924)	1923-1924
10569	Puschin, Mr. & Mrs. A.J.	Barrington	RI	0	1977
05972	Sargent, William P./Sargent, William Parker	Barrington	RI	6 (1914)	1914-1915
03959	Spencer, Everett L./Spence, Everett L.	Barrington	RI	0	1910
07771	McColl, William B.	Bristol	RI	0	1927
07092	Nicholson, Paul C.	Bristol	RI	31 (1924-1934)	1924-1935
10522	Sisson, Mr. & Mrs. George L.	Bristol	RI	0	1975
02286	Smith, J. W.	Cranston	RI	0	
06429	Hodgeman, Mrs. William	East Greenwich	RI	0	1916
07686	Lisle, Arthur B.	East Greenwich	RI	35 (1923-1930)	1926-1930
01144	Pierce, D. A.	East Greenwich	RI	5 (1889)	1889-1894
03451	Dexter, Abbie S.	East Providence	RI	0	1908-1910
07126	Flint, D. W.	Edgewood	RI	0	1923
06776	Arnold, E. E./Arnold, Edward E.	Green	RI	7 (1920)	1919-1924
01033	Schuyler, Miss L. L.	Jamestown	RI	0	1865 (?); 1886-1895
00641	Schuyler, Montgomery/Schuyler, L.L.	Jamestown	RI	26 (1874-1889)	1882-1883
07718	Truesdale, Philemon Dr.	Little Compton	RI	5 (1926-1928)	1924-1928
05976	Behrend, Ernst R. Mrs.	Middletown	RI	15 (1915-1920)	1914-1919
05554	Baldwin, Sarah R. Miss	Narragansett Pier	RI	152 (1912-1924)	1912-1920; 1939
07694	Blanding, P. H.	Nayatt	RI	0	1926
07031	Buker, Henry	Nayatt	RI	11 (1922)	1922
07000	Chafee, Henry/Sharp(e), Henry/Sharpe, Henry D./Chafee, Henry S.	Nayatt	RI	106 (1921-1944)	1921-1950
09322	Coats, A. M./Coats, Alfred M.	Nayatt	RI	1 (1932)	1932
05577	Ballou, F. A./Ballou, Frederick A.	Nayatt Point	RI	11 (1912-1915)	1912-1915; 1939-1940
06145	Watson, Edward L. Mrs.	Nayatt Point	RI	20 (1915-1916)	1915-1916
06172	Abney, Mr.	Newport	RI	0	1915
07090	Aspegren, John	Newport	RI	31 (1922-1932)	1922-1924
03794	Auchincloss, H. D./Auchincloss, Hugh D./Hammersmith Farm	Newport	RI	58 (1909-1946)	1910-1911; 1945-1946; 1977-1978
01726	Brown, Harold	Newport	RI	136 (1894-1927)	1894-1900; 1912-1915; 1926-1927; 1934-1936
01220	Brown, John Nicholas Mrs./Brown, John Nicholas	Newport	RI	151 (1913-1926)	1890-1915
01387	Burden, W. T.	Newport	RI	6 (1893)	1893-1894
01299	Busk, J. R.	Newport	RI	6 (1890-1891)	1890-1892

Job #	Job Name/Alternative Name	Job Location		Plans	Correspondence
12417	Clews, Henry	Newport	RI	0	1886; 1889
00684	Davis, T. M.	Newport	RI	36 (1882-1891)	1882-1884; 1890-1891
01073	Dorsheimer, William	Newport	RI	22 (1885-1886)	1885-1891
05432	Duncan, Stuart	Newport	RI	21 (1911-1926)	1911-1915; 1926
01015	Ellis, J. W.	Newport	RI	40 (1883-1886)	1883-1887
00337	Emery, T. J. Mrs./Emery, Thomas J.	Newport	RI	18 (1902-1908)	1902-1908; 1912
01029	Fiske, J. M.	Newport	RI	45 (1885)	1885-1887
01130	Gammell, Mrs. E.A.	Newport	RI	11 (1888)	1888
01203	Goelet, Ogden	Newport	RI	126 (1888-1893)	1890-1895
05353	Hoffman, Mrs. C. F./Armsea Hall	Newport	RI	0	1911-1918
01808	Hutton, G. M.	Newport	RI	10 (1895)	1893-1895
10309	Ingersoll, Stuart	Newport	RI	5 (1970)	1970
03558	James, Arthur Curtiss	Newport	RI	160 (1908-1921)	1908-1929
07106	Jelke, Ferdinand Frazier	Newport	RI	59 (1922-1924)	1922-1924
03085	King, George Gordon	Newport	RI	10 (1905-1906)	1905-1906; 1922
00257	Mason, Ellen F.	Newport	RI	55 (1882-1920)	1881-1883; 1902-1903; 1919-1925
02261	Olmsted "King Lot"/Olmsted, A. H./Wildacre (in King-Glover tract)	Newport	RI	2 (1900)	1899-1901
02221	Olmsted, A. H.	Newport	RI	14 (1899-1902)	1894; 1899-1916
01225	Perry, M. J./Winans, R. Ross/Perry, Marsden J.	Newport	RI	15 (1892-1893)	1892-1909
01369	Pope, John R./Lippitt, Charles W./Lippitt, C. W.	Newport	RI	112 (1894-1898; 1929-1931)	1892-1898; 1930-1932
01036	Rough Point/Vanderbilt, F. W.	Newport	RI	36 (1887-1890)	1887-1890
00615	Sands, Mahlon	Newport	RI	4 (1879)	1879
00640	Stokes, A. P./Stokes, Anson P./Miantinomi Hill	Newport	RI	12 (1881-1916)	1882-1891; 1915-1918
07161	Taylor, Moses	Newport	RI	45 (1921-1933)	1923-1924
01010	The Misses Jones	Newport	RI	26 (1886-1887)	1886-1887
06268	Wetmore, George Peabody Hon./Chateau-sur-Mer	Newport	RI	12 (1915-1916)	1915-1918
07331	Jones, L. W./Coats, Alfred - old job	Nyatt	RI	12 (1920-1930)	1924-1927
06330	Gallagher, Mathew J.	Pawtucket	RI	0	1916
06561	Goff, D. L. Jr./Goff, Darius	Pawtucket	RI	4 (1917)	1917-1918
06532	Goff, D. L./Goff, Darius L.	Pawtucket	RI	4 (1917)	1917
06629	Lumb, R. W./Lumb, Ralph G.	Pawtucket	RI	3 (1917-1918)	1918
06503	Potter, J. C./Potter, James C.	Pawtucket	RI	4 (1914-1917)	1917
03582	Read, Charles O.	Pawtucket	RI	2 (1905)	1908-1909
06508	Shaw, C. T. Mrs./Shaw, C.T.	Pawtucket	RI	4 (1917)	1917-1918
05520	Steele, Mrs. T. Sedgwick	Pawtucket	RI	0	1912
01202	Hazard, Rowland/Castle Estate	Peace Dale	RI	21 (1892-1894)	1891-1895
07270	Aldred, Arthur L.	Providence	RI	17 (1924-1931)	1924-1932
00335	Arnold, Edward E.	Providence	RI	14 (1903-1916)	1903-1916
03454	Beckwith, Mrs. Daniel	Providence	RI	0	1908

Job #	Job Name/Alternative Name	Job Location		Plans	Correspondence
00604	Brown, J. C./Brown, John Carter	Providence	RI	34 (1890-1895)	1890-1892
07089	Coates, Mrs. Alfred	Providence	RI	0	1922-1932
07672	Coats, A. M./Jackson, Donald E.	Providence	RI	16 (1926-1927; 1948)	1926-1932; 1948
07451	Davis, F. B.	Providence	RI	4 (1925)	1925
07460	DeWolf, Paul C.	Providence	RI	0	1925; 1930
06407	Freeman, John R. Mrs.	Providence	RI	2 (1902; 1916)	1916
02229	Gammel, R. I.	Providence	RI	3 (1899)	1900
01045	Gammell, William	Providence	RI	24 (1888-1892)	1886-1892; 1916
06556	Gladding, John R.	Providence	RI	1 (1917)	1917
00646	Goddard, Col. R.H.J.	Providence	RI	15 (1880-1889)	1886-1895; 1916
01042	Goddard, T. P. I.	Providence	RI	23 (1887-1889)	1886-1890
01126	Harkness, Prof.	Providence	RI	15 (1887-1888)	1887-1891
07988	Hoffman, Harold W.	Providence	RI	4 (1928)	1928-1929
07409	Iselin, C. Oliver Mrs./Iselin, Oliver	Providence	RI	24 (1924-1925)	1925-1929
03694	McColl, J. R./McColl, James R.	Providence	RI	6 (1909-1914)	1909-1915
07062	Metcalf, Mrs. Jesse H.	Providence	RI	0	1922
06739	Nicholson, Paul C.	Providence	RI	65 (1920-1931)	1921-1936
02916	Olney, Frank F.	Providence	RI	0	1903
02397	Perry, Marsden	Providence	RI	2 (1903-1904)	1903-1905
01028	Russell, H. G.	Providence	RI	14 (1885-1886)	1885-1890; 1939
07131	Spencer, E. L.	Providence	RI	11 (1922)	1922-1923
01093	Sturgis, H. O. Estate	Providence	RI	18 (1889-1890)	1885-1891
03690	Welsh, Edward L./Shadow Farm	Wakefield	RI	7 (1909-1911)	1909-1913
06074	Gerry, Peter G.	Warwick	RI	0	1914-1916
06730	Curtis, F. R.	Watch Hill	RI	0	1919
06766	Grant, J. P.	Watch Hill	RI	6 (1919-1920)	1919-1921
06651	Mellon, R. B.	Watch Hill	RI	45 (1916-1930)	1918-1919; 1929-1932
09232	Scaife, Alan M. Mrs./Scaife, Alan M.	Watch Hill	RI	6 (1930)	1930-1931
06069	Starkweather, J. U.	West Barrington	RI	0	
07854	Tully, William J.	West Barrington	RI	13 (1927-1930)	1927-1931
07083	Dunn, H. T.	Westerly	RI	0	1922
06717	Milner, Harry B./Wilner, Harry R.	Westerly	RI	2 (1919-1920)	1919-1921
06899	Ward, Wilfred/Sherman, Chas.	Westerly	RI	29 (1920-1926)	1920-1923
09918	Darman, Arthur I.	Woonsocket	RI	79 (1951-1955)	1951-1956
03457	Jenks, Mrs.	Woonsocket	RI	0	1908
00056	Smith, Stanley G./Rathbun, E. H. and Stanley G. Smith	Woonsocket	RI	3 (1902)	1902
05279	Schiller, W. B./Boykin, Newton C.	Camden	SC	10 (1911-1913)	1911-1914; 1923
09259	Archbald, Joseph A/Yeamans Hall	Charleston	SC	9 (1931)	1931
09205	Coe, W. R./Coe, William R./Cherokee Plantation	Charleston	SC	4 (1930)	1930-1935
09302	Colt, Samuel G./Yeamans Hall	Charleston	SC	5 (1931)	1931

Job #	Job Name/Alternative Name	Job Location		Plans	Correspondence
09213	Hartford, Edward V. Mrs./Hartford, Edward V./Wando Plantation	Charleston	SC	306 (1909-1940)	1930-1946
09260	Mason, George G./Mason, George Grant/Yeamans Hall	Charleston	SC	9 (1927; 1931)	1931
09287	McFaddin, Harrison D./Yeamans Hall	Charleston	SC	4 (1931)	1931-1932
09279	Milbank, Dunlevy/Yeamans Hall	Charleston	SC	5 (1931)	1931
09130	Robertson, Hugh S./Yeamans Hall	Charleston	SC	11 (1929)	1929
09252	Wiggin, Albert H./Yeamans Hall	Charleston	SC	19 (1929-1932)	1930-1932
05094	Urquhart, James B.	Columbia	SC	0	1910-1911
09105	Goose Creek Estates/Stuart, Francis Lee	New Charleston	SC	28 (1925-1930)	1929-1931
02957	Cherry, J. M.	Rock Hill	SC	0	1904
03115	Hastre, Mrs. William S./Magnolia on the Ashley/Hastie, Julia Drayton	Runnymede	SC	0	1906
06964	Reynolds, E. R.	Bristol	TN	0	1921
03082	Montague, D. P.	Chattanooga	TN	17 (1905-1907)	1905-1907
07253	Olmsted, Roland W.	Chattanooga	TN	33 (1923-1927)	1923-1927; 1936; 1978
09569	Rawlings, B. M./Fairyland/Subdivision	Chattanooga	TN	0	1937-1940
09782	Hunter, E. G.	Kingsport	TN	4 (1947)	1947-1953
07241	Sanford, A. F.	Knoxville	TN	71 (1923-1930)	1923-1939
07734	Sanford, Hugh	Knoxville	TN	23 (1927)	1926-1927
06078	Strong, R. R.	Knoxville	TN	0	1914
05501	Bradford, James C./Franklin Pike	Nashville	TN	0	1912
07637	Farrell, Herbert	Nashville	TN	30 (1925-1928)	1926-1931; 1950
03131	Felder, Thomas J.	Nashville	TN	6 (1906)	1906
09802	Kerrigan, Philip Jr.	Nashville	TN	34 (1948-1954)	1947-1954
07825	Shwab, J. Briant	Nashville	TN	0	1927
07041	Aldredge, Mrs. George M.	Dallas	TX	0	1922
07739	Camp, Alex	Dallas	TX	26 (1926-1927)	1926-1963
08261	Neal, J. Robert	Houston	TX	219 (1921-1932)	1930-1939
05450	Withers, John T.	San Antonio	TX	0	1911-1912
04071	Neale, W. J./Waco Park/Neals, W. J.	Waco	TX	0	1910
07404	Littleton, Frank C.	Aldie	VA	2 (1921; 1925)	1925-1927
09319	Rinehart, W. A.	Charlottesville	VA	27 (1932-1933)	1932-1934
09311	Lambert, Gerard B./Carter Hall	Clarke County	VA	39 (1930-1932)	1932-1934
07350	Peter, G. F./Peter, G. Freeland	Cobham	VA	15 (1924-1929)	1924-1928
06000	Hertle, Louis/Gunston Hall	Fairfax County	VA	0	1914
06497	Baldwin, F. C.	Fredericksburg	VA	0	1917
06221	McLean, Edward B.	Leesburg	VA	0	1915-1916
02978	Rontzahn, E. G./Routzahn, E. G.	Richmond	VA	0	1904
07129	Grasty, J. H. C./Cottage Park	Staunton	VA	1 (1923)	1923-1925
07699	Woodward, Edward	Staunton	VA	1 (1923-1926)	1926
02982	Coolidge, Archibald	Tuckahoe	VA	0	1904
05264	Everett, E. H.	Bennington	VT	6 (1911)	1911

Job #	Job Name/Alternative Name	Job Location		Plans	Correspondence
07371	Clark, Julian B./Overlake Park	Burlington	VT	23 (1881; 1925)	1924-1925; 1946-1947
07397	Cowles, Clarence P.	Burlington	VT	1 (1925)	1924-1926; 1952
01167	Holt, Henry/Fairholt	Burlington	VT	91 (1890-1937)	1890-1897; 1908-1931; 1936-1941
01031	Webb, William Seward/Shelburne Farms	Burlington	VT	37 (1886-1889)	1886-1891; 1979
09588	Allen, Sherman Vail	Fair Haven	VT	0	1939
03167	Clark, C. M. - Wyndhurst/Clark, Clarence M.	Manchester	VT	10 (1906-1916)	1906-1916; 1926-1928
09688	Flower, Henry C. Jr.	Manchester	VT	33 (1930-1945)	1944-1947
00437	Harvey, G. S./Harvey, George L.	Manchester	VT	0	1902
09671	Lambert, Gerard B.	Manchester	VT	29 (1944-1945)	1944-1964
09005	Dunsmore, W. Rowland	Proctor	VT	6 (1928-1929)	1928-1930
07839	Fletcher, Allen M. Mrs./Charlton, Mary Fletcher	Proctorsville	VT	6 (1927)	1927; 1972-1980
10164	Babbott, Dr Frank L. Jr	Shelburn	VT	11 (1963-1964)	1963-1964
06237	Brown, W. W.	Springfield	VT	0	1915
05448	Jones, Frank A.	Aberdeen	WA	0	1911
03725	Griggs, Everett G.	American Lake	WA	4 (1910-1923)	1909-1911; 1922-1923
03494	Thorne, Chester	American Lake	WA	41 (1908-1911)	1908-1915; 1930; 1938

Biltmore estate grounds (Biltmore Village), date unknown. Job #170 – George W. Vanderbilt/Biltmore (Asheville, NC).

Job #	Job Name/Alternative Name	Job Location		Plans	Correspondence
03877	Bolcom, W. M./Bolcom, William	Ballard	WA	0	1910-1911
06635	Gordon, E. M.	Bellevue	WA	0	1918
06171	Dunn, Arthur G.	Bitter Lake	WA	20 (1914-1916)	1915-1916
03355	Trimble, W. P.	Blake Island	WA	0	1907
09281	Bonnell, J. J. Nursery	Bryn Mawr	WA	4 (1931)	1931
03720	Spanton Company, The/Subdivision of former Poor Farm Tract	Multnomah County	WA	0	1909
03273	Moran, Robert	Orcas Island	WA	3 (1906-1907)	1907-1909
03421	Donworth, George	Port Orchard Bay	WA	3 (1908)	1907-1908
03723	Anderson, A. H.	Port William	WA	3 (1908-1909)	1909
06075	Agen, John B.	Seattle	WA	33 (1915-1916)	1914-1920; 1940
05971	Arnold, M. A./Highlands/Arnold, N.A	Seattle	WA	30 (1910-1927)	1914-1916; 1927-1929
03717	Backus, M. F./Country Club	Seattle	WA	10 (1909-1917)	1903-1909; 1917-1919
08217	Bailargeon, C. J.	Seattle	WA	10 (1929)	1928-1929
03871	Baker, B. W.	Seattle	WA	0	1909; 1914
03204	Baker, F. W.	Seattle	WA	0	1906
06692	Ballinger, J. H./Highlands	Seattle	WA	30 (1919-1929)	1919-1930; 1936; 1957
03956	Beaton, Wilford	Seattle	WA	0	
08245	Beck, B. C.	Seattle	WA	0	1929-1930
03168	Black, C. H.	Seattle	WA	19 (1907)	1906-1909
05877	Boeing, W. E./The Highlands	Seattle	WA	6 (1913)	1914-1916
06798	Bogle, Lawrence/The Highlands	Seattle	WA	2 (1920)	1920
05859	Bolcom, H. S./Bolcom, Harry S.	Seattle	WA	6 (1913)	1913-1917
03324	Burke, Thomas/Seattle Country Club/estate in Seattle Golf and Country Club	Seattle	WA	2 (1908)	1907-1909; 1915
03490	Clarke, C. H./Clarke, Charles H./estate in Highlands subdivision	Seattle	WA	0	1908-1912
03592	Clise, J. W.	Seattle	WA	14 (1906-1909)	1908-1909; 1978
04082	Conner, Herbert S.	Seattle	WA	3 (1909-1910)	1910
04081	Donahue, M.	Seattle	WA	0	1910
08091	Douglas, J. F./Highlands	Seattle	WA	40 (1927-1929)	1927-1929
08092	Douglas, Walter T./Day, Lew V./Highlands	Seattle	WA	73 (1927-1929; 1935)	1927-1940
03718	Edwards, J. H. & Smith, W. R.	Seattle	WA	2 (1909-1910)	1908-1910
03875	Farnsworth, Clare/Farnsworth, Clare E.	Seattle	WA	4 (1909-1910)	1909-1910
03425	Farrell, J. D.	Seattle	WA	6 (1908)	1908
05095	Force, Ridgely	Seattle	WA	1 (1911)	1911
06712	Foster, Newton	Seattle	WA	0	1919
05788	Frederick, D. E.	Seattle	WA	201 (1913-1933)	1912-1922; 1929-1939; 1953-1959
04083	Frink, J. M.	Seattle	WA	3 (1910)	1910-1915
09552	Garrett, Edward I./Highlands/The Highlands	Seattle	WA	13 (1927-1939)	1934-1942
08208	Garrett, Lewis Edward	Seattle	WA	2 (1928)	1926-1930

Job #	Job Name/Alternative Name	Job Location		Plans	Correspondence
05888	Hambach, A.	Seattle	WA	0	1913
03872	Hamm, David	Seattle	WA	1 (1910)	1909-1910
05787	Heffernan, J. T./Bush School	Seattle	WA	12 (1912-1915)	1912-1915
03499	Heineman, M. C.	Seattle	WA	4 (1908)	1908-1912
03205	Hill, Samuel	Seattle	WA	0	1906
03870	Hoge, James D.	Seattle	WA	6 (1910)	1909-1910; 1919
03873	Hughes, E. C.	Seattle	WA	3 (1909-1910)	1909-1911
04070	Hyde, Samuel	Seattle	WA	4 (1910)	1910-1911
06217	Jones, Ray W./Wight, M. F.	Seattle	WA	0	1915
03206	Jones, W. G.	Seattle	WA	0	1906
03724	Kerry, A. S.	Seattle	WA	5 (1908-1910)	1909-1912
08075	Krauss, Arthur J. Mrs.	Seattle	WA	33 (1926-1931)	1927-1939
03207	Leary, Mrs. John	Seattle	WA	0	1906
05911	Lewis, L. D.	Seattle	WA	4 (1914)	1913-1915
03878	Merrill, R. D.	Seattle	WA	35 (1909-1914)	1912-1915; 1924
06002	Merrill, R. D. - City Home	Seattle	WA	6 (1914-1924)	1914-1915; 1924-1929
08221	Milburn, Anna	Seattle	WA	19 (1928-1931)	1928-1935
06089	Moss, D. H./The Highlands	Seattle	WA	14 (1914-1916)	1914-1917
06619	Ostrander, H. F./Gunn, George	Seattle	WA	7 (1913; 1917; 1946)	1917-1920
08242	Paine, Alexander B.	Seattle	WA	14 (1929-1930)	1929-1930
04053	Peterson, Peter	Seattle	WA	0	1910
06056	Phillips, W. R.	Seattle	WA	0	1914
03208	Sheffield, W. M.	Seattle	WA	0	1906
03589	Smith, C. J.	Seattle	WA	3 (1909)	1909
03446	Spooner, Charles P.	Seattle	WA	0	1907
03709	Stewart, A. B. Country Club	Seattle	WA	14 (1909-1913)	1909-1913; 1925-1928
03491	Stimson, C. D./Estate in Highlands subdivision	Seattle	WA	12 (1909-1921)	1908-1913; 1921
03590	Stimson, F. S./Stimson, T.D./Stimson, F. L./Stimson, Thomas D.	Seattle	WA	28 (1908-1939)	1908-1909; 1921-1923; 1938-1939
03447	Struve, F. K.	Seattle	WA	0	
03210	Upper, H. S.	Seattle	WA	0	
06364	Whitcomb, David/Arcade Building & Realty Company	Seattle	WA	5 (1917)	1916-1917
05278	White, C. F./Bullitt, A. Scott/Highlands	Seattle	WA	15 (1911-1922)	1911-1914; 1922-1928
05676	Wight, M. F.	Seattle	WA	10 (1891-1913)	1912-1913
03354	Brown, David/Estate in Rockwood subdivision	Spokane	WA	7 (1907-1909)	1907-1921
03587	Coman, T. E./Coman, Edwin T.	Spokane	WA	1 (1908-1909)	1908-1909
03813	Cowles, W. H.	Spokane	WA	7 (1909-1912)	1909-1912
03427	Davenport, L. M.	Spokane	WA	28 (1908-1910)	1908-1911; 1922
08055	Davenport, L. M./Little Spokane River/Country Place on Little Spokane River	Spokane	WA	44 (1925-1926)	1908-1911; 1925-1931
03641	Finncane, F. J./Finucane, F. J.	Spokane	WA	0	1909-1913

Job #	Job Name/Alternative Name	Job Location		Plans	Correspondence
04085	Galland, S.	Spokane	WA	1 (1910)	1910-1911
08068	Goodwin, E. S.	Spokane	WA	4 (1926)	1926-1927
08059	Gordon, B.L. Mrs. Farm	Spokane	WA	10 (1915; 1925-1926)	1925-1926
04007	Grant, A. E.	Spokane	WA	0	
03879	Graves, J. Ranch/Waikiki Ranch/Graves, Jay P./Waikiki Farm	Spokane	WA	24 (1909-1914)	1909-1915
04005	Ham, D. J.	Spokane	WA	0	
05800	Hansen, C. T.	Spokane	WA	0	1912
06506	Humbird, T. J.	Spokane	WA	3 (1917)	1917
04059	Jones, C. H.	Spokane	WA	7 (1911)	1910-1911; 1935
08067	Leuthold, W. M.	Spokane	WA	15 (1926)	1926-1927
03638	Martin, F. N.	Spokane	WA	0	1909
05096	Mason, Fred	Spokane	WA	0	1910-1912
06188	Mathews, C. L./Matthews, Charles L.	Spokane	WA	0	1915
03736	McGoldrick, J. F.	Spokane	WA	0	1909
03350	Paine, James L.	Spokane	WA	5 (1910-1912)	1907-1914
03639	Pfile, J. W.	Spokane	WA	0	1909
05801	Porter, J. D.	Spokane	WA	0	1912-1913
09370	Powell, W. W./Powell, William	Spokane	WA	56 (1931-1936)	1933-1938
03360	Richards, J. P. M./estate in Pettet subdivision	Spokane	WA	1 (1907)	1907
04006	Ryland, A. S.	Spokane	WA	0	
05490	Sherwood, J. D.	Spokane	WA	6 (1912)	1912-1913
05262	Traver, Alice C.	Spokane	WA	0	1911
05261	Turner, Senator	Spokane	WA	0	1911
05499	Twohy, D. W.	Spokane	WA	2 (1912)	1912
03550	White, A. L. Mrs. Ranch/White, Aubrey L.	Spokane	WA	1 (1907-1908)	1908-1912; 1932
05455	White, A. L./Brown Addition	Spokane	WA	8 (1911-1912)	1911-1925
03109	White, A. L./White, Aubrey L.	Spokane	WA	3 (1906-1908)	
03552	White, Aubrey L.	Spokane	WA	0	1908
04086	Witherspoon, A. W.	Spokane	WA	0	1910
03416	Blattner, F. S.	Tacoma	WA	0	1907-1914
03422	Rust, William R.	Tacoma	WA	0	1907-1908
07014	Weyerhaeuser, J. P./Weyerhauser, J. P.	Tacoma	WA	98 (1922-1923)	1922-1923
03874	Wilkinson, Samuel	Tacoma	WA	0	1909
03211	Fletcher, A. H.	Walla Walla	WA	0	1906
03239	Langden, John W.	Walla Walla	WA	0	1906
03217	Webb, John	Walla Walla	WA	0	1906
09888	Stone, Stanley	Fox Point	WI	15 (1949-1950)	1950
07351	Kohler, Walter/Kohler, Walter J.	Kohler	WI	123 (1920-1925)	1924-1925; 1934-1935; 1947-1949
01420	Ayer, Edward E.	Lake Geneva	WI	0	1901
03038	Bartlett, A. C./Leiter Property	Lake Geneva	WI	9 (1905-1906)	1905-1907

Job #	Job Name/Alternative Name	Job Location		Plans	Correspondence
05679	Countiss, Frederick H.	Lake Geneva	WI	0	1912
03744	Harris, Albert W.	Lake Geneva	WI	0	1909-1911
05776	Harris, N. W./30 Acre Farm	Lake Geneva	WI	0	1912
03040	Harris, N. W./Leiter Property	Lake Geneva	WI	16 (1904-1915)	1902-1914
00416	Hutchinson, C. L.	Lake Geneva	WI	7 (1901-1902)	1896; 1901-1904
00276	Linn, W. R.	Lake Geneva	WI	5 (1902)	
02287	Ryerson, Martin/Bonnie Brae	Lake Geneva	WI	12 (1902-1903)	1895; 1902-1903
00201	Young, Mr. Otto	Lake Geneva	WI	0	1900
09125	Sensenbrenner, F. J.	Lake Winnebago	WI	281 (1928-1937)	1929-1938; 1943
12163	Roby, Sydney	Madison	WI	2 (N.D.)	1890-1893
00082	Stout, J. H.	Menomonie	WI	7 (1895-1896)	1894-1896
06244	Brown, Victor/Brown, Victor L.	Milwaukee	WI	0	1915-1916
02384	Christensen, N. A.	Milwaukee	WI	3 (1902)	1902-1905
06255	Goodrich	Milwaukee	WI	0	
06245	Hayssen, Robert/Green, Nathanael	Milwaukee	WI	0	1915
06176	Plankinton, William W./Plankinton, William Woods	Milwaukee	WI	0	1915-1916
07368	Kohler, J. M. Mrs./Kohler, J.M.	Sheboygan	WI	9 (1924-1925)	1924-1925
10582	Gallagher, Mr. & Mrs. Robert	Beckley	WV	0	1971-1976
05809	VanRensselaer, Mrs. Eugene/Van Rensselaer, Eugene/Fruit Hill Tract	Berkeley Springs	WV	3 (1916)	1912-1916
06894	Kingdom, Arthur T.	Bluefield	WV	126 (1922-1928)	1919
07168	Bierne, Samuel	Huntington	WV	0	1923
06738	McKinley, J. C. Mrs./McKinley, J.C.	Wheeling	WV	16 (1916-1919)	1919-1920
	CANADA				
09461	Aubeneu, Henry	Vancouver	BC	0	1936-1938
05381	Marpole, C. M./Marpole, Clarence M.	Vancouver	BC	2 (1911)	1911-1912
09402	Taylor, A. J. T. - Kew Beach House	Vancouver	BC	0	
03419	Dunsmeir, Lord/Dunsmuir, James	Victoria	BC	0	1907-1911
05815	Rogers, B. T.	Victoria	BC	7 (1913)	1913
09403	Taylor, A. J. T. - Glen Eagles	West Vancouver	BC	0	1944
09401	Taylor, A. J. T./British Pacific Properties	West Vancouver	BC	69 (1935-1936)	1935-1936
09666	Taylor, A. J. T./Capilano Heights	West Vancouver	BC	13 (1944)	1944-1946
09400	Taylor, Austin C.	West Vancouver	BC	15 (1935)	1935-1936
05057	Byerley, Ralph Reed	Winnipeg	MB	0	1910
03819	Doupe, J. L./Doupe, J. Lonsdale	Winnipeg	MB	4 (1909)	1909
03955	Glines, George A.	Winnipeg	MB	0	1910
05856	Jukes, H. A.	Winnipeg	MB	0	1913
06744	Loring, Robert	Saint Andrews	NB	13 (1919-1920)	1919-1922
06770	Wilson, Norman Mrs.	Saint Andrews	NB	8 (1919)	1919-1920
05775	Rieder, T. H.	Berlin	ON	0	1912
00203	Wilks, E. L./Wilkes, Langdon	Blair	ON	3 (1902)	1902

Job #	Job Name/Alternative Name	Job Location		Plans	Correspondence
00185	Fulford, G. T.	Brockville	ON	10 (1897-1931)	1896-1902; 1914; 1931
06333	Grant, Harry G.	Clark Hill	ON	0	1916-1917
06734	Hamilton Harbor Commissioners	Hamilton	ON	0	1919
00348	McCagg, T. D. Mrs./McCagg, E.B.	Murray Bay	ON	4 (1899)	1869-1876; 1888; 1899-1904
05871	Ryrie, Harry	Oakville	ON	0	1913
00026	Flavelle, J. W.	Toronto	ON	6 (1901-1902)	1901-1903
07877	Gundy, J. H.	Toronto	ON	1 (1927)	1927-1928
07882	Hunter, Horace T.	Toronto	ON	16 (1904-1929)	1927-1929
00069	Janes, S.H.	Toronto	ON	21 (1890-1891)	1890-1891
06722	Maclean, J. B. Col./MacLean, John B.	Toronto	ON	119 (1920-1929)	1919-1929
00446	Nicholls, Frederick	Toronto	ON	0	1901
00051	Pellatt, H. M. Col./Davenport Hill	Toronto	ON	1 (N.D.)	1901-1902
00433	Small, John T.	Toronto	ON	0	1902
09013	Tyrrell, H. V.	Toronto	ON	18 (1928-1929)	1928-1930
09256	Vaughan, J. J./Culham, Gordon	Toronto	ON	0	1926-1934
10702	Gilday, Mr. & Mrs. Angus M.	Brome	QC	0	1899; 1979
10655	Gales, Mr. & Mrs. D. Lorne	Como	QC	0	1978
00232	MacDougall, Hartland	Dorval	QC	4 (1899)	1899
10705	Peterson, Mr. & Mrs. H.J.L.	Hudson	QC	0	
10703	McKenna, Mrs. Richard	Magog	QC	0	1979
00214	Angus, R. B.	Montreal	QC	105 (1899-1902)	1898-1903
05254	Burland, Colonel Jeffrey	Montreal	QC	0	1911
10656	Hale, Mr. & Mrs. John	Montreal	QC	0	1978
00057	Ross, James	Montreal	QC	4 (1899)	1899-1900
10704	Courtois, Mr. & Mrs. Jacques	North Hatley	QC	0	
00157	Clouston, E. S.	Saint Anne's	QC	5 (1899)	1899
00180	Forget, L. J.	Sainte Anne-de-Bellevue	QC	7 (1899-1900)	1899-1901; 1906
07154	Mitchell, Mrs. James S.	Sherbrooke	QC	0	1923
00132	Ross, W. G.	Woodlands	QC	4 (1899-1900)	1899-1901

OTHER COUNTRIES

Job #	Job Name/Alternative Name	Job Location		Plans	Correspondence
06065	Olmsted, F. L./Daniels' Head Property	Daniels' Head	BER	2 (1914)	1911-1923
07217	Roosevelt, George	Tuckers Town	BER	13 (1923-1924)	1924
01017	Cadogan Estates	London	ENG	1 (N.D.)	
03011	Rayner, Dr. Henry/Hampstead	London	ENG	0	1892
09396	Taylor, A. J. T.	London	ENG	4 (1935)	
03401	Workman, Mrs. Giles - Cottage/Abinger Common	Surrey	ENG	0	

Model of the Masonic Memorial to George Washington, date unknown. Job #6991 – Masonic Memorial (Alexandria, VA).

Background: Detail of general plan of Hillside Cemetery, June 1909. Job #3277 – Hillside Cemetery Association (Torrington, CT).

Cemeteries, Burial Lots, Memorials and Monuments

Arleyn A. Levee

While the Olmsted firm provided designs for the settings of monuments of all types — in parks, public squares and other locations — the majority of the 275 projects (approximately 200 with at least one plan) in this thematic category relate to cemeteries and to individual burial lots, with the latter predominating. Most of these commissions took place in the 1920s. Designing landscaped grounds for the final resting places for many clients was an appropriate extension of the Olmsted firm's work, as the home grounds, businesses and philanthropic endeavors of many of these individuals or families had been similarly graced by the Olmsted landscape aesthetic. Likewise, many of the monument and memorial projects not involving cemeteries were the result of work done on other commissions. In particular, the prominence of Frederick Law Olmsted Jr. in the emerging discipline of city planning and his work for the Fine Arts Commission in Washington, D.C., especially after World War I, brought clients to the firm seeking tasteful solutions or redesigns for civic memorials.

The Olmsted firm designed very few cemeteries as complete, separate new projects. Frederick Law Olmsted set forth his concerns about cemeteries in his 1865 *Preface to the Plan for Mountain View Cemetery, Oakland, CA.* For him there was an inherent conflict in creating a place of suitable expression of "those feelings, sentiments and aspirations which religion and civilization make common to all in the presence of the dead" and achieving his ideal of landscape beauty where the ground was of necessity "cut up" into small divisions.[1] As he later wrote to English landscape gardener William Robinson, "[I]f art should do anything in a place of rest for our dead it should produce an impression of restfulness.... I do not think I could lay out a burial place without making conditions about monuments such as I fear few but Quakers would be willing to accept."[2]

Mountain View Cemetery in Oakland, California, was the major project of this sort that Olmsted undertook, beginning in 1864, with subsequent design work by the Olmsted Brothers in the 1940s. Among the examples of Olmsted Brothers cemetery projects were Hillside Cemetery in Torrington, Connecticut, and North Purchase Cemetery in Attleboro, Massachusetts. After World War II, the firm designed the American Military Cemetery in Cambridge, England. The later firm of Olmsted Associates designed Puritan Lawn Memorial Park, in West Peabody, Massachusetts, a project that had started during the Depression but was fully developed in the late 1950s-1960s.

However, most of the Olmsted firm's work involved improvements or additions to existing landscapes, some of these being nineteenth century rural cemeteries, which required expansion or accommodation to meet twentieth century needs, such as automobiles. The firm made extensive additions to the Memorial Cemetery of Saint John's Church (listed as Saint John's Memorial Cemetery) in Cold Spring Harbor and to Locust Valley Cemetery, both on Long Island, New York; to Pittsfield Cemetery in Pittsfield, Massachusetts; to Kingsport Cemetery in Kingsport, Tennessee; and to the Charles Evans Cemetery in Reading, Pennsylvania. The firm also designed private cemetery grounds or tombs for several of their prominent clients such as the Kohler family in Kohler, Wisconsin; the Vanderbilt family in New Dorp on Staten Island, New York; and the Rockefeller family at Pocantico, New York, (listed as Tarrytown). In some cases, these projects are incorporated under the residential estate job number, rather than being listed as a separate project. Likewise, there are cemetery grounds incorporated into some of the Olmsted Brothers' campus planning, such as that for Phillips Academy in Andover, Massachusetts, and for Mount Holyoke College in South Hadley, Massachusetts.

As John Charles Olmsted wrote in a series of articles in *Garden & Forest* published in 1888, cemeteries should be spaces set apart for the prime purpose of memorializing the dead in a respectful, contemplative setting. The Olmsted design credo of integrated whole compositions subordinating component elements, such as structures, within the landscape's comprehensive aesthetic was particularly challenged to create an artistic unity over all the heterogeneous individual units inevitable in a cemetery. Using plant groupings and working within topographic irregularities wherever possible, firm employees shaped burial lots into individual family "rooms" for dignified privacy, best exemplified by the lots for prominent clients such

Right: Plan for Mountain View Cemetery, date unknown. Job #9685 – Mountain View Cemetery (Oakland, CA). See also Job #12118.

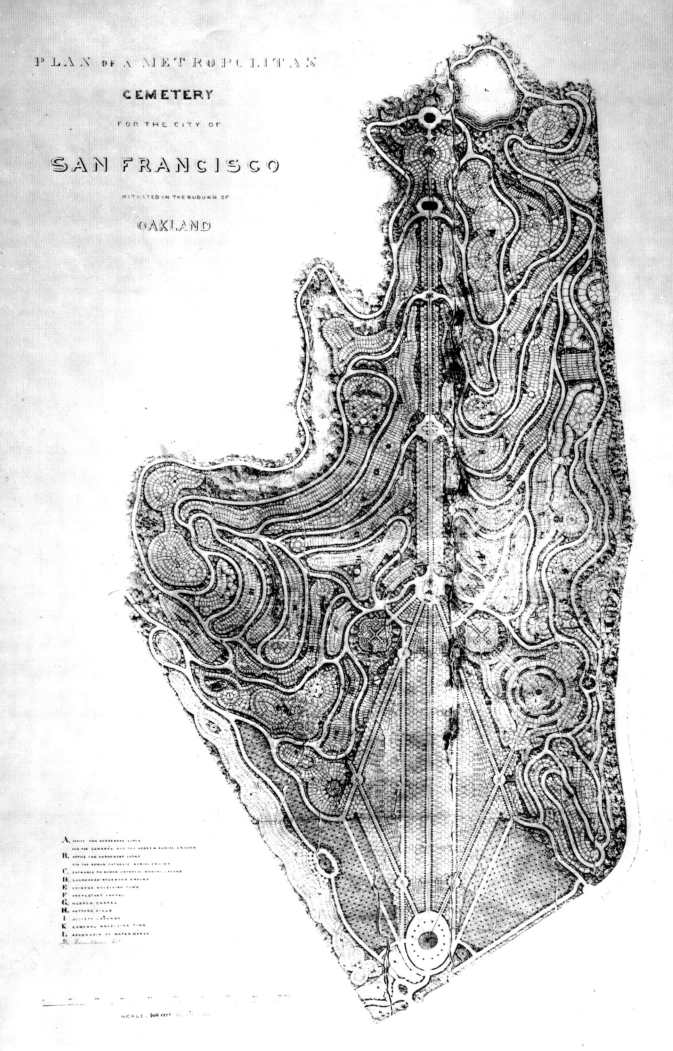

PLAN OF A METROPOLITAN

CEMETERY

FOR THE CITY OF

SAN FRANCISCO

SITUATED IN THE SUBURB OF

OAKLAND

A. OFFICE AND GARDENERS LODGE
    FOR THE GENERAL AND THE HEBREW BURIAL GROUND
B. OFFICE AND GARDENERS LODGE
    FOR THE ROMAN CATHOLIC BURIAL GROUND
C. ENTRANCE TO ROMAN CATHOLIC BURIAL GROUND
D. GARDENERS RESERVED GROUND
E. CHINESE RECEIVING TOMB
F. PROTESTANT CHAPEL
G. HEBREW CHAPEL
H. POTTERS FIELD
I. SOCIETY GROUNDS
K. CENTRAL RECEIVING TOMB
L. RESERVOIR OF WATER WORKS

SCALE 400 FEET

Laura Spelman Rockefeller Memorial at Great Smoky Mountains National Park, November 27, 1939. Job #9516 – Laura Spelman Rockefeller Memorial (Gatlinburg, TN).

as the De Forests, the Coes, J. P. Morgan and others in the Long Island cemeteries, including those at Cold Spring, Cold Spring Harbor and Locust Valley.

In a similar fashion, the Olmsted work for civic monuments and memorials involved the integration of the various structures into appropriate settings, either as individual focal units or within a park landscape. Some of this work involved statuary settings, such as the War Memorials at Capron Park in Attleboro, Massachusetts, and the Francis Scott Key Monument in Baltimore, Maryland. Other projects concerned the surrounds of prominent structures as in the Masonic Memorial to George Washington in Alexandria, Virginia, and the Laura Spelman Rockefeller Memorial at Great Smoky Mountains National Park in Gatlinburg, Tennessee. Moreover, not all memorial projects are listed in this thematic category (e.g., Memorial Hall in North Easton, Massachusetts, which is listed in the category Grounds of Public Buildings), so research inevitably involves making creative links to associated categories and projects.

See Introductory Guide on pages 33-35 for information on the use of this list.

Cemeteries, Burial Lots, Memorials and Monuments

Job #	Job Name/Alternative Name	Job Location		Plans	Correspondence
06696	War Memorials other than professional or numbered works			0	

UNITED STATES

Job #	Job Name/Alternative Name	Job Location		Plans	Correspondence
08315	Donner Monument/California State Parks	Donner County	CA	0	
08314	Marshall's Monument/California State Parks	El Dorado County	CA	0	
06878	National Cemetery Association	Los Angeles	CA	0	1920
09685	Mountain View Cemetery	Oakland	CA	12 (1872; 1944-1949)	1938; 1944-1949
12118	Mountain View Cemetery	Oakland	CA	0	1864-1868; 1871; 1874; 1884-1894; 1921
01140	Sharon Mausoleum/Laurel Hill Cemetery/Sharon, G. W.	San Francisco	CA	4 (1890)	1890; 1894
09223	Bryant, Waldo C. Cemetery Lot/Bryant, W. C.	Bridgeport	CT	11 (1930)	1930-1932
06210	Mountain Grove Cemetery Association	Bridgeport	CT	1 (1915)	1915
09963	Field, John Burial Lot	Fairfield	CT	3 (1953)	1953-1955
06411	Jennings Cemetery Lot	Fairfield	CT	1 (1916)	
01891	Colt Memorial	Hartford	CT	4 (1895-1896)	1895-1896
07477	Connecticut State Capitol/Burr Memorial	Hartford	CT	205 (1925-1931)	1925-1932; 1944
09583	Dillon Memorial - Saint Francis Hospital	Hartford	CT	119 (1938-1952)	1939-1953
00812	Keney Memorial	Hartford	CT	8 (1897)	1897-1898
02933	Olmsted Tomb - North Cemetery/Olmsted Family Burial Vault	Hartford	CT	34 (1958-1959)	1907; 1919-1921; 1930-1932; 1948-1967
09305	Alvord, Mrs. Charles H. - Burial Lot/Hillside Cemetery	Litchfield	CT	0	1932
05275	Cunningham, Seymour Cemetery Lot	Litchfield	CT	3 (1911)	1911
07256	Cedar Grove Cemetery/The New London Cemetery Association	New London	CT	68 (1923-1966)	1922-1925; 1941-1969
09359	Bryant, T. W. Mrs. Burial Lot/Bryant, Thomas W.	Torrington	CT	17 (1934)	1934-1935
07145	Doughty Cemetery Lot/Doughty, Marion/Burial Lot Hillside Memorial	Torrington	CT	25 (1922-1924)	1922-1925; 1931; 1938
06001	Fuessenich, F. F. Cemetery Lot/Fuessenich, Frederick F./Burial Lot/Hillside Cemetery	Torrington	CT	2 (1914)	1914
06959	Fyler Burial Lot/Flyer, O .R./Burial Lot in Hillside Cemetery	Torrington	CT	7 (1921-1922)	1921-1922
03277	Hillside Cemetery Association	Torrington	CT	100 (1907-1969)	1907-1937; 1943-1980
04001	Migeon et al. Cemetery Lots/Swayze Memorial/Hillside Cemetery	Torrington	CT	53 (1909-1931)	1909-1912
09799	Reid, W. R. Cemetery Lot	Torrington	CT	1 (1947)	1947-1948
05523	Swayze Memorial/Migeon Cemetery Lot/Hillside Cemetery/Migeon, Elizabeth	Torrington	CT	16 (1909-1931)	1913-1918; 1931-1936
07690	Turner, L. G. Cemetery Lot/Burial Lot Hillside Cemetery	Torrington	CT	1 (1927)	1926-1928

Job #	Job Name/Alternative Name	Job Location		Plans	Correspondence
03750	Turner, Luther G.	Torrington	CT	0	1909
09329	Calvary Cemetery/Roman Catholic Cemetery	Waterbury	CT	23 (1932-1933)	1932-1933
06965	Chase Burial Lot, Riverside Cemetery/Chase, F. S.	Waterbury	CT	7 (1920-1923)	1921-1923
02838	Grant Monument	Washington	DC	15 (1907)	1906-1908; 1920
02847	Roosevelt Memorial/Roosevelt Memorial Association	Washington	DC	19 (1925)	1919-1926; 1934-1937
02848	Washington Monument Grounds	Washington	DC	51 (1930-1933)	1930-1935
07013	Cummer, A. G. Mrs. Burial Lot/Cummer, Arthur	Jacksonville	FL	2 (1921)	1922
07777	Bok Testimonial/Hubert Fountain	Mountain Lake	FL	29 (1928-1929)	1927-1931
03049	Oakland Cemetery	Iowa City	IA	0	1905
06634	Vanderlip Burial Lot	Aurora	IL	0	1918-1919
12501	Wacker Burial Plot/Wacker, C.H./Grace-land Cemetery	Chicago	IL	2 (1905)	
07759	Nancy Hanks Lincoln Memorial	Lincoln City	IN	63 (1922-1938)	1926-1939
07660	Kentucky Pioneer Memorial Park/KY Pioneer Memorial Association	Harrodsburg	KY	23 (1923-1930)	1925-1932; 1938
03018	Potter's Field	Lexington	KY	0	
07782	Cemetery	Louisville	KY	0	1927
06309	Colonial Dames Monument/Cort Nelson Monument/Fort Nelson	Louisville	KY	0	1915
03045	Hite, Allen R./Cherokee Pk 01263/Cave Hill Cemetery Corner	Louisville	KY	51 (1848; 1905; 1912; 1952-1954)	1905-1969
06869	Newman Burial Lot	New Orleans	LA	0	1920
07354	Abington Memorial/American Legion Building	Abington	MA	11 (1925-1928)	1924-1928
05173	Arnold, Moses N./Civil War Memorial/Soldiers Monument	Abington	MA	1 (1911)	1911-1913
02235	Amherst Cemetery	Amherst	MA	2 (1899)	1887; 1899
05337	Amherst Memorial Fountain	Amherst	MA	7 (1911-1914)	1911-1915
06664	Attleboro Soldiers Memorial	Attleboro	MA	8 (1919-1920)	1919-1920
07950	Attleboro Spanish War Memorial	Attleboro	MA	0	
07948	Attleboro Spanish War Memorial/Capron Park	Attleboro	MA	17 (1904-1929)	1928-1929
06941	North Purchase Cemetery	Attleboro	MA	70 (1921-1922; 1933-1934; 1970-1978)	1921-1980
07003	Woodlawn Cemetery	Attleboro	MA	31 (1921-1931)	1921; 1930-1931
09940	Work, G. R. Cemetery Lot	Barre	MA	3 (1952)	1952-1953
	* See also Charlestown and Jamaica Plain	Boston	MA		
09858	Clark, Paul F. Cemetery Lot/Cemetery Lot in Forest Hills Cemetery/Clark, Paul F.	Boston	MA	7 (1949)	1949-1950
07748	Copley Square War Memorial, Lowell, Guy/Howell, Guy	Boston	MA	0	1926-1927
01511	Eliot Memorial/Blue Hills project/Metropolitan Park Commission/Great Blue Hills	Boston	MA	13 (1900-1905)	1895-1906

Job #	Job Name/Alternative Name	Job Location		Plans	Correspondence
12018	J. B. O'Reilly Statue	Boston	MA	0	1893-1899
00949	Nurses' Monument - Boston Common/Patriotic Societies	Boston	MA	0	1910
09793	Patton Memorial Comm.	Boston	MA	5 (1939-1947)	1947
01344	Van Brunt, Mrs. Charles/Forest Hills Cemetery/Van Brunt, Agnes	Boston	MA	1 (1893)	1893-1895
00969	War Memorial - Charles River Basin	Boston	MA	0	1894; 1921
02045	White, George R. Cemetery Plot/Forest Hills Cemetery	Boston	MA	5 (1898-1901)	1897-1910; 1924
07423	White, George R. Memorial/George R. White Memorial/Bradbury, Mrs. F.	Boston	MA	0	1928
09860	Blue Hill Cemetery	Braintree	MA	8 (1949-1954)	1949-1954
03041	Holland, Charles P. - Cemetery	Brockton	MA	1 (1902; 1905)	1905
01322	Blake, A.W. Cemetery	Brookline	MA	5 (1892-1899)	1892-1893
01309	Brookline Soldiers Monument	Brookline	MA	0	1911-1912
09513	Prouty-Oakes Burial Lots	Brookline	MA	12 (1937-1950)	1937-1974
09394	Bryant, John Cemetery Lot	Cambridge	MA	6 (1935)	1935
01490	City of Cambridge Old Town Burial Ground, Harvard Square/Old Town Burying Ground	Cambridge	MA	0	1922
01402	Harvard Class of 1880	Cambridge	MA	2 (1902)	1901-1905
09306	Higgins Burial Lot/Higgins Family/Burial Lot, Cambridge Cemetery	Cambridge	MA	2 (1932)	1932-1934
09557	Hornblower-Greenough Burial Lot, Mount Auburn Cemetery	Cambridge	MA	95 (1938-1963)	1938-1963
07390	Howells, John Mead Cemetery Lot/Howells, John Mead/Burial Lot, Cambridge Cemetery	Cambridge	MA	8 (1920-1925)	1924-1925
01469	Improvement of Old Town Burying Ground	Cambridge	MA	0	
09466	Johnston, Dr. William B. and Janet - Lot	Cambridge	MA	0	1936
10505	Rowley Burial Lot	Cambridge	MA	0	1974
07932	Knollwood Cemetery	Canton	MA	2 (N.D.)	1928
01555	Bunker Hill Monument Grounds	Charlestown	MA	0	1919-1920
07828	Alcott Memorial/Carved Tablet/Alcott Memorial Association	Concord	MA	0	1927-1928
07757	Catholic Cemetery/Fairview Cemetery	Dalton	MA	0	1926-1929
07412	Crane Memorial/W.M. Crane Memorial	Dalton	MA	28 (1925)	1925-1926
07135	Dalton Cemetery	Dalton	MA	10 (1923-1929)	1923-1931
01606	Memorial Commission	Fall River	MA	0	1924
09571	Montgomery Burial Lot	Falmouth	MA	7 (1939)	1939-1941
09794	National Cemetery	Fort Devens	MA	48 (1947)	1947-1948
02954	Ray Memorial	Franklin	MA	0	1904
12503	Hingham Cemetery	Hingham	MA	1 (N.D.)	
00020-PC	Saint Jerome Cemetery	Holyoke	MA	4 (1939)	
10150	Draper, George William F. Mausoleum	Hopedale	MA	34 (1889; 1919; 1960-1963)	1962-1963; 1974
10057	Kennedy, J. P. Mausoleum	Jamaica Plain	MA	16 (1956-1957)	1957

Job #	Job Name/Alternative Name	Job Location		Plans	Correspondence
06918	Evergreen Cemetery Fountain	Kingston	MA	0	1921
06932	Massachusetts Society of Mayflower Descendants/Bradford Boulder Lot	Kingston	MA	3 (1921)	1921-1922
05449	Lexington Cemetery	Lexington	MA	4 (1912-1913)	1911-1913
09679	Brooks, J. E. Cemetery Lot/Cemetery Lot, Longmeadow Cemetery	Longmeadow	MA	4 (1944)	1944-1945
09919	Burbank Cemetery	Longmeadow	MA	1 (1951)	1951
01718	Malden Soldiers & Sailors Monument	Malden	MA	1 (1907)	1907-1908
06141	Middleton Cemetery/Moore, Charles	Middleton	MA	1 (N.D.)	1914-1915
01191	Milton Civil War Memorial	Milton	MA	0	1939
09608	Ball, Sidney Burial Lot/Burial Lot in Prospect Hill Cemetery	Nantucket	MA	8 (1940-1941)	1940-1942
09102	Saint Mary's Cemetery	New Bedford	MA	71 (1923-1930)	1928-1931
09835	Burial Lot for Mrs. Charles R. Leonard, Newton Cemetery	Newton	MA	11 (1949-1962)	1948-1974
10323	Morrill Burial Lot	Newton	MA	2 (1968; 1970)	1970
10059	Newton Cemetery	Newton	MA	3 (1957)	1891; 1896-1897; 1957
09865	Parker, William A. Mrs. Cemetery Lot	North Easton	MA	7 (1949-1950)	1949-1950
06956	Farley, Owen F. Jr. Cemetery Lot/Farley, Owen F. Jr./Proposed Cemetery	North Saugus	MA	2 (1921)	1921-1925
00447	Norwood Cemetery	Norwood	MA	0	1902
06623	Peabody Institute/Soldiers Memorial	Peabody	MA	1 (1918)	1918
09107	Graves, Merle Cemetery Lot/Graves, Merle D.	Pittsfield	MA	5 (1929)	1929
05492	Pittsfield Cemetery	Pittsfield	MA	52 (1912-1915)	1912-1918; 1942
01152	National Monument to the Forefathers	Plymouth	MA	0	1926
06908	Provincetown Pilgrim Memorial/Pilgrim Tercentenary Commission/Pilgrim Monument Approach	Provincetown	MA	10 (1893; 1921)	1920-1921
09673	Riverside Cemetery	Saugus	MA	15 (1944)	1944-1945
06008	Wells Cemetery Lot/Wells Burial Lot	Southbridge	MA	27 (1913-1933)	1914-1916; 1933-1934
07335	Hill Crest Park Cemetery/Green, Samuel M. Co.	Springfield	MA	44 (1924-1925)	1924-1929; 1934
03291	Skinner Burial Lot/Skinner, Henry H.	Springfield	MA	2 (1907)	1902-1910; 1921; 1926-1927
09943	Springfield Cemetery	Springfield	MA	15 (1948; 1952)	1952-1953
06296	Choate Burial Lot	Stockbridge	MA	5 (1915-1925)	1915-1926
04004	Pine Grove Cemetery/Topsfield Park/Pine Grove Cemetery	Topsfield	MA	2 (1910)	1910-1911
09842	Liebman, Joshua L. Mrs. Burial Lot/Liebman, Joshua Loth	Wakefield	MA	5 (1949)	1949
09664	Puritan Lawn Memorial Park	West Peabody	MA	504 (1934-1968)	1934-1980
06806	Townsend, Prescott/Soldiers Memorial and Town Plan	Westminster	MA	0	1920
00110	Wildwood Cemetery	Winchester	MA	12 (1937-1938)	1899; 1937-1939
00109	Winchester War Memorial	Winchester	MA	14 (1925-1926)	1925-1926

Grounds of the Masonic Memorial to George Washington, date unknown. Job #6991 – Masonic Memorial (Alexandria, VA).

Job #	Job Name/Alternative Name	Job Location		Plans	Correspondence
02938	Green Mount Cemetery	Baltimore	MD	6 (1904-1913)	1904; 1913
02432	Key Monument (Francis Scott Key)/Eutaw Place	Baltimore	MD	18 (1909-1910)	1909-1910
07934	Saint Charles College Burial Lot/St. Charles Cemetery/St. Charles College	Baltimore	MD	9 (1928-1929)	1928-1930
06856	Blaine Memorial	Augusta	ME	21 (1920)	1920-1924; 1929
09398	Burleigh Cemetery Lot	Augusta	ME	0	1936
09003	Downing, Charles Cemetery Lot	Augusta	ME	1 (1928)	1928
07316	Ogden, David B. Gravestone/Ogden, Mrs. David B./Ogden, Harriet	Bar Harbor	ME	14 (1924-1937)	1924-1925; 1937
09789	Camden War Memorial/Village Green	Camden	ME	16 (1947-1949)	1947-1969
09368	Crimmins, Thomas Mrs. Burial Lot	Camden	ME	8 (1933-1934)	1934-1937
06860	Corinna Memorial/Soldiers Memorial	Corinna	ME	11 (1920)	1920
07243	Sharples, Stephan Paschall Cemetery Lot/Sharples, S. P. Estate	Deer Isle	ME	13 (1923)	1923-1924
09756	Dennis Cemetery/Dennis, H.R.	Litchfield	ME	5 (1946)	1946-1949
06876	Bird, Elmer S. Cemetery Lot	Rockland	ME	4 (1920-1921)	1920
01423	Fogg Memorial	South Berwick	ME	1 (1894)	1894

Job #	Job Name/Alternative Name	Job Location		Plans	Correspondence
09206	Knox Memorial/Knox, Henry/Montpelier	Thomaston	ME	19 (1930)	1930
09142	Washtenong Memorial Park	Ann Arbor	MI	19 (1929-1931)	1929-1939; 1944; 1952; 1959
00665	Detroit Soldiers' Memorial	Detroit	MI	0	1922-1923
03538	Louisiana, Missouri Cemetery	Louisiana	MO	0	1908
12028	Soldiers' Monument	Concord	NH	0	1891
09238	Lovejoy, J. R. Cemetery Lot	Enfield	NH	5 (1930-1931)	1930-1933
07865	Gibson Cemetery Lot/Gibson, Harvey D.	North Conway	NH	4 (1927)	1927-1928
09216	Hillside Cemetery	Weare	NH	57 (1930-1933)	1929-1934
06784	Memorial to Dr. Peck/Essex County Park Commission	Caldwell	NJ	0	1919-1920
07888	Evergreen Cemetery	Elizabeth	NJ	14 (1927-1930)	1927-1930
06659	Montclair Soldiers Memorial/Memorial to Soldiers	Montclair	NJ	25 (1919)	1918-1919
01201	Higgins, Eugene/Glen Farm	Morristown	NJ	22 (1890-1891)	1890-1892
03671	Mount Pleasant Cemetery	Newark	NJ	0	1909
09064	Paterson War Memorial	Paterson	NJ	3 (1929)	1929-1931
09341	Old Tennent Church Cemetery	Tennent	NJ	0	1933
01183	Cemetery Land/Hill, E. C.	Trenton	NJ	0	1906-1908
07664	Fairview Cemetery	Westfield	NJ	2 (1902; 1904)	1926
05774	Roman Catholic Cemetery Association	Buffalo	NY	0	1912
12038	Soldiers' Memorial Arch	Buffalo	NY	0	1876; 1894
05571	DeForest Burial Plot/DeForest, Henry W./Memorial Cemetery	Cold Spring	NY	78 (1912-1924)	1914-1940
07862	Ayer, James C. Cemetery Lot/Coe Cem. Lot #7403/Burial Lot in St. John's Memorial Cemetary	Cold Spring Harbor	NY	15 (1925-1928)	1927-1929
09077	Blair, James A. Cemetery Lot/Blair, James A./Cemetery Lot in Memorial Cemetery	Cold Spring Harbor	NY	3 (1929)	1929; 1947; 1956-1957
03058	Brooklyn Institute of Arts & Sciences	Cold Spring Harbor	NY	2 (1905)	1905-1907
09061	Campbell, Oliver A. Cemetery Lot/Burial Lot in Memorial Cemetery	Cold Spring Harbor	NY	6 (1929)	1929; 1953
07403	Coe Cemetery Lot/Coe, William R./Burial Lot Memorial Cemetery	Cold Spring Harbor	NY	18 (1925-1927)	1925-1928
09550	Gardner, Mrs. Paul Edgerton/Burial Lot, St. Johns' Memorial Cemetery	Cold Spring Harbor	NY	7 (1938)	1938-1939; 1973
07128	Garver, John A. Cemetery Lot/Garver, John A./Burial Lot in Memorial Cemetery	Cold Spring Harbor	NY	13 (1923)	1923-1924
09499	Harris, H. U. Burial Lot/Harris, H. U./Cemetery Lot in Memorial Cemetery	Cold Spring Harbor	NY	9 (1937)	1937-1938; 1950
06907	James, Walter Dr. Cemetery Lot/James, Walter/Burial Lot - St. John's Cemetery	Cold Spring Harbor	NY	6 (1920-1921)	1920-1921
06904	Jennings, Walter Cemetery Lot/Jennings, Walter/Burial Lot - St. John's Cemetery	Cold Spring Harbor	NY	17 (1920-1921)	1920-1923; 1938
07671	Kahn, Otto Burial Lot/Burial Lot, St. Johns Cemetery	Cold Spring Harbor	NY	8 (1925-1926)	1926-1927
07018	Kalbfleisch, F. H. - Lot in Memorial Cemetery	Cold Spring Harbor	NY	0	1922

Job #	Job Name/Alternative Name	Job Location		Plans	Correspondence
09286	Kennedy, William Cemetery Lot/Burial Lot in St. John's Memorial Cemetery	Cold Spring Harbor	NY	12 (1931-1932)	1931-1932
06343	McKelvey, Chas. W. Cemetery Lot	Cold Spring Harbor	NY	17 (1916-1921)	1916-1921
09006	Moore, Benjamin Burial Lot	Cold Spring Harbor	NY	4 (1928)	1928
07108	Morris, Ray Memorial Slab/Morris, Ray/ Burial Lot in Memorial Cemetery	Cold Spring Harbor	NY	7 (1923)	1922-1923
06967	Nichols Cemetery Lot/Nichols, W. T.	Cold Spring Harbor	NY	18 (1921)	1921-1922
06621	Saint John's Memorial Cemetery/St. John's Cemetery/Memorial Cemetery	Cold Spring Harbor	NY	58 (1918-1958)	1917-1958; 1970
09328	Sloan Burial Lot/Sloan, Alfred P./Burial Lot in St. John's Memorial Cemetery	Cold Spring Harbor	NY	26 (1932)	1932-1934
09241	Snow, Fred. A. Burial Lot/St. Johns Memorial Cemetery/Snow, Frederick A.	Cold Spring Harbor	NY	27 (1930-1939)	1931-1932; 1937-1938
09494	Stimson, Henry L. Burial Lot	Cold Spring Harbor	NY	15 (1937)	1937-1949
09496	Trowbridge, E. Q. Cemetery Lot	Cold Spring Harbor	NY	25 (1937; 1939)	1937-1940
07133	War Memorial at Cold Spring Harbor	Cold Spring Harbor	NY	0	1922
07650	Glen Cove Soldiers Memorial/War Veterans Monument/James Erwin Donohue Post	Glen Cove	NY	3 (1926)	1926-1927
09024	Mount Hope Cemetery	Greenburgh	NY	20 (1925; 1928-1930)	1928-1930; 1940, 1956-1957
05459	Kensico Cemetery	Kensico	NY	13 (1912)	1911-1915; 1935
09937	Maple Grove Cemetery	Kew Gardens	NY	29 (1942-1947; 1952)	1951-1954
09351	Babbott, F. L. Dr. Burial Lot/Locust Valley Cemetery	Locust Valley	NY	10 (1934)	1931-1937; 1942-1946; 1952
07925	Burchard, Mrs. A. W. - Burial Lot/Locust Valley Cemetery	Locust Valley	NY	0	1928
07337	Coffin, C. A. Cemetery Lot/Coffin, C. A. Burial Lot/Locust Valley Cemetery	Locust Valley	NY	4 (1924)	1924-1925
07224	Davison, H. P. Mrs. Cemetery Lot/Davison, K. T./Burial Lot Locust Valley Cemetery Addition	Locust Valley	NY	21 (1923-1927)	1923-1924
09314	Dickinson Burial Lot/Dickinson, Hunt C./Burial Lot Locust Valley Cemetery Addition	Locust Valley	NY	11 (1932-1933)	1932-1933
07338	Hodenpyl, A. Cemetery Lot/Hodenpy (cravath), Anton Burial Lot/Locust Valley Cemetery	Locust Valley	NY	5 (1924)	1924-1925
09745	King, Rufus Cemetery Lot/Locust Valley Cemetery	Locust Valley	NY	4 (1946)	1946-1947
07050	Locust Valley Cemetery, Addition to/Davison, H.P. Cemetery Lot/Locust Valley Cemetery	Locust Valley	NY	263 (1922-1946)	1922-1948
07299	Morgan Cemetery Lot/Morgan, J. P./ Burial Lot # 20 Locust Valley Cemetery	Locust Valley	NY	9 (1924)	1924
07980	Nichols, W. H. Burial Lot/Locust Valley Cemetery	Locust Valley	NY	0	1928
07792	Percy (Burial Lot), Locust Valley Cemetery/Chubb, Percy	Locust Valley	NY	0	1927
09270	Smith, R. W. Burial Lot/Smith, Robert Waverly/Burial Lot Locust Valley Cemetery Addition	Locust Valley	NY	14 (1931; 1938)	1931; 1938-1939

CEMETERIES, BURIAL LOTS, MEMORIALS AND MONUMENTS

Job #	Job Name/Alternative Name	Job Location		Plans	Correspondence
07659	Stettinius Cemetery Lot/Locust Valley Cemetery/Stettinius Burial Lot	Locust Valley	NY	34 (1926-1939)	1926-1927; 1938-1939
09457	White, T. J. Cemetery Lot	Long Island	NY	10 (1936)	1936
12128	Hillside Cemetery	Middletown	NY	0	
00218	Vanderbilt Mausoleum/Sloane Tomb	New Dorp	NY	138 (1886-1899)	1869-1901; 1972-1978
05345	Baker, George F. Cemetery Lot/George Baker Monument/Kensico Cemetery	New York City	NY	6 (1911-1921)	1911-1914; 1920-1921
03074	Constable Burial Lot/Constable, F. A./Woodlawn Cemetery	New York City	NY	9 (1905; 1926-1927)	1905-1921; 1926-1928
12048	Farragut Statue	New York City	NY	0	1879-1880; 1896
09237	Garvan Mausoleum/Garvan, Francis P./Mausoleum/Woodlawn Cemetery	New York City	NY	8 (1930-1931)	1930-1933
00537	Grants Tomb	New York City	NY	16 (1928-1933)	1873-1889; 1928-1932
03437	Greenwood Cemetery	New York City	NY	0	
05812	Pulitzer Fountain	New York City	NY	0	1912
00239	Sloan Tomb/Vanderbilt Tomb	New York City	NY	0	1869-1897
06970	Stauffen, E. Jr. Cemetery Lot/Stauffen, Ernest Jr./Cemetery Lot in Woodlawn Cemetery	New York City	NY	93 (1920-1929)	1921-1922
03953	Woodlawn Cemetery	New York City	NY	0	1910

Richly planted family burial 'room' with flat marker in the Memorial Cemetery of Saint John's Church, October 3, 1916. Job #5571 – DeForest Burial Plot (listed as Cold Spring, NY).

Job #	Job Name/Alternative Name	Job Location		Plans	Correspondence
06906	Matheson, William J. Cemetery Lot/Matheson, William J./Burial Lot - St. John's Cemetery	Oyster Bay	NY	58 (1920-1922)	1920-1922
07596	Roosevelt - Path to Burial Lot/North Country Garden Club	Oyster Bay	NY	2 (1926)	1925-1927
05999	Greenwood Union Cemetery	Rye	NY	0	1914
06537	Bodman, Edward Mrs./Sleepy Hollow Cem./Bodman Burial Lot/Cemetery	Scarborough	NY	6 (1917)	1917-1922
06803	Carnegie, Andrew Mrs. Burial Lot/Carnegie, Andrew/Burial Lot Sleepy Hollow Cemetery	Tarrytown	NY	83 (1905-1921)	1920-1923
03008	Dunham Cemetery Lot/Dunham, Carroll/Sleepy Hollow Cemetery	Tarrytown	NY	10 (1904-1905)	1904-1905
00245	Rockefeller, John D. Jr. Cemetery Lot/Sleepy Hollow Cemetery Lot	Tarrytown	NY	203 (1938-1951)	1939-1942; 1974
03395	Forest Hills Cemetery/Utica Cemetery Association	Utica	NY	0	1906-1907
02628	Brookside Cemetery Plot	Watertown	NY	4 (1903)	
03009	Canfield, A. Cass Cemetery Lot/Woodlawn Cemetery	Woodlawn Cemetery	NY	4 (1904-1905)	1904-1905
06656	Sanderson, Henry Burial Lot	Yonkers	NY	4 (1918)	1918-1919
06086	Hanna Mausoleum/Mark Hanna Mausoleum	Cleveland	OH	1 (1911)	1914-1915
06718	Deeds Mausoleum/Deeds, E.A./Mausoleum Woodlawn Cemetery	Dayton	OH	16 (1917-1920)	1919-1920
06298	Patterson Cemetery Lot	Dayton	OH	0	N.D.
06267	Patterson, Col. Robert Memorial/Rubicon	Dayton	OH	0	1915-1916
05453	Woodland Cemetery	Dayton	OH	0	1911-1912; 1949
05771	Wright Memorial/Wright Brothers Memorial	Dayton	OH	8 (1912-1919)	1912-1916
10121	Stranahan, R. A. Cemetery Plot	Toledo	OH	10 (1959-1960)	1960-1961
03797	Portland Cemetery	Portland	OR	0	1909
00039	Allegheny Cemetery	Allegheny	PA	1 (1901)	1901
04099	Chambersburg Cemetery	Chambersburg	PA	0	1910
07121	Strong, C. H. Mausoleum	Erie	PA	0	1923
09611	Jones Memorial/Merion (?) Cricket Club/Bobby Jones Memorial	Haverford	PA	4 (1928-1940)	1940-1941; 1947
06675	Lock Haven War Memorial	Lock Haven	PA	0	1919
09455	Bok-Curtis Burial Lot/Laurel Hill Cemetery	Philadelphia	PA	5 (1936)	1936
09113	Thaw, William Burial Lot/Burial Lot Allegheny Cemetery	Pittsburgh	PA	9 (1929-1930)	1929-1930
06987	Evans, Charles Cemetery/Charles Evans Cemetery Company	Reading	PA	74 (1921-1923)	1921-1939
07584	Janssen Cemetery Lot/Evans Memorial Cemetery/Janssen, Henry/Charles Evans Cemetery	Reading	PA	52 (1925-1926)	1925-1932
07333	Thun Cemetery Lot/Thun, Ferdinand Burial Lot/Charles Evans Cemetery	Reading	PA	2 (1924)	1924

Job #	Job Name/Alternative Name	Job Location		Plans	Correspondence
04009	Fuller, E. L. Burial Lot/Fuller, E. L./Dunmore Cemetery	Scranton	PA	5 (1911)	1910-1911
09700	Sunset Memorial Park	Somerton	PA	46 (1941-1946)	1945-1946; 1961
09080	Boies, David Mrs. Cemetery Lot/Boies, David/Burial Lot in Hickory Grove Cemetery	Waverly	PA	2 (1929)	1929-1931
07571	Fuller, Mortimer B. Cemetery Lot/Hickory Grove Cemetery Lot	Waverly	PA	22 (1928)	1928-1930
04079	Barrington Cemetery	Barrington	RI	0	1910
05172	Forest Chapel Cemetery	Barrington	RI	7 (1911-1912)	1911-1914
06410	Hoffman, W. H. Burial Lot/Princess Hill Cemetery/Hoffman, William H.	Barrington	RI	15 (1917-1918)	1916-1917; 1928
00413	Prince's Hill Cemetery/Hoffman, W.H.	Barrington	RI	54 (1907-1911)	1907-1911
05810	Tyler Point Cemetery	Barrington	RI	0	
01830	Bath Road War Memorial/War Memorial and Bath Road Widening	Newport	RI	4 (1945)	1945
01828	Soldiers' Memorial	Newport	RI	0	1918-1920
06636	Wetmore, G. P., Hon. Burial Lot/Wetmore, George Peabody/Burial Lot, Island Cemetery	Newport	RI	4 (1918)	1918-1919
09011	Hazard Memorial	Peace Dale	RI	6 (1928)	1928-1930
02271	Brown Burial Lot/Brown, Mrs. John Nicholas	Providence	RI	3 (1900)	1900-1902
07024	Location of Monument to Music	Providence	RI	0	1921-1922
00334	Swan Point Cemetery	Providence	RI	3 (1911-1914)	1869; 1894-1895; 1911-1914
03509	World War Memorial	Providence	RI	0	1924-1926
09516	Rockefeller, Laura Spelman Memorial/Great Smoky National Park	Gatlinburg	TN	54 (1938-1939)	1937-1942
09861	Dennis Burial Lot	Kingsport	TN	16 (1949-1952)	1949-1952
09707	Kingsport Cemetery	Kingsport	TN	107 (1927-1955)	1940-1955
06687	El Paso Park Commission War Memorial	El Paso	TX	0	
06991	Masonic Memorial/Masonic Memorial to George Washington/Shuter's (Shooters) Hill	Alexandria	VA	77 (1921-1942)	1921-1950
09741	Robert Marlow burial plot/National Memorial Park	Falls Church	VA	0	1946
07385	Anderson, Christian S. - Cemetery Lot	Hot Springs	VA	0	1924-1925
03455	Bennington Vermont Cemetery/Bennington Park Lawn Cemetery	Bennington	VT	0	1908
03014	Dellwood Cemetery	Manchester	VT	2 (1904)	1897; 1904-1905
05784	King County Crematorium/Kings County Crematory	King County	WA	2 (1907-1913)	1912-1913
09566	Bonnell Cemetery Lot/Evergreen Cemetery	Seattle	WA	0	1939-1941
06773	Evergreen Cemetery Company	Seattle	WA	1 (1921)	1919-1920
05502	Bolster Memorial/White, A. L.	Spokane	WA	1 (1912)	1912-1914
08048	Cemetery in Spokane	Spokane	WA	0	

Kohler family burial lot, August 1941. Job #9600 – Kohler Family Burial Lot (Kohler, WI).

Job #	Job Name/Alternative Name	Job Location		Plans	Correspondence
08047	Greenwood Cemetery/Greenwood Cemetery Extension	Spokane	WA	6 (1923-1925)	1924-1925
05813	Riverside Park Company/Riverside Land Company Cemetery	Spokane	WA	1 (1913)	1912-1916
03588	Woodlawn Cemetery	Spokane	WA	0	1908
08077	Wenatchee Cemetery	Wenatchee	WA	7 (1915)	1926
06644	Kiernan, William H. Burial Lot/Kiernan, W.H./Burial lot Woodlawn Cemetery	Green Bay	WI	92 (1918-1936)	1918-1920; 1936
09697	Brotz Burial Lot/Brotz, Anton F.	Kohler	WI	9 (1945)	1945
09600	Kohler Family Burial Lot	Kohler	WI	181 (1940-1957)	1939-1962
09658	Kohler, Carl J. Cemetery Lot	Kohler	WI	5 (1943)	1943-1953
09998	Kohler, J. M. Cemetery Lot	Kohler	WI	1 (1955)	1954-1955
	CANADA				
07162	Crieff Churchyard/Crieff Churchyard Cemetery/Maclean, J. B.	Crieff	ON	17 (1923-1930)	1923-1931
	OTHER COUNTRIES				
09790	American Military Cemetery	Cambridge	ENG	146 (1947-1953)	1947-1967; 1976

Historic view of the National Cash Register factory, date unknown. Job #280 – National Cash Register (Dayton, OH). Listed in Subdivisions and Suburban Communities.

Background: Detail of topographical map for the International Garden Club, October 1916. Job #6376 – International Garden Club (Pelham Bay, NY).

Grounds of Commercial
and Industrial Buildings

Lauren Meier

As the nation's economy expanded in the final decades of the nineteenth century, the Olmsted firm gradually added both commercial and industrial landscape projects to its portfolio, although such jobs constituted a late addition and focus to the firm's design work. This aspect of the firm's work is particularly diverse in scope, ranging from early civic improvements focused on transportation systems and utility projects to a broad sector of commercial enterprises such as banks, nurseries, laboratories, life insurance companies, corporate headquarters, shopping centers and manufacturing facilities. There are more than 175 projects included in this category, of which approximately 70% advanced into design plans, with the vast majority completed after Frederick Law Olmsted's retirement in 1897.

A notable early exception is the substantial project for the Boston and Albany Railroad, which consisted of some ninety-five plans between 1880 and 1884 and was later completed by Olmsted, Olmsted & Eliot. This project represents an important evolution in the urban fabric of Boston, for it provided a new public transportation system that connected the growing suburbs to the city. Although listed only as Boston, this single job represents distinct design elements for multiple stations, primarily in Wellesley, Newton and the Allston/Brighton section of Boston, Massachusetts, that address site grading, track layout, platform location, bridge design and planting. At the same time, the Olmsted firm's work on behalf of the Ames family in North Easton, Massachusetts, included plans completed in 1883 for the North Easton Train Station designed by H. H. Richardson, which coincided with a distinctive body of work nearby. This category also includes a significant design project for Rockaway Point on Jamaica Bay in Queens, New York, (listed as New York City), completed in 1879 to create a summer resort in association with the new rail service.

During the first decades of the twentieth century, the Olmsted firm's commercial projects increased substantially. The list includes a significant number of projects completed for the growing utility and communication industries (e.g., Western Electric Company in Chicago, Illinois, and Baltimore, Maryland; the Wyman and Androscoggin Dams for the Central Maine Power Company; Bell Telephone Labs facilities in Deal, Holmdel, Mendham, Summit and Whippany, New Jersey; and sewage treatment plants in Fitchburg and North Adams, Massachusetts). This period of affluence prior to the Depression also generated demand for landscaped grounds associated with commercial buildings, especially financial institutions and insurance companies, evidenced by several projects undertaken by the firm (e.g., Aetna Fire Insurance Company in Hartford, Connecticut; the First Brunswick Federal Savings and Loan Association in Brunswick, Maine; the Maryland Casualty Company in Baltimore, Maryland; and the Massachusetts Mutual Life Insurance Company in Springfield, Massachusetts).

Several jobs included in this section relate directly to more extensive work referenced in other thematic categories, or which came about because of the Olmsted firm's involvement nearby. For example, on Mount Desert Island, Maine, the work of Frederick Law Olmsted Jr. with John D. Rockefeller Jr. in the development of the motor road system for Acadia National Park may have led to the firm's involvement from 1942 to 1950 in the Jackson Laboratories, located in Bar Harbor, adjacent to the park. Following World War II through the later years of the Olmsted Associates, the firm experienced a surge in commercial and industrial projects that included continued work for insurance companies (e.g., John Hancock Mutual Life Insurance Company in Boston and Brookline, Massachusetts; State Mutual Life Assurance Company in Worcester, Massachusetts; and the Berkshire Life Insurance Company in Pittsfield, Massachusetts) as well as corporate offices, retail centers and manufacturing complexes (e.g., Crane and Company in Dalton, Massachusetts; Sears, Roebuck and Company in Saugus, Massachusetts; General Motors Frigidaire Division in Dayton, Ohio; and the Jack Daniel Distillery in Lynchburg, Tennessee). This period also includes noteworthy projects related to hospitals and medical research centers such as Ledgemont Laboratory in Lexington, Massachusetts, and the Sloan-Kettering Foundation in Rye, New York. Finally, an interesting aspect of the firm's later commercial and industrial work includes design plans for nurseries and garden centers, such as Weston Nurseries in Hopkinton, Massachusetts. These businesses may have provided plant material for the firm's other projects.

See Introductory Guide on pages 33-35 for information on the use of this list.

Grounds of Commercial and Industrial Buildings

Job #	Job Name/Alternative Name	Job Location		Plans	Correspondence
00061	Barbour Stockwell Company			0	
07408	Consolidated Realty Company			0	

UNITED STATES

Job #	Job Name/Alternative Name	Job Location		Plans	Correspondence
09950	Vestavia Hills Shopping Center	Birmingham	AL	34 (1948; 1953-1955)	1953-1956
08235	Burbank United Airport	Burbank	CA	9 (1929-1930)	1929-1930
08321	Custom House - Old Theater/California State Parks	Monterey County	CA	0	
08256	Sub-station for Edison Co.	Palos Verdes	CA	2 (1930)	1930-1931
05949	Spring Valley Water Company	San Francisco	CA	0	1913-1914
07851	North Eastern Forestry Company Nursery/Bryant, E.S.	Chesire	CT	0	1927; 1933-1934
09274	Millane Tree Expert & Nurseries Company	Cromwell	CT	10 (1931)	1931
07508	Aetna Fire Insurance Company	Hartford	CT	17 (1925-1926)	1925-1927
07035	Aetna Life Insurance Company	Hartford	CT	0	1922
10011	Cascio, P. Garden Center	Hartford	CT	4 (1955)	1955-1956
09336	Milford Sewage Treatment Plant/Metcalf & Eddy, for	Milford	CT	3 (1933)	1933
10317	Norwich Shopping Center	Norwich	CT	0	1970
09312	Greenwich Sewage Disposal Works/Old Greenwich Sewage Disposal Works	Old Greenwich	CT	3 (1932)	1932
09481	Ridgebury Company/Mallory, Harry B.	Ridgebury	CT	0	1937
09170	Bartlett, F. A. Tree Expert Company/F. A. Bartlett Tree Expert Company	Stamford	CT	7 (1929-1931)	1929-1930
06535	Torrington Mfg. Company	Torrington	CT	5 (1917-1927)	1917; 1927-1928; 1931
06671	Chase Companies Inc.	Waterbury	CT	17 (1919-1920)	1919-1920
07009	Chase Companies North Main Street Project	Waterbury	CT	0	1921
05873	Chase Rolling Mill Company/Chase, F.S.	Waterbury	CT	3 (1913)	1913
07765	Waterbury Medical Society	Waterbury	CT	7 (1926-1927)	1927
00698	Mesa Group	Miami	FL	0	1964-1967
00689	The Mesa Group (mis-numbered)	Miami	FL	0	1964-1967
03803	American Textile Company	Cartersville	GA	0	1909; 1918
05485	International Recreation Company	Chicago	IL	0	1912
09198	Western Electric Company/Hawthorne Street	Chicago	IL	97 (1929-1945)	1930; 1937-1948
05937	Wildwood Builders Company	Fort Wayne	IN	0	1913
10165	Brown-Forman Distillers Corporation	Utica	IN	26 (1962-1968)	1963-1969
09763	Brown-Forman Distillers Corporation	Louisville	KY	242 (1943-1970)	1947-1977

Job #	Job Name/Alternative Name	Job Location		Plans	Correspondence
07501	Hydro-Electric Plant of Kentucky Utilities Company/Kentucky Utilities Company/Dix River Hydro-Electric Plant	Louisville	KY	0	1925
05170	McAllister & Co./McAlister & Company	Louisville	KY	0	1910-1911
09765	Brown-Forman Distillers Corporation	Shirley	KY	164 (1935; 1945-1968)	1947-1955
09764	Brown-Forman Distillers Corporation/Labrot & Graham	Versailles	KY	63 (1943; 1947)	1947
06992	Attleboro Springs Company	Attleboro	MA	0	1921-1922
	*See also Roxbury andWest Roxbury	Boston	MA		
00647	Boston and Albany Railroad	Boston	MA	95 (1880-1884)	1883-1897; 1921
10203	Boston Council, Inc. Boy Scouts of America	Boston	MA	33 (1965-1966)	1966
10714	Episcopal Diocese of Massachusetts	Boston	MA	0	N.D.
09891	H. A. Johnson Company	Boston	MA	3 (1950)	1950
09740	John Hancock Mutual Life Insurance Company/John Hancock Board of Consultants/Housing Committee	Boston	MA	0	1946-1947
02896	Women's Educational and Industrial Union	Boston	MA	0	1906
09703	Hancock, John Mutual Life Insurance Company/John Hancock Insurance Company Housing	Boston & Brookline	MA	47 (1944-1947)	1941-1948
10202	Howard Johnson Company	Braintree	MA	34 (1956; 1959; 1964-1966)	1966-1974
10727	Red Coach Grill	Braintree	MA	0	1979
	* See also Boston & Brookline	Brookline	MA		
00673	Olmsted, F. L./99 Warren St. (office property)/Fairsted	Brookline	MA	160 (1880-1968)	1883-1899; 1904-1907; 1918-1950; 1960-1980
09953	Torf Funeral Home	Brookline	MA	7 (1943; 1953)	1952
01136	Western Union Telegraph Company	Brookline	MA	0	
10171	Burlington Shopping Center	Burlington	MA	6 (1963-1964)	1963-1964
10730	Harvard University Press	Cambridge	MA	0	1893; 1979-1980
09768	Houghton Mifflin Company/Riverside Press	Cambridge	MA	36 (1946-1950)	1947-1950
06235	Norris, F. W. and Company	Cambridge	MA	0	1915
10456	The Garage/Wasserman Development Corporation	Cambridge	MA	0	1973
10473	Minute Man Companies/Minuteman Companies	Concord	MA	11 (1972-1973)	1973-1975
10220	Crane and Company	Dalton	MA	112 (1960-1969)	1967-1970
07102	Sawyer, Regan Company Mill	Dalton	MA	1 (1922)	1922-1923
10724	Howard Johnson's Restaurant	Danvers	MA	0	1979
10590	Dedham Medical Associates Partnership	Dedham	MA	6 (1976-1977)	1977-1978
05779	Fitchburg Sewage Filtration Plant	Fitchburg	MA	5 (1912)	1912-1913
10725	Howard Johnson's Restaurant	Framingham	MA	0	1979

Job #	Job Name/Alternative Name	Job Location		Plans	Correspondence
03064	Bass Rock Station/Boston and Maine Railroad/Bass Rocks Station	Gloucester	MA	2 (1905)	1905
10047	Weston Nurseries Garden Center	Hopkinton	MA	6 (1956-1957)	1956-1957
10232	Amicon Corporation	Lexington	MA	5 (1967)	1967-1968
10141	Ledgemont Laboratory/Kennecott Copper Co.	Lexington	MA	878 (1961-1972)	1962-1974
10449	One Nineteen Corporation/Mill Pond Site	Littleton	MA	16 (1969; 1973)	1966-1973
03320	Cuticura Soap Factory/Cuticura Soap Works/White, George R.	Malden	MA	1 (1907)	1907-1908
10176	Sears Roebuck - Filene's Shopping Center	Natick	MA	35 (1963-1965)	1964-1965
09810	Winslow Nurseries Inc.	Needham	MA	11 1948)	1948
10315	Reliable Homes Inc.	New Bedford	MA	20 (1970)	1970
09902	Jenney Manufacturing Company	Newton	MA	19 (1947; 1951-1952)	1951-1960
09360	North Adams Sewage Treatment Plant/North Adams Mass. Sewage Disposal Plant	North Adams	MA	8 (1934)	1934-1935
00670	North Easton Station Grounds	North Easton	MA	3 (1883)	1883
10556	Washington Mills Abrasive Co., Inc.	North Grafton	MA	6 (1970; 1976)	1976
10020	Elaine Development Company/Torf, H. J.	Norwood	MA	6 (1955)	1955-1956
10723	Red Coach Grill	Pembroke	MA	0	1979
10044	Berkshire Life Insurance Company	Pittsfield	MA	118 (1956-1959)	1956-1961; 1969
02396	Pittsfield Street Railroad Company/Pittsfield Electric Street Railway Co./Pontoosuc Park	Pittsfield	MA	1 (1901)	1903
10719	Ocean Spray Cranberries, Inc.	Plymouth	MA	0	1979
03792	Plant, Thomas G. Company	Roxbury	MA	7 (1909)	1909-1910
10118	Sears, Roebuck and Company	Saugus	MA	42 (1959-1960)	1960-1961
06007	American Optical Company/Park at Mills	Southbridge	MA	32 (1911-1961)	1914; 1930-1961
09188	Southbridge National Bank	Southbridge	MA	5 (1929-1930)	1930-1933
09100	Fiberloid Company	Springfield	MA	2 (1929)	1929-1930; 1935
07400	Massachusetts Mutual Life Insurance Company	Springfield	MA	104 (1925-1951)	1925-1937; 1945-1971
09878	Springfield Fire & Marine Insurance Company	Springfield	MA	116 (1945; 1950-1952)	1950-1955
10263	Strathmore Shoe Company Inc.	Stoughton	MA	10 (1968-1969)	1968-1969
10431	Upton Inn	Upton	MA	7 (1972)	1973-1975
10721	Red Coach Grill	Wayland	MA	0	1979
09957	Elm Farm Foods Co.	West Roxbury	MA	0	1953
10019	Lee Development Company/Torf, H. J.	West Roxbury	MA	3 (1955)	1955-1956
09116	United Electric Light Company	West Springfield	MA	3 (1929)	1929
03012	Whitinsville Park/Whitinsville National Bank	Whitinsville	MA	6 (1904-1907)	1904-1907
09935	Wilmington Rotary Park, Inc.	Wilmington	MA	0	1951-1952
09698	Heald Machine Company	Worcester	MA	36 (1944-1952)	1945-1952

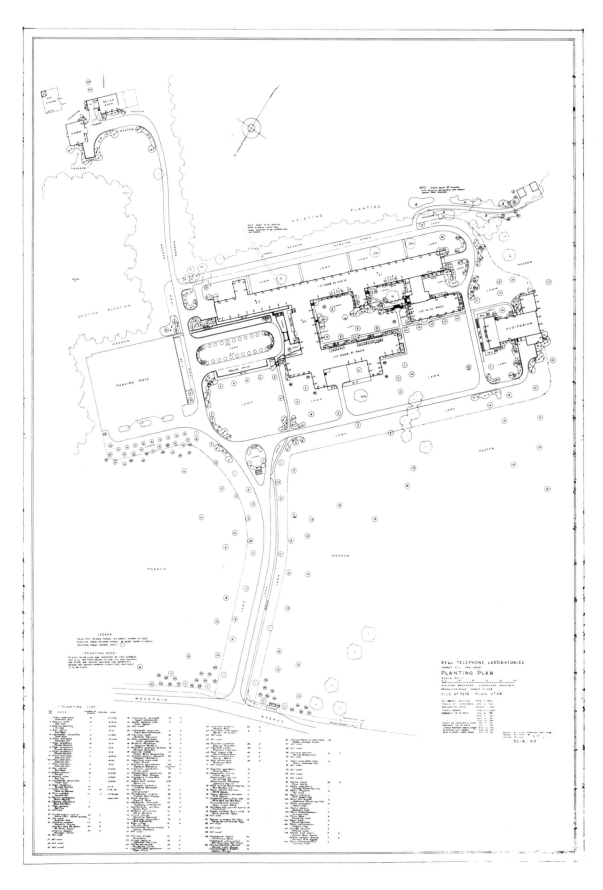

Planting plan for the Bell Telephone Laboratories, August 1940. Job #9218 – Bell Telephone Labs (Summit, NJ).

Job #	Job Name/Alternative Name	Job Location		Plans	Correspondence
10017	State Mutual Life Assurance Company	Worcester	MA	110 (1955-1958)	1955-1959; 1968-1969
06769	Maryland Casualty Company	Baltimore	MD	47 (1919-1921)	1919-1922; 1939
09035	Western Electric Company Cable Factory/Point Breeze Plan	Baltimore	MD	255 (1921; 1928-1931)	1928-1934; 1939
06563	Dundalk Company	Saint Helena	MD	0	1917-1918
07376	Central Maine Power Company	Androscoggin Dam	ME	60 (1925-1927)	1924-1928
09866	Jackson, Roscoe B. Memorial Laboratory	Bar Harbor	ME	53 (1942-1950)	1948-1950
09020	Wyman Dam - Central Maine Power Company	Bingham	ME	21 (1928-1930)	1928-1931
10516	First Brunswick Federal Savings & Loan Association	Brunswick	ME	10 (1974-1975)	1974-1976
09777	Camden Yacht Club	Camden	ME	7 (1947-1948)	1947-1949; 1966-1969
03628	Huron Farms Company		MI	0	
03618	Barton Power Plant/Barton Plant/Detroit Edison Company	Barton	MI	9 (1911-1914)	1911-1914
03663	Eastern Michigan Edison Co./Huron River	Dearborn	MI	0	1910;1913
03627	Detroit Edison Company/Huron Farms Company/Washtenaw Light and Power Co.	Detroit	MI	0	1925; 1929
03617	Detroit Edison/Delray Plant/Detroit Edison Company	Detroit	MI	5 (1911-1912)	1911-1912; 1924
03660	Eastern Michigan Edison Co., Oakwood River Substation	River Rouge	MI	0	1913
05069	Eastern Michigan Edison Company	Rochester	MI	13 (1910-1915)	1910-1913
03615	Superior Plant - Huron River Improvement/Detroit Edison Company	Superior	MI	8 (1911-1915)	1911-1912
03662	Eastern Michigan Edison Co., Trenton Plant/Huron River	Trenton	MI	9 (1909-1911)	1911; 1913
07598	Washtenaw Council Boy Scouts of America	Washtenaw	MI	4 (1925-1926)	
06185	Hartley, G. G. - Office	Duluth	MN	0	1915
07098	Long Bell Lumber Company	Kansas City	MO	0	1922
10181	Mississippi Research and Development Center	Jackson	MS	20 (1963-1966)	1962-1967
02380	High Shoals Cotton Mills	High Shoals	NC	1 (1902)	
09807	Western Electric Company	Winston-Salem	NC	0	1948
09887	American Guernsey Cattle Club	Peterboro	NH	39 (1946; 1949-1951)	1950-1951
10436	Rockingham Mall	Salem	NH	5 (1971-1973)	1972-1973
09243	Bell Telephone Labs	Deal	NJ	24 (1930-1931)	1930-1931
03078	Hackensack Water Company	Hackensack	NJ	63 (1906-1907; 1922-1929; 1939-1940)	1905-1909; 1922-1925; 1931; 1939-1940
09246	Bell Telephone Labs/Holmdel Township	Holmdel	NJ	17 (1929-1931)	1930-1931
09103	Western Electric Company - Kearney	Kearny	NJ	0	1927-1948
10155	Wiley Mission, Inc.	Marlton	NJ	1 (1957)	1963
09234	Bell Telephone Labs	Mendham	NJ	3 (1930)	1930-1931

Job #	Job Name/Alternative Name	Job Location		Plans	Correspondence
07747	Mutual Benefit Life Insurance	Newark	NJ	2 (1927)	1927-1928
09955	Scott, O. M. & Sons Company	Princeton	NJ	71 (1953-1954)	1952-1954
09218	Bell Telephone Labs/Bell Telephone Laboratories, Inc	Summit	NJ	3 (1930)	1930-1931; 1939-1944; 1949
09233	Bell Telephone Labs	Whippany	NJ	7 (1929-1930)	1930-1931
02903	Ontario Power Company	Buffalo	NY	5 (1903-1904)	
05359	Harmony Mills	Cohoes	NY	0	1911
07649	Cord-Meyer Office Grounds/Cord Meyer Development Company	Forest Hills	NY	12 (1926-1927)	1926-1927
09830	Newsday	Garden City	NY	13 (1948-1949)	1948-1949
06886	Patterson, J. H./Camp No. 4	Lowville	NY	3 (1920)	1920-1921
00538	Barnard Studios/Fort Tryon, found in with/Barnard, George Grey	New York City	NY	0	1931-1932
07867	Electric Ferries Inc.	New York City	NY	4 (1927)	1927-1928
12515	New Casino/Casino Theater/Casino Theatre/New York Concert Co. Ltd.	New York City	NY	2 (1882)	
00515	Rockaway/Rockaway Beach & Jamaica Bay	New York City	NY	105 (1879)	1876-1884; 1975
05850	Hydraulic Power Company	Niagara Falls	NY	0	1907-1908; 1913
07728	Community Plate Company Ltd./Oneida Community, Ltd.	Oneida	NY	4 (1926)	1926-1936
06376	International Garden Club	Pelham Bay	NY	3 (1915-1916)	1916
10067	Sloan-Kettering Foundation	Rye	NY	57 (1957-1960)	1957-1962
00077	Solvay Process Company	Syracuse	NY	3 (1901)	1901-1902
09596	Nassau Smelting & Mining Company/Nassau Smelting & Refining Co.	Tottenville	NY	8 (1939-1940)	1940
05920	New York Air Brake Company	Watertown	NY	14 (1913-1918)	1913-1919
06365	Taggart Brothers Company Factory	Watertown	NY	0	
02042	Lane & Bodley/Lane & Bodley Manufacturing Co.	Cincinnati	OH	1 (1897)	1897-1901
06430	Baker, Dunbar-Allen Company	Cleveland	OH	0	1916
06118	Holden, Elizabeth Davis Memorial/Holden Memorial Mortuary Association	Cleveland	OH	40 (1914-1916)	1915-1916
06538	Aviation Field	Dayton	OH	0	
07832	Dayton Sewage Treatment Plant/Sewage Disposal Plant	Dayton	OH	4 (1927)	1927
06248	Deeds, E. A. Conservancy Building	Dayton	OH	12 (1915)	1915-1916
09951	Delco Products	Dayton	OH	81 (1951-1953)	1952-1966
09906	General Motors Frigidaire Division	Dayton	OH	124 (1949; 1951-1952)	1951-1966
10055	Montgomery County Airport	Dayton	OH	7 (1955-1957)	1956-1957
06699	Moraine Flying Field	Dayton	OH	0	1919
05508	Patterson Miscellaneous/Patterson, J. H.	Dayton	OH	22 (1912-1921)	1912-1922
09966	Patterson, J. H. Farm	Dayton	OH	21 (1953-1955)	1953-1955
06555	Wright Field/Wright Aviation Field	Dayton	OH	2 (1917)	1917
06367	Youngstown Sheet & Tube Company	Youngstown	OH	13 (1913-1917)	1916-1937

Job #	Job Name/Alternative Name	Job Location		Plans	Correspondence
09757	Johnson, Howard	Allentown	PA	7 (1940; 1947)	1946-1947
07821	Klines Island - Sewage Disposal Plant	Allentown	PA	10 (1927)	1927
09725	Western Electric Company	Allentown	PA	51 (1949-1951)	1946-1948
06632	Hammermill Paper Company	Erie	PA	7 (1916-1920)	1918-1920; 1935
06764	Fort Pitt - Malleable Iron Company	Pittsburgh	PA	17 (1920-1921)	1919-1921
09728	Curtis Publishing Company	Sharon Hills	PA	75 (1923; 1928; 1945-1947)	1946-1948
06289	Conrad and Jones Office Grounds	Westgrove	PA	0	1915
06911	Berkshire Knitting Mills	Wyomissing	PA	13 (1921-1925)	1920-1933
09257	Wyomissing Sewage Disposal Plant	Wyomissing	PA	1 (1931)	1931
01825	Newport Railroad Station Grounds	Newport	RI	1 (1914)	1914-1915
07726	Counting House Corporation	Providence	RI	5 (1926-1927)	1926-1928
09871	Securities Co.	Kingsport	TN	1 (1950)	1950-1955
09353	Tennessee Valley Authority/TVA	Knoxville	TN	13 (1934-1935)	1933-1937
10083	Jack Daniel Distillery	Lynchburg	TN	111 (1958-1968)	1958-1972
10438	American Horticultural Society Headquarters/Wellington/A.H.S. River Farm/Riverfarm	Alexandria	VA	23 (1973)	1973-1979
07132	Virginia Hot Springs Company	Hot Springs	VA	45 (1922-1931)	1922-1934
06419	Van Amringe Granite Company (cemetery)/clients of Mortuary Monument Richmond VA	Redmond	VA	0	1916; 1923-1926
10051	National Life Insurance Company	Montpelier	VT	137 (1956-1961)	1957-1969
09773	National Carbon Company	Saint Albans	VT	35 (1946-1947)	1947
05957	Peyton Investment Company	Spokane	WA	0	1913-1914
03734	Western Union Life Insurance Company	Spokane	WA	1 (1909)	1909-1910
07392	Kohler Company/Kohler Company - Factory Grounds	Kohler	WI	10 (1925)	1925
09250	Smith, A. O. Corporation	Milwaukee	WI	22 (1930-1931)	1930-1931; 1938

CANADA

Job #	Job Name/Alternative Name	Job Location		Plans	Correspondence
05820	Winnipeg Hunt Club	Winnipeg	MB	0	1913
07881	Crieff Manse and Farm/MacLean, J.M.	Crieff	ON	20 (1928-1929)	1927-1930; 1942
05252	Riordan Paper Co. Limited	Hawkesbury	ON	0	1911-1912
05858	United States Steel Corporation	Industrial Village	ON	0	1913
07735	Community Plate Company Ltd./Oneida Community, Ltd.	Niagara Falls	ON	3 (1925-1926)	1926; 1929-1938
02968	Finley and Spence/Guardian Building	Montreal	QC	0	1904
00231	Meredith, Mr. H. V./Bank of Montreal	Montreal	QC	6 (1895-1915)	1894-1907; 1911-1915

OTHER COUNTRIES

Job #	Job Name/Alternative Name	Job Location		Plans	Correspondence
07250	Saint George Hotel/Bermuda Development Company	Saint Georges	BER	1 (1923)	1923

View of the Caracas Country Club, date unknown. Job #7947 – Caracas Country Club
(Caracas, Venezuela).

Background: Detail of plan for The Country Club, Brookline, MA, July 1934.
Job #1048 – The Country Club (Brookline, MA).

Country Clubs, Resorts, Hotels and Clubs

Lucy Lawliss

In the 1880s Frederick Law Olmsted may have been part of designing another first: in this case, America's first true country club. According to James M. Mayo's *The American Country Club*,[1] The Country Club at Clyde Park in Brookline, Massachusetts — the same town in which Olmsted's home and office was located — was an important step in the evolution from the elitist nineteenth century city club to the popular twentieth century institution known as the country club. Prior to the formation of the first country club, the Olmsted firm had been involved in other fashionable nineteenth century health and recreation developments. The firm worked at some of the best known resorts of the day, including Hot Springs, Arkansas, and Saratoga, New York. These jobs are listed in other thematic categories.

Another first according to Mayo is the Olmsted firm's work at Roland Park, a project listed in the category of Subdivisions and Suburban Communities. Developed in the late 1890s at the northern limits of Baltimore, Roland Park — one of five planned communities by the Olmsted firm in the area — is noted by Mayo (without crediting the Olmsted firm) as the first incorporation of a golf course with a planned community. The success of this project spawned a series of golf club communities with the surge in golf's popularity through the first decades of the twentieth century. Golf became the sport inextricably linked with the American country club, and the Olmsted firm was involved in many of the outstanding clubs of the period. Additional research needs to be done to learn how many of the Olmsted firm subdivisions and planned communities that post-date the Roland Park development include golf courses and country clubs. For example, it is likely that the project listed as the Druid Hill Hotel in Atlanta, Georgia, is related to the Druid Hills Country Club that occupies the same location on the subdivision plans developed by the Olmsted firm for the Kirkwood Land Company.

Of the approximately 150 projects in this category, the golf club is an important sub-category. This uniquely American adaptation is probably best represented by the Augusta National Golf Club — arguably the country's most prestigious golf club — a development that the Olmsted firm was involved with for more than a decade. It is important to note that the Olmsted firm worked with the great golf course architect, Dr. Alister Mackenzie, at Pasatiempo Country Club and Estates at Santa Cruz, California, before both were invited to Augusta by Bobby Jones to work on Jones's visionary course.

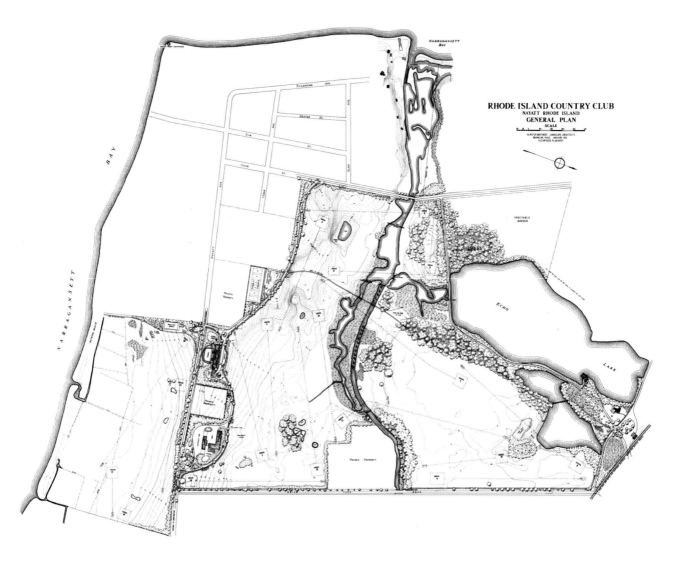

General plan for the Rhode Island Country Club, January 1912. Job #5103 – Rhode Island Country Club (Nyatt, RI).

See Introductory Guide on pages 33-35 for information on the use of this list.

Country Clubs, Resorts, Hotels, and Clubs

Job #	Job Name/Alternative Name	Job Location		Plans	Correspondence
		UNITED STATES			
09811	Vestavia Hills Golf & Riding Club	Birmingham	AL	51 (1948-1951)	1948-1951
03575	Montgomery Country Club/Country Club of Montgomery	Montgomery	AL	4 (1908)	1908
08078	Grand Canyon/El Tovar Hotel	Grand Canyon	AZ	2 (1926)	1907; 1926-1927; 1942-1944
08254	California Club	Los Angeles	CA	14 (1929-1930)	1930-1933
08003	McCloud River Club	McCloud	CA	6 (1922-1923)	1922
08255	Midwick Country Club	Montebello Park	CA	16 (1929-1930)	1930-1931
08216	Morro Bay Vista	Morro Bay	CA	4 (1925-1928)	1928-1929
08094	Palm Springs Golf Course	Palm Springs	CA	4 (1925)	1927-1932
08093	Vista Valmonte Hotel/Hotel Vista Val Monte	Palm Springs	CA	10 (1927)	1927-1932
08063	Portugese Beach Club/Portugese Bend Beach Club	Palos Verdes	CA	3 (1925)	1926
02394	Santa Catalina Island Company	Santa Catalina	CA	3 (1890-1903)	1903; 1919
08209	Hollins, Marion Miss/Pasatiempo Estates Co./Pasatiempo Golf Club and Estates Co./Santa Cruz Development Co.	Santa Cruz	CA	51 (1927-1930)	1928-1937
08097	Meadow Club of Tamalpais/Dibbler	Tamalpais	CA	14 (1927-1928)	1927-1929
06451	Broadmoor Hotel	Colorado Springs	CO	222 (1908-1921)	1916-1923; 1930
01206	Denver and Lookout Mountain Resort	Denver	CO	5 (1890)	1890-1891
05876	Lookout Mountain Property	Denver	CO	0	1913
06152	Branford Hunt Club	Branford	CT	0	1915
00694	Bridgeport Municipal Golf Course/Public Golf Course	Bridgeport	CT	4 (1930)	1930-1931
07670	Hartford Country Club	Hartford	CT	0	1926
07366	Litchfield Country Club	Litchfield	CT	0	1924
09200	Day, Irvin W.	Waterbury	CT	13 (1930)	1930; 1950
05913	Greenwoods Country Club	Winsted	CT	0	1913
07577	Clewiston Country Club District	Clewiston	FL	4 (1925)	1925-1926
07383	Timquana Country Club	Jacksonville	FL	0	1924
06553	Philip and Hover Hotel	Mountain Lake	FL	0	1917
07143	Cochran, William F./West Florida Club	Sarasota	FL	63 (1923-1925)	1923-1926; 1937
06431	Sarasota Hotel/Hotel at Sarasota/L. Barth & Son	Sarasota	FL	2 (1916)	1916
07800	Tampa Garden Club/Bayshore Boulevard	Tampa	FL	4 (1927)	1927-1930
06107	Indian River Islands Company	Vero Beach	FL	39 (1930-1940)	1925-1933; 1940; 1950
04000	Druid Hill Hotel/Kirkwood Land Company	Atlanta	GA	4 (1910)	1910-1911
03133	Piedmont Driving Club/Dargan, Milton	Atlanta	GA	0	1906-1907

Job #	Job Name/Alternative Name	Job Location		Plans	Correspondence
09275	Augusta National Golf Club	Augusta	GA	45 (1931-1932; 1940-1941)	1931-1936; 1941-1947; 1957-1962; 1974-1980
07280	Appalachian Estates Country Club/Tallulah Park	Tallulah Park	GA	0	1924
03597	Lake Shore Country Club/Highland Illinois Country Club	Glencoe	IL	34 (1909-1911)	1908-1919
03271	Lexington Country Club	Lexington	KY	7 (1907-1915)	1907-1911
07760	Big Spring Golf Club/T.H. Gamble	Louisville	KY	0	1926-1927
05838	Douglass Park Jockey Club	Louisville	KY	0	1913
06983	Louisville Country Club	Louisville	KY	57 (1925-1946)	1921-1926; 1934-1947
07654	Davis, E. K./Seapuit Club	Barnstable	MA	254 (1913-1952)	1926; 1937; 1952-1961
10252	Belmont Hill Club	Belmont	MA	0	
03000	Repton Club	Boston	MA	0	
01094	Somerset Club	Boston	MA	2 (1888)	1888; 1897
01048	Country Club, The/Brookline Country Club	Brookline	MA	37 (1886-1946)	1888-1889; 1937-1947
10162	Faulkner Farm/American Academy of Arts and Sciences	Brookline	MA	2 (1963)	1963-1964
02981	Tavern Club	Brookline	MA	0	1904
09748	Owl Club	Cambridge	MA	26 (1946)	1946-1948
06083	Concord Golf Club	Concord	MA	0	1914
09547	Bass Rocks Beach Club	Gloucester	MA	4 (1948)	1938-1939
09560	Y. M. C. A.	Halifax	MA	4 (1939)	
04073	Mount Tom Golf Club	Holyoke	MA	72 (1922-1924)	1910; 1921-1925
06942	Jones River Club/Jones River Village Club/John Bradford House	Kingston	MA	2 (1920-1921)	1921
04017	Lawrence Country Club	Lawrence	MA	0	1910
07301	Longmeadow Country Club	Longmeadow	MA	1 (1924)	1924; 1928
09313	Tedesco Country Club	Marblehead/Salem	MA	15 (1932)	1932-1934
09458	Kittansett Club	Marion	MA	4 (1936)	1932-1936
09179	Milton Women's Club	Milton	MA	13 (1930)	1930
00216	Country Club	New Bedford	MA	5 (1902)	1902-1905
09958	Brae Burn Country Club	Newton	MA	0	1947-1953
03174	Home Culture Club Company/Home-Culture Clubs/Cable, G. W.	Northampton	MA	5 (1903-1906)	1906-1909
09391	Clara Barton Homestead Camp	Oxford	MA	30 (1928; 1935-1938)	1935
09209	Pittsfield Country Club	Pittsfield	MA	3 (1930)	1930
01774	Shellton Hotel	Quincy	MA	6 (1895-1896)	1896
10327	Spring Valley Country Club	Sharon	MA	0	
10037	Myopia Hunt Club	South Hamilton	MA	0	1956
09187	Cohasse Country Club	Southbridge	MA	15 (1923-1930)	1930; 1935
09189	Wells Camps	Southbridge	MA	7 (1930)	1930
09894	Colony Club	Springfield	MA	14 (1951)	1951-1954

Job #	Job Name/Alternative Name	Job Location		Plans	Correspondence
09570	The Inn/Montgomery, W.P.	West Falmouth	MA	14 (1929-1933)	1939-1941
10673	Pine Brook Country Club	Weston	MA	0	1978-1979
09744	Wianno Club	Wianno	MA	23 (1931; 1946-1947)	1946-1947
06064	Worcester Golf Club	Worcester	MA	0	1914
07591	Annapolis Roads/Armstrong, R. A./Belmont Hotel/Armstrong, Rella A.	Annapolis	MD	86 (1894-1927)	1926-1935; 1973-1977
07814	Woodholme Club	Pikesville	MD	0	1927
07512	Augusta House	Augusta	ME	1 (1925)	1922-1927
07802	Wickyup Club	Hancock County	ME	0	1927
06352	Parmachenee Club	Oxford County	ME	6 (1915)	1916
07856	Sprague Corporation/Black Point Inn	Prouts Neck	ME	15 (1927)	1927
06550	Washtenaw Country Club	Ann Arbor	MI	2 (1917)	1917
06841	Detroit Aviation Country Club	Detroit	MI	17 (1919-1920)	1920-1926
07680	Kansas City Country Club District	Kansas City	MO	0	1926
07480	Golf Club	Laurel	MS	0	
06821	Kamuga Lake Development	Hendersonville	NC	0	1920

Broadmoor Hotel grounds, July 1936. Job #6451 – Broadmoor Hotel (Colorado Springs, CO).

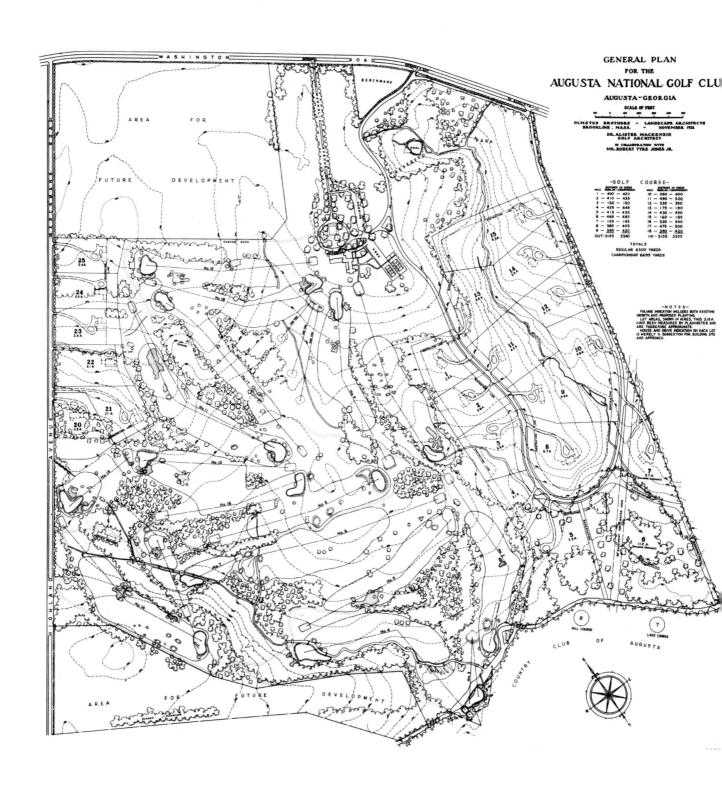

General plan for the Augusta National Golf Club, November 1932. Job #9275 – Augusta National Golf Club (Augusta, GA).

Job #	Job Name/Alternative Name	Job Location		Plans	Correspondence
05266	Hale, Henry S./Tract in White Mountains/ Dixville Notch	Dixville Notch	NH	1 (1911)	1911
06885	Wentworth Hall Hotel	Jackson	NH	0	1920-1921
09515	Y. M. C. A.	Lake Winnipasaukee	NH	38 (1937-1948)	1937-1952
06765	Stoneleigh Manor/Rye Beach Hotel/ Stonleigh Manor Hotel/Philbrick, Shirley S.	Rye Beach	NH	37 (1915-1920)	1919-1922
09591	Y. M. C. A. - North Woods	Wolfeboro	NH	0	
07425	Golf Club/Douglas, W. J.		NJ	0	1925
07067	Baltusrol Golf Club	Baltusrol	NJ	18 (1922-1924)	1922-1924
07755	Camden Country Club/Camden County Park Commission	Camden	NJ	0	1926-1927
02155	Essex County Golf Course/Golf Course - Branch Brook Extension	Essex County	NJ	4 (1926-1929)	1928-1929
07144	Maplewood Country Club	Maplewood	NJ	0	1922-1923
07642	Essex County Country Club	Orange	NJ	0	1926
07043	Civic Club/Proposed Park	Summit	NJ	0	1922
09310	Summit Women's Club	Summit	NJ	0	1932
09269	Ardsley Club	Dobbs Ferry	NY	0	1928-1931
07551	Chocomount Homes Inc./Six Syndicate Lots	Fishers Island	NY	47 (1925-1926)	1926-1930
07015	Creek Club/Locust Valley C.C./Walker & Gillette C.C./Clients of Walker and Gillette/Cavath Property Lots A & D	Glen Cove	NY	67 (1922-1923)	1922-1923
07169	Nassau Country Club	Glen Cove	NY	0	
09346	Women's National Golf and Tennis Club	Glen Cove	NY	0	1933
06344	Grand View Hotel	Lake Placid	NY	1 (1911; 1916)	1896; 1916
09506	Lake Placid Club	Lake Placid	NY	2 (1937)	1937-1944
07249	Hempstead Country Club	Long Island	NY	2 (1923)	1923-1924
02211	Atlantic Yacht Club	New York City	NY	0	1898
09364	Canarsie Race Track	New York City	NY	11 (1934)	1934-1935
00621	Coney Island Jockey Club	New York City	NY	29 (1880)	1879-1880; 1887
00515	Rockaway/Rockaway Beach & Jamaica Bay	New York City	NY	105 (1879)	1876-1884; 1975
09155	Century Country Club	Purchase	NY	26 (1922-1934)	1929-1934
06745	Engineers Country Club/Engineers Club Golf Course	Roslyn	NY	37 (1919-1920)	1919-1924; 1935; 1944
02880	Columbus Country Club	Columbus	OH	0	1904
03229	Dayton Country Club/formerly Kramer property, Oakwood subdivision	Dayton	OH	4 (1907-1912)	1907-1910; 1917-1919
06679	Dayton Polo Club/Polo Club — (Deeds)/ Miami Valley Hunt & Polo Club	Dayton	OH	10 (1919)	1919
06682	Dayton Women's Club	Dayton	OH	3 (1919-1922)	1919
06700	Eby Club House	Dayton	OH	0	
06189	Kidder, Walter S./Miami Valley Golf Club House/Dayton View Country Club	Dayton	OH	31 (1915-1919)	1915-1919; 1961

View from the Capilano Golf Club to the Vancouver skyline, February 8, 1937. Job #9273 – British Pacific Properties (Vancouver, BC, Canada). Listed in Subdivisions and Suburban Communities.

Job #	Job Name/Alternative Name	Job Location		Plans	Correspondence
06236	Miami Hotel/Miame Hotel Gardens	Dayton	OH	0	1915-1916
06968	Old Barn Club/Patterson, J. H.	Dayton	OH	9 (1920-1921)	1922
06071	Hamilton Country Club	Hamilton	OH	0	1914
07749	Congress Lake Club	Hartville	OH	0	1926-1927
10025	Armco Steel Company	Middletown	OH	84 (1955-1965)	1955-1971
07474	Westlake Hotel	Rocky River	OH	0	1925
05510	Waverly Country Club	Clackamas County	OR	3 (1912-1919)	1912
02689	Portland Country Club	Portland	OR	0	1907
02882	Allegheny Country Club	Allegheny	PA	0	1901; 1908
07242	Buck Hill Falls Inn/Buck Hill Falls Company	Buck Hill Falls	PA	145 (1923-1931)	1923-1934; 1940; 1944
07607	Sky Top Lodge Inc.	Buck Hill Falls	PA	96 (1921-1930)	1926-1934
06359	Sunnybrook Golf Club	Chestnut Hill	PA	0	
07104	Kennett Square Golf & Country Club/Kennett Country Club	Kennett Square	PA	3 (1923)	1922-1923
06760	Rolling Rock Club	Laughlinstown	PA	155 (1919-1931)	1919-1920; 1930-1932; 1948
03325	McIlhenny, John D.	Philadelphia	PA	2 (1906)	1907; 1936-1937
03798	Philadelphia Cricket Club	Philadelphia	PA	0	1909-1910; 1914-1915
05384	Pike County Shooting Club	Pike County	PA	0	1911
06913	Longue Vue Club/Longue Vue Country Club	Pittsburgh	PA	0	1921-1923
00233	Schenley Hotel	Pittsburgh	PA	6 (1898)	1898-1905

Job #	Job Name/Alternative Name	Job Location		Plans	Correspondence
07990	Scranton Country Club	Scranton	PA	9 (1928-1929)	1928-1932
07136	Westmoreland Club	Wilkes-Barre	PA	9 (1922-1923)	1922-1923; 1934
07500	York Country Club	York	PA	0	1925
07196	Wannamoisett Country Club	East Providence	RI	0	
00678	Narragansett Casino	Narragansett	RI	2 (1884)	1884
05103	Rhode Island Country Club	Nyatt	RI	31 (1911-1923)	1911-1924
03645	Pomham Club	Providence	RI	0	1909
06742	Misquamicut Golf Club	Watch Hill	RI	17 (191-1930)	1919-1930
07199	Charleston Country Club/Wappoo Country Club	Charleston	SC	19 (1923-1926)	1923-1927; 1946
07347	The Allegendoah Club/The Allegendoab Club	Goshen	VA	0	1924
07431	Hotchkin, E. B. Jr. Country Club Project/Hotchkiss, E. B. Jr./Golf Club Project	Richmond	VA	0	1925
07564	Yorktown Hotel Corporation/Yorktown Country Club	Yorktown	VA	0	1925-1926
09674	Ekwanok Club	Manchester	VT	0	1944
08207	Bainbridge Island Country Club	Seattle	WA	4 (1905; 1928)	1927-1929
08065	Nile Temple Country Club	Seattle	WA	20 (1926-1927)	1926-1927
03353	Seattle Golf & Country Club/Highlands	Seattle	WA	4 (1891-1925)	1907-1915
05943	Davenport Hotel/Roof Garden	Spokane	WA	25 (1913)	1913-1914
06156	Pendleton Arms Hotel/Berkeley Springs Hotel	Berkeley Springs	WV	8 (1916)	1915-1916
09178	Greenbrier Hotel	White Sulphur Springs	WV	19 (1930)	1929-1930
02395	Rocky Mountain Country Club	Laramie	WY	2 (1903)	1903-1906
	CANADA				
05259	Calgary Golf and Country Club	Calgary	AB	0	1911
09661	British Pacific Development Company/Sentinel Hill	West Vancouver	BC	15 (1927-1944)	1944-1946
03757	Manitoba Club	Winnipeg	MB	0	1909
	OTHER COUNTRIES				
05255	Panama Hotel		PAN	0	1911
07947	Caracas Club/Caracas Country Club	Caracas	VEN	72 (1928-1930)	1928-1932; 1941

Saint Michael's Episcopal Church, July 1921. Job #6950 – Saint Michael's Episcopal Church (Litchfield, CT).

Background: Detail of preliminary general plan for the National Cathedral grounds, March 1910. Job #3297 – Washington Cathedral (Washington, DC).

Grounds of Churches

Lucy Lawliss

The list of projects associated with church grounds is not long, which is not surprising because the focus in this type of development is on the structure, not the landscape. However, there are a few notable exceptions. During the career of Frederick Law Olmsted it would appear that there was only one commission of note that he designed: Brookline's First Parish Church, which is very close to Fairsted, Olmsted's home and office in Brookline, Massachusetts. In addition to the proximity and setting of the church, this congregation founded in 1717 notes in its history that it survived the schism of Congregationalists and Unitarians in the early nineteenth century and the two communities continued to worship together and dedicate this notable structure and setting in 1893, a decade after Olmsted's move to Brookline. It is likely that the age and tolerance of this community would have appealed to Olmsted, who was a seventh-generation New Englander and not known to have had any strong connection to a particular church or denomination.

Another significant commission for the Olmsted firm in this thematic category includes the long association of Frederick Law Olmsted Jr. with the National Cathedral in Washington, D.C. The Cathedral's All Hallows Guild, a volunteer organization, was founded in 1916 to work with Olmsted Jr. to oversee the beautification and maintenance of the Cathedral gardens and grounds. On the Guild's seventy-fifth anniversary, Olmsted historian Susan L. Klaus (see Subdivisions and Suburban Communities) noted that the relationship with the Cathedral grew out of the role of Olmsted Jr. with the McMillan Commission, the three-person team organized by Congress in 1900 to extend the L'Enfant plan for Washington, D.C., and the Capitol area. In the true Olmsted tradition, Olmsted Jr. was involved at the National Cathedral as early as 1907 to help select a site "most rare in picturesqueness and beauty" and was still consulting in the mid-1920s to oversee the completion of three phases of planning and construction that included a campus of buildings, gardens and woodland.

A thorough study of this category should include a review of Subdivisions and Suburban Communities as well as College and School Campuses for church grounds that may have been developed as part of larger community plans.

Top: Panorama northwest on San Marco Avenue, Mission Nombre de Dios, June 1964.

Bottom: Panorama northeast on San Marco near Pine Street, Mission Nombre de Dios, June 1964. Job #10172 – Mission of Nombre de Dios (Saint Augustine, FL).

See Introductory Guide on pages 33-35 for information on the use of this list.

Grounds of Churches

Job #	Job Name/Alternative Name	Job Location		Plans	Correspondence
		UNITED STATES			
09589	Saint Joseph Cathedral	Hartford	CT	143 (1938-1958)	1939-1950; 1957-1962
06950	Saint Michael's Episcopal Church	Litchfield	CT	6 (1919-1921)	1921-1922
09792	Saint Rose's Church	Meriden	CT	13 (1947)	1947-1948
06040	Torrington Central Congregational Church	Torrington	CT	10 (1914-1917)	1914-1917; 1934
06657	Torrington-Trinity Rectory/Trinity Church Rectory	Torrington	CT	15 (1917-1920)	1918-1920
07909	Waterbury Church of the Immaculate Conception	Waterbury	CT	24 (1928)	1928
07924	Waterbury First Congregational Church	Waterbury	CT	2 (1928)	1928
07275	Christ Church	Watertown	CT	13 (1924)	1924
09992	National Shrine of the Immaculate Conception	Washington	DC	258 (1953-1967)	1954-1969
03297	Washington Cathedral/Boys Choir Grounds	Washington	DC	343 (1905-1927)	1895; 1907-1929; 1939-1944
06178	Bethesda by the Sea Church Competition	Palm Beach	FL	0	
10172	Mission of Nombre de Dios	Saint Augustine	FL	22 (1963-1964)	1960-1965
09597	Lexington Second Presbyterian Church	Lexington	KY	1 (1940)	1940; 1950
09780	Broadway Baptist Church	Louisville	KY	8 (1947-1948)	1947-1948
09984	Fourth Avenue Presbyterian Church	Louisville	KY	38 (1954-1956)	1954-1957
09749	Saint Francis in the Fields Church	Louisville	KY	91 (1943-1958)	1946-1958
09974	Second Presbyterian Church	Louisville	KY	72 (1953-1958)	1954-1958
09893	Saint Matthew's Episcopal Church	Louisville	KY	81 (1951-1966)	1950-1967
09812	Plymouth Congregational Church	Belmont	MA	8 (1946-1948)	1948
09073	Saint John's Church	Beverly Farms	MA	7 (1929)	1929
	* See also Mattapan and Roxbury	Boston	MA		
09910	Arlington Street Church	Boston	MA	9 (1945; 1951-1952)	1951-1953
09321	Christian Science Church Park/Christian Science Park	Boston	MA	2 (1932)	1932-1933
10111	Church of the Advent	Boston	MA	2 (1960)	
02976	All Souls Church	Braintree	MA	0	1904
01178	First Parish Church	Brookline	MA	23 (1887-1938)	1889-1894; 1900-1907; 1917; 1936-1938
00687	Saint Paul's Church	Brookline	MA	19 (1885)	1898-1903
10096	Unitarian Church	Cambridge	MA	10 (1959-1960)	1959-1961
07828	Alcott Memorial/Carved Tablet/Alcott Memorial Association	Concord	MA	0	1927-1928
07931	Fall River - Saint Mary's Cathedral	Fall River	MA	15 (1927-1928)	1928
05772	First Congregational Church	Fall River	MA	1 (1912)	1912-1916

Job #	Job Name/Alternative Name	Job Location		Plans	Correspondence
01424	Falmouth Church	Falmouth	MA	8 (1890-1894)	1889-1895
03129	Hingham Church/St. John the Evangelist Parish	Hingham	MA	3 (1906)	1906
09146	Aldred, John Memorial Chapel	Lawrence	MA	1 (1929)	1929-1931
06462	Lawrence Street Congregational Church	Lawrence	MA	1 (1916)	1916-1918
10070	Christian Science Church	Lynn	MA	10 (1958)	1958-1960
12076	Rotch Memorial Chapel	Mattapan	MA	17 (1886-1887)	1886-1887; 1895
12505	Parkway Community Methodist Church	Milton	MA	6 (1969)	
10149	Tifereth Israel Synagogue	New Bedford	MA	10 (1961-1962)	1962
	* See also West Newton	Newton	MA		
07051	Newton Center Methodist Church/ Newton Episcopal Church/Speare, E. Ray	Newton	MA	0	1922
00445	Newton Centre First Church	Newton	MA	0	1900
02280	First Church in Newton/First Unitarian Church in Newton	Newton Centre	MA	2 (1899)	1906
10119	First Church of Christ Scientist	Newtonville	MA	9 (1960)	1960-1961
09914	Saint Theresa's Church	Pittsfield	MA	0	1951-1952
06223	Home for Aged Couples Chapel	Roxbury	MA	0	1915
02925	Unitarian Society	Roxbury	MA	0	1903
05513	Walnut Park Methodist Episcopal Church/Walnut Avenue Church/Walnut Avenue Methodist & Episcopal Church	Roxbury	MA	2 (1912)	1912-1913
10420	Unitarian Church	Sharon	MA	3 (1973)	1972-1975
09872	Taunton Church	Taunton	MA	0	
10439	Trinitarian Congregational Church	Wayland	MA	0	1973
09729	Wellesley First Church of Christ Scientist	Wellesley	MA	32 (1946-1953)	1946-1953
10116	First Congregational Church	Wellesley Hills	MA	14 (1958-1961)	1960
09522	Saint Bernard's Church	West Newton	MA	18 (1938)	1938-1952
03122	West Newton Unitarian Church	West Newton	MA	7 (1906)	1906-1907
10689	Saint Demetrios Church	Weston	MA	0	1979
07737	Weston Baptist Parsonage/Weston First Baptist Church	Weston	MA	5 (1926)	1926
07738	Weston First Baptist Church	Weston	MA	1 (1926)	1926
02212	Whitinsville Congregational Church	Whitinsville	MA	3 (1897-1899)	1899
09701	Congregational Church	Worcester	MA	0	1945
10069	Temple Beth Israel	Worcester	MA	10 (1957-1959)	1957-1960
09946	Cathedral of the Assumption of the Blessed Virgin Mary	Baltimore	MD	292 (1952-1962)	1954-1962
05271	Jenkins Memorial Church/Jenkins, Michael	Baltimore	MD	3 (1911)	1911
09057	Saint Ambrose Church	Baltimore	MD	1 (1929)	1929
10036	First Congregational Church	Camden	ME	10 (1955-1956)	1956; 1964
05675	Brown Chapel	Falmouth	ME	2 (1913)	1913
10693	Trinity Chapel	Kennebunk Beach	ME	0	1978-1979

The main entrance to Saint John's Church, July 1940. Job #9605 – Saint John's Church, Kohler Village (Kohler, WI).

Job #	Job Name/Alternative Name	Job Location		Plans	Correspondence
06788	Saint Ann's Church	Kennebunkport	ME	0	1920
09881	Knox Church	Thomaston	ME	5 (1930)	1950
07754	Cranbrook Christ Church	Birmingham	MI	5 (1926-1928)	1926-1929; 1935
05383	North Woodward Avenue Congregational Church	Detroit	MI	2 (1911)	1911-1914
10136	Shrine of Saint Therese	Hampton Beach	NH	3 (1961)	N.D.
09576	Union Chapel/Fuller, A. T.	Rye Beach	NH	3 (1939)	1939-1940
07938	East Orange Church of the Holy Name of Jesus	East Orange	NJ	3 (1928)	1928-1929
07565	Montclair Congregational Church/ Montclair Sunday School	Montclair	NJ	16 (1914-1929)	1925-1929
03472	Saint George's Church/Strong, Mrs. William E.	Seabright	NJ	5 (1908)	1908-1909
09038	Saint James Church	Albany	NY	8 (1925-1929)	1928-1931
03809	Sage Memorial Church	Far Rockaway	NY	7 (1906-1910)	1879; 1909-1914

Job #	Job Name/Alternative Name	Job Location		Plans	Correspondence
09975	Church of Our Lady - Queen of Martyrs	Forest Hills	NY	8 (1954-1958)	1954
03126	Glen Cove Church	Glen Cove	NY	3 (1906)	1873; 1906
03570	Saint Barnabas Protestant Episcopal Church/Dunham, Carroll	Irvington	NY	0	1908-1909
06786	Saint John's Lattingtown Rectory	Locust Valley	NY	12 (1919-1928)	1920-1931
09285	Mamaroneck Methodist-Episcopal Church	Mamaroneck	NY	0	1931
07543	Saint Thomas Episcopal Church	Mamaroneck	NY	3 (1925)	1925
09069	New Rochelle First Presbyterian Church	New Rochelle	NY	4 (1929-1930)	1929-1930
00539	Riverside Church	New York City	NY	34 (1929-1941)	1931-1941
01037	Roche Memorial Chapel	New York City	NY	0	1907
05559	Saint John the Divine Cathedral	New York City	NY	0	1912
09900	Saint Paul's Episcopal Church	Akron	OH	20 (1946-1951)	1951-1952
09934	Greek Orthodox Church	Dayton	OH	7 (1952)	1952-1953
10043	Shiloh Congregational Christian Church	Dayton	OH	54 (1952-1957)	1956-1959
09909	Saint Timothy's Parish	Garfield Heights	OH	2 (1951)	1951
07065	Presbyterian Synod of Ohio	Sidney	OH	0	1922
07915	Wernersville Novitiate Order of Jesuits	Wernersville	PA	22 (1927-1929)	1928-1930
06988	Lutheran Church of the Atonement	Wyomissing	PA	6 (1920)	1921-1923
10128	Temple Sinai	Cranston	RI	8 (1961)	1961-1962
10326	Cathedral of Saints Peter and Paul	Providence	RI	38 (1963; 1968-1972)	1971-1973
10217	Chancery Office Building	Providence	RI	74 (1966-1970)	1967-1969
09625	Lutheran Church/Bethany Evangelical Lutheran Church	Kohler	WI	18 (1941-1942)	1941-1943
09605	Saint John's Church/Kohler Village	Kohler	WI	12 (1939-1940)	1940-1945
	CANADA				
07162	Crieff Churchyard/Crieff Churchyard Cemetery/Maclean, J. B.	Crieff	ON	17 (1923-1930)	1923-1931

Left (top): View of the long walk and boxwood hedge, National Cathedral, Fall 1926. Job #3297 – Washington Cathedral (Washington, DC).

Left (bottom): South steps of the National Cathedral, July 1935. Job #3297 – Washington Cathedral (Washington, DC)

Seattle Arboretum in Washington Park. Job #2699 – Seattle Arboretum (Seattle, WA).

Background: Detail of topographical map of the Bussey farm, now the Arnold Arboretum, date unknown. Job #902 – Arnold Arboretum (Boston, MA).

Arboreta and Gardens

Lauren Meier

Arboreta and gardens constitute a relatively minor category for the Olmsted firm, with about twenty projects, about fifteen of which produced design plans. It represents, however, a project type associated with a handful of major arboreta completed in association with park systems in Boston, Louisville and Seattle, as well as important arboreta/botanic gardens in cities such as Brooklyn, New York. The earliest of these projects and the one most closely associated with Frederick Law Olmsted is the Arnold Arboretum (1879-1897). It is located in the Jamaica Plain section of Boston between Franklin Park and Jamaica Pond along the Arborway, and forms a significant piece of the Emerald Necklace park system. Created as one of the first successful American arboreta open to the public, the Arnold Arboretum serves as a prototype, with dual functions as a scientific study collection of hardy trees and as a scenic pleasure ground that provides shelter and respite from the city.[1] While the Arboretum's first director, Charles Sprague Sargent, sought to create a museum for the display of living specimens, Olmsted brought his park experience, noting his design intent:

> We want a ground to which people may easily go after their day's work is done, and
> where they may stroll for an hour, seeing, hearing, and feeling nothing of the bustle
> and jar of the streets, where they shall, in effect, find the city put far away from
> them…. What we want most is a simple, broad, open space of clean greensward, with
> sufficient play of surface and a sufficient number of trees about it to supply a variety of
> light and shade…. We want depth of wood enough about it not only for comfort in
> hot weather, but to completely shut out the city from our landscapes.[2]

After several years of negotiations between Harvard University and the City of Boston and a long series of design studies, Olmsted and Sargent created a plan for the Arnold Arboretum in which trees were grouped by family and genus following their phylogenetic order, with a curvilinear road system that negotiated the site's undulating topography so that visitors would

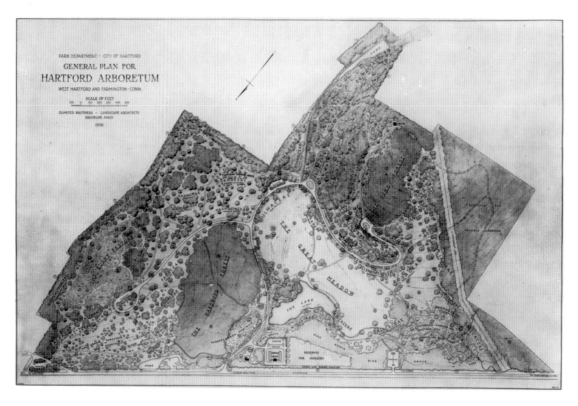

Top: Vestavia Gardens temple from the east lawn, August 15, 1949. Job #9800 – Vestavia Gardens (Birmingham, AL).

Bottom: General plan for the Hartford Arboretum, 1936. Job #813 – Hartford Arboretum (Hartford-Farmington, CT).

experience the tree collection in a strictly logical order.[3] This dual function of scientific museum and aesthetic pleasure ground is still intact more than a century after the Arnold Arboretum's creation.

The firm was consulted as early as 1893 on the future of the Missouri Botanical Garden, which was in a period of transition following the death of its founder, Henry Shaw, in 1889. Shaw had been instrumental in founding both the botanic garden and later a School of Botany at Washington University in Saint Louis, and was involved in negotiations regarding the role the university would play in the care and upkeep of the botanic garden. Unlike the Arnold Arboretum, the Missouri Botanic Garden was established as a not for profit institution rather than a direct affiliate or extension of the university. The Board of Trustees asked the Olmsted firm to submit a plan to both evaluate the current condition of Shaw's garden and make plans for its future. Although the Olmsted master plan was adopted by the Trustees, only a portion was implemented. Listed in the *Master List* in both the parks and arboreta categories, the Missouri Botanical Garden is, like the Arnold Arboretum, a scientific botanical garden that is open to the public and serves as a pleasure ground.

Much of the Olmsted firm's arboreta/botanic garden work occurred in the mid-1930s, with several projects completed concurrently with work by the WPA. The Olmsted firm created plans for the Seattle Arboretum (1884, 1903-1906, 1934-1939), Morris Arboretum in Philadelphia (1909-1933), listed as Chestnut Hill, Bernheim Arboretum in Louisville, Kentucky, (1929-1957) and the Brooklyn Botanic Garden (1907-1919). Frederick Law Olmsted Jr. and James Frederick Dawson are largely credited with the implementation of the plans for the Seattle Arboretum at Washington Park, which opened in 1934, and with the Olmsted firm's plans for the Bernheim Arboretum, implemented the following year. While the *Master List* indicates sixteen plans prepared for the Hartford Arboretum between 1934 and 1936, it is difficult to ascertain the full extent of the firm's design work there. In addition to the large public arboreta, between 1933 and 1935 the Olmsted Brothers completed more than fifty design plans for the interior courtyard, fountain and front planting at the Frick Museum (Collection) in New York City. The *Master List* includes other lesser-known botanic gardens that progressed into design in Birmingham and Kellyton, Alabama, and Sebring, Florida.

Top: Lilacs at the Arnold Arboretum, date unknown. Job #902 – Arnold Arboretum (Boston, MA).

Bottom: Arnold Arboretum, July 1939. Job #902 – Arnold Arboretum (Boston, MA).

Arboreta and Gardens

Job #	Job Name/Alternative Name	Job Location		Plans	Correspondence
		UNITED STATES			
09800	Vestavia Gardens	Birmingham	AL	42 (1928-1951)	1958-1962
09272	Jordan, Ann Game Preserve Inc./Mitchell, Sidney Z.	Kellyton	AL	118 (1931-1932)	1925-1926
08239	Rancho Santa Ana Botanic Gardens	Long Beach	CA	55 (1928-1939)	1927-1952
00813	Hartford Arboretum/Batterson Park	Hartford-Farmington	CT	16 (1934-1936)	1931-1932
02845	Botanic Garden/National Arboretum	Washington	DC	0	1934-1936
09451	Rosarium for American Rose Society	Washington	DC	0	1935
07029	Bok, Edward Sanctuary for Birds/Mt. Lake Sanctuary/Bok, Edward W./Sanctuary and Singing Tower	Mountain Lake	FL	303 (1922-1959)	1920-1978
06168	Handleman Memorial Garden	Mountain Lake	FL	0	1919
09352	Florida Botanic Garden & Arboretum	Sebring	FL	20 (1933-1934)	1912; 1941
06669	Lincoln Farm Association, Arboretum Project	Hodgenville	KY	0	1931-1965
09278	Bernheim, I. W. Arboretum & Herbarium	Louisville	KY	143 (1929-1957; 1968)	1976
10563	Andover Bicentennial Garden	Andover	MA	2 (1976)	1932-1940
00902	Arnold Arboretum/Parkway	Boston	MA	252 (1879-1897)	1947-1956
10649	Houghton Garden (Webster Conservation Area)	Chestnut Hill	MA	0	1904-1939; 1977-1978
07683	Springfield Garden Club/Springfield Garden Club Competition	Springfield	MA	0	1877-1898; 1921-1934; 1945; 1958; 1966; 1977-1979
00081	Missouri Botanic Gardens/Missouri Botanical Garden	Saint Louis	MO	96 (1896-1905)	1892-1912; 1959-1966
05500	William Mason Gardens	Laurel	MS	0	1928; 1934-1940
03960	Brooklyn Botanic Gardens/Brooklyn Institute of Arts and Sciences/Brooklyn Botanic Garden	New York City	NY	53 (1907-1919)	
09382	Frick Museum/The Frick Collection	New York City	NY	58 (1933-1935)	1910-1919; 1970-1971
10126	Holden Arboretum	Mentor	OH	0	1897-1899
09331	Morris Arboretum/University of Pennsylvania	Chestnut Hill	PA	246 (1909-1933)	1978-1979
01899	Philadelphia Economic Plants Garden/Phila. Com. Museum	Philadelphia	PA	9 (1897-1899)	1897; 1936-1938
02699	Seattle Arboretum/Washington Park/University of Washington Arboretum	Seattle	WA	117 (1884; 1903-1906; 1934-1939)	1917-1945; 1953

World's Columbian Exposition. Job #274 – World's Columbian Exposition (Chicago, IL).

Background: Detail of map of buildings and grounds of the Jackson Park and Midway Plaisance, World's Columbian Exposition, 1893. Job #274 – World's Columbian Exposition (Chicago, IL).

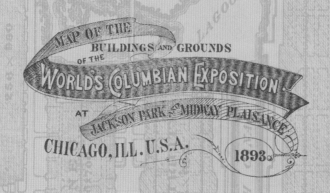

Exhibitions and Fairs

Julia S. Bachrach

Frederick Law Olmsted and the Olmsted Brothers played a significant role in planning and designing some of the nation's most influential exhibitions and fairs. In 1890, when Chicago won the honor of hosting the World's Columbian Exposition, Frederick Law Olmsted was asked to help select the site for the fair. While groups throughout the city lobbied for their own neighborhoods, Olmsted envisioned a site that would provide dramatic views of Lake Michigan as the backdrop for the fairgrounds. Two decades earlier, Olmsted and Vaux had laid out the 1055-acre South Park, which included Eastern and Western Divisions and a wide swath to connect them, the Midway Plaisance. The Western Division, renamed Washington Park, was largely implemented by the time the fair was being planned. In contrast, the Eastern Division, which had become Jackson Park, had only a small area of finished landscape. Because of Jackson Park's lakefront setting and its incomplete state, Olmsted advocated for it as the site of the World's Columbian Exposition.

Olmsted and Henry Codman articulated a guiding theme similar to that of the original South Park Plan—a series of navigable waters that would be linked to Lake Michigan. In a meeting with consulting architects Daniel H. Burnham and John Welborn Root, the planners sketched the scheme at a large scale on brown paper. The plan featured a great architectural court with a formal canal leading to a series of lagoons. In the middle of the lagoon system, Olmsted suggested carving a natural sandy peninsula into a large secluded wooded island meant to remain free of buildings or structures. Although he had pressure to build various exhibits on the island, Olmsted argued to protect its sylvan character, and only the Japanese pavilion and a garden that coincided with the Horticultural Building were allowed. The island would stand in stark contrast to the magnificent campus of white neoclassical buildings that would be accessed by boat and train.

After the death of John Welborn Root in 1891, Burnham continued as Director of Works for the World's Columbian Exposition, and Olmsted's role as consulting landscape architect remained pivotal. When the fair opened on May 1, 1893, visitors were dazzled by the gleaming "White City." Six months later, after the fair closed, many of its plaster buildings were destroyed by fire, and almost all of the rest were razed. The South Park Commissioners retained Olmsted, Olmsted & Eliot to transform the site back to parkland. The firm's 1895 plan featured the lake, lagoons and playfields in a manner similar to that of Olmsted and Vaux's original plan. The later plan did, however, retain the Fine Arts Palace as the Field Columbian Museum (now Museum of Science and Industry) as a vestige of the fair.

After Frederick Law Olmsted's death, the Olmsted Brothers continued the legacy by designing a number of other fairs and expositions. The Olmsted Brothers developed numerous plans for the 1915 Panama-California Exposition in San Diego's Balboa Park. These plans were not fully realized, however, because local authorities insisted on altering the location of the fair, and the Olmsted Brothers withdrew from the project. The firm had better success in planning other fairs, including the 1905 Lewis & Clark Exposition in Portland, Oregon, and the 1909 Alaska-Yukon-Pacific Exposition in Seattle (also listed in Parks, Parkways, Recreation Areas and Scenic Reservations), now the Rainier Vista in the heart of the University of Washington campus. The firm also designed exhibition sites within important American fairs, such the National Cash Register Exhibit at the 1939 New York World's Fair.

Fountain in the Alaska-Yukon-Pacific Exposition, now part of the Rainier vista at the University of Washington. Job #2739 – Alaska-Yukon-Pacific Exposition (Seattle, WA).

See Introductory Guide on pages 33-35 for information on the use of this list.

Exhibitions and Fairs

Job #	Job Name/Alternative Name	Job Location		Plans	Correspondence
02411	Arundell Club Exhibition			0	
02921	Exhibition Plans/plans used for exhibitions			53 (1893-1925)	1904-1965

UNITED STATES

Job #	Job Name/Alternative Name	Job Location		Plans	Correspondence
08275	Cabrillo Exposition	Los Angeles	CA	0	1935-1938
04051	Balboa Park/City Park/San Diego Exposition/Panama-California Exposition (1915)	San Diego	CA	38 (1911-1915)	1910-1915; 1940-1948
05380	Panama-Pacific New York State Bldg. Exposition/ASLA, Exhibit of/San Francisco Exhibition	San Francisco	CA	4 (1914)	1911-1915
03957	Iowa State Fair Grounds	Des Moines	IA	0	1910
00274	World's Columbian Exposition	Chicago	IL	141 (1891-1893)	1888-1899
03445	Kentucky State Fair Grounds	Lexington	KY	0	1908
00936	Boston Parks Dept. Exhibit/Chicago Worlds Fair 1893	Boston	MA	11 (1879-1893)	1893-1894
01536	Paris Exposition/Paris Exhibition Exhibit/Metropolitan Parks Commission exhibit	Boston	MA	4 (1899-1900)	1878-1879; 1899-1900
02930	Turin Exhibit	Boston	MA	0	
03702	Boston 1915/Boston 1915 Exposition	Brookline	MA	4 (1909)	1909-1910
02889	Louisiana Purchase Exposition	Saint Louis	MO	1 (1904)	1899-1901
01548	Saint Louis Exposition/Metropolitan Parks Commission exhibit	Saint Louis	MO	2 (1903-1904)	1903-1905
07627	Atlantic City Exposition/International Exposition	Atlantic City	NJ	20 (1919-1926)	1926
00410	Pan-American Exposition	Buffalo	NY	0	1899
09533	National Cash Register - New York World's Fair Exhibit/National Cash Register Company/ Exhibit, New York World's Fair (1939)	New York City	NY	40 (1937-1938)	1938-1940
09514	New York World's Fair	New York City	NY	0	1879-1889; 1936-1939
03367	New York State Fair Commission	Syracuse	NY	0	1907
00099	County Fair Grounds	Dayton	OH	0	1898
06817	Patterson, J. H. - New Fair Grounds	Dayton	OH	0	
02399	Lewis & Clark Exposition	Portland	OR	5 (1902-1903)	1903-1904
05174	Lewis & Wiley Exposition Tract	Portland	OR	7 (1910)	1911
07039	Philadelphia Sesquicent. International Expo./Sesqui-Centennial Exposition	Philadelphia	PA	13 (1925-1926)	1921-1929
01551	Jamestown Exposition/Metropolitan Parks Commission exhibit	Hampton Roads	VA	3 (1907)	1907
02974	Jamestown Exposition	Jamestown	VA	0	1904-1907
02739	Alaska-Yukon-Pacific Exposition	Seattle	WA	43 (1906-1910)	1961

CANADA

Job #	Job Name/Alternative Name	Job Location		Plans	Correspondence
05175	Winnipeg Exposition	Winnipeg	MB	0	
05761	Winnepeg Exhibition/Canadian Industrial Exposition Association/Canadian Industrial Exhibition	Winnipeg	MB	17 (1912-1913)	1912-1914

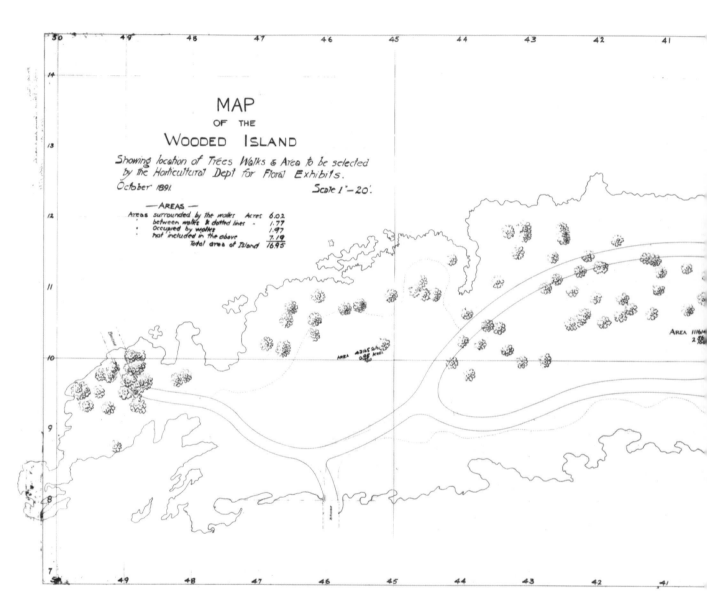

Plan for the wooded island, World's Columbian Exposition, October 1891.
Job #274 - World's Columbian Exposition (Chicago, IL).

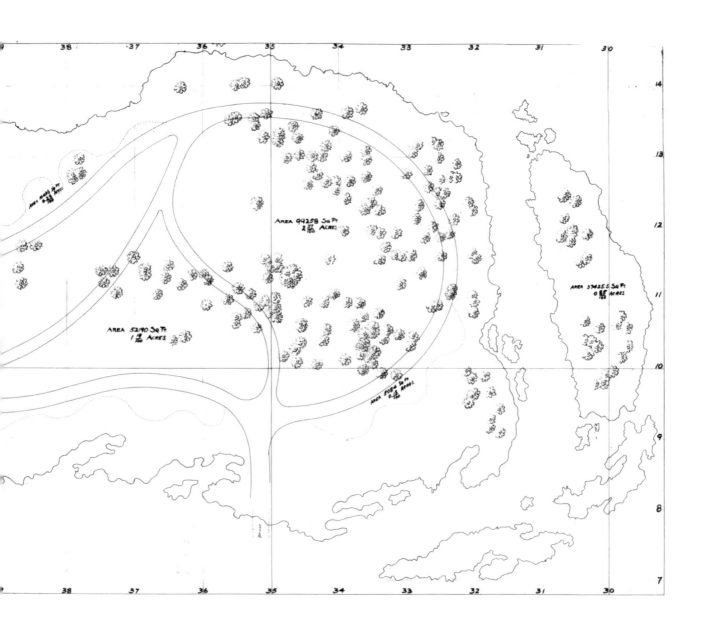

East Garden of the White House, July 1935. Job #2843 – Fine Arts Commission (Washington, DC).

Background: Detail of plan for the Jefferson Memorial showing location of structure and relocation of roads and shoreline, 1938. Job #2843 – Fine Arts Commission (Washington, DC).

Miscellaneous Projects

Anthony Reed

The vast majority of Olmsted projects can be grouped by type and are therefore included in
the previous sections of the *Master List*. However, a few outstanding projects remain (numbered as such by the Olmsted firm) that defy any sort of thematic categorization. Given the
diversity of the work that the firm and individual members of the firm engaged in, it is not
surprising to find project files that do not relate to specific physical landscape design jobs, but
rather to more conceptual and less clearly defined work. For example, committee work or
membership organizations associated with individual firm members were given project numbers, such as the Save the Redwoods League in Berkeley, California, and the New England
Committee on Dutch Elm Disease in Boston. Additionally, project numbers were also assigned
to administrative files as a means of tracking correspondence, as in the case of Carpenter
Shop, Olmsted Brothers, (location not specified) and Financial Records/Olmsted Brothers in
Brookline, Massachusetts. Or a Miscellaneous designation may be assigned because a deter-
mination has not been made as to the nature of the firm's work for a given project, as with
Wilkinson and Wilkinson, of Knoxville, Tennessee, or because the project confounds simple
categorization, such as Plimoth Plantation in Plymouth, Massachusetts. The job number for
the Fine Arts Commission, Washington, D.C., includes work for a wide variety of projects
of different types in a number of locations. For this reason, it, too, has been included in the
Miscellaneous category. As with many true project-related job numbers, sometimes no records
exist for a particular Miscellaneous project, beyond a notation in one of the firm's numerous
project lists, making the contents of a particular project all the more inscrutable. Fortunately,
these projects are fairly few and are presented here so that the *Master List* is inclusive and illus-
trative of the firm's archival record.

See Introductory Guide on pages 33-35 for information on the use of this list.

Miscellaneous Projects

Job #	Job Name/Alternative Name	Job Location	Plans	Correspondence
06796	American Academy in Rome/Fellowship Matters		0	1905-1938
06895	American Society for Municipal Improvement		0	1921-1923
00064	Carpenter Shop, Olmsted Brothers		0	
03568	Coram Court		0	
07944	Donnelly, John and Sons		0	1928
06582	Federal Housing Authority, Consulting Services of H. V. Hubbard		0	
07407	Forest Highway Projects Bureau of Roads/U. S. Department of Agriculture		0	1924-1930
02944	French and Bryant		0	
07410	Frohman, Robb and Little - Washington Cathedral Model		0	
09924	G. I. Loan on properties in subdivisions		0	1953-1954
02637	General Information		0	
00753	Hastings Pavement Co.		0	
03389	Indoors and Out (publication)		0	1907-1908
06581	International Federation for Housing and Town Planning		0	
03698	Landscape Architecture and Parks Periodicals		0	
02080	Metropolitan Water Board		0	
02090	Metropolitan Water Board		0	
02110	Metropolitan Water Board		0	
02898	National Advisory Board on Civic Art		0	1903-1908; 1924
06583	National Defense prospective jobs		0	1940-1941
02893	New England Association of Park Superintendents/American Institute of Park Executives/American Park Society		0	1904-1911; 1917-1926; 1948; 1953
02412	Olmsted, Frederick Law Lecture		0	
02964	Olmsted, Frederick Law Sr., writings		0	1898-1956; 1968
02639	Olmsted, Gideon Writings		0	1808; 1898; 1904-1908
02906	Olmsted, John C. - Guardian to Carolyn Olmsted and Margaret Olmsted		0	1917-1920; 1967
02904	Olmsted, Sarah (Mrs. Frederick Law)		0	1889
02905	Olmsted, Sophia (Mrs. John Charles)		0	
02907	Pacific Coast Chapter of ASLA (American Society of Landscape Architects)		0	1927-1938
06584	Public Building Administration - New England Defense Housing Projects		0	

Job #	Job Name/Alternative Name	Job Location		Plans	Correspondence
02602	Public Parks Association/Metropolitan Park Commission			0	
00252	U. S. Department of Agriculture/Printed Bulletins/U. S. Government Publications			0	1913-1914; 1921-1923
07002	U. S. Department of Commerce Committee on Zoning			0	1921-1938

UNITED STATES

Job #	Job Name/Alternative Name	Job Location		Plans	Correspondence
07970	Alabama (general)		AL	0	1928-1933
08025	Yeoman's Association/Brotherhood of American Yeomen/City of Childhood		CA	0	1923
01809	Save the Redwoods League	Berkeley	CA	0	1865; 1879; 1938-1954
08241	Redondo Beach, City of, (Oil Leases)	Redondo Beach	CA	0	1924-1931
08203	Hassler, Robert H. Polo Field	Serena	CA	50 (1928)	1927-1929
06858	Torrington D.A.R./D.A.R. Drinking Fountain	Torrington	CT	7 (1920-1921)	1920-1922
09704	Bunker Hill Improvement Association	Waterbury	CT	0	1944-1945
03749	American Federation of Arts	Washington	DC	0	1909-1925
02961	Eighth Annual Geographic Conference	Washington	DC	0	1904
02843	Fine Arts Commission/Fine Arts Council/Fine Arts post 1911/District of Columbia	Washington	DC	889 (1901-1954)	1909-1954; 1961-1973
07290	Parks National Conference/National Conference on State Parks	Washington	DC	0	1929-1932; 1947-1948

South Lawn of the White House, July 1935. Job #2843 – Fine Arts Commission (Washington, DC).

Job #	Job Name/Alternative Name	Job Location		Plans	Correspondence
02832	U. S. Coast and Geodetic Survey	Washington	DC	0	1884-1904
02835	U. S. Geological Survey	Washington	DC	0	1890-1899; 1904-1905
02849	Washington Sesqui-centennial	Washington	DC	0	1949
03604	Wilderness Society	Washington	DC	0	1935-1953
06123	Lake Wales Town Clock	Mountain Lake	FL	12 (1930-1931)	1930-1932
07426	Texel Jungle/Babson Park/Bok, Edward	Polk County	FL	6 (1915-1925)	1925; 1943; 1966
03599	American Society of Planning Officials	Chicago	IL	0	1942
03706	National Conference On City Planning/American Institute of Planners/American City Planning Institute	Chicago	IL	4 (1912-1913)	1909-1935; 1940-1943
00020-8	Womans National Farm & Garden Association	Chicago	IL	1 (1922)	
02390	American Park & Outdoor Art Association	Louisville	KY	3 (1902)	1897-1904
02922	American Park and Outdoor Art Association/American Civic Association	Louisville	KY	0	1897-1917
02002	Association of Commerce - Civic Betterment Campaign	New Orleans	LA	0	1915
02039	Board of Commissioners of St. Charles Ave.	New Orleans	LA	0	1904
02010	New Orleans	New Orleans	LA	0	1899
02020	New Orleans	New Orleans	LA	0	
02030	New Orleans	New Orleans	LA	0	
00227	Massachusetts Fish and Game Commission/Fells Reservation		MA	0	1894-1900
09826	Massachusetts State Housing - general		MA	0	1948-1952
09581	Camp Becket	Becket	MA	2 (1939)	1939-1944
00941	Boston Schoolhouse Commission	Boston	MA	0	1904-1909; 1914-1915
03034	Boston Society of Architects	Boston	MA	0	1905-1913
03640	Chamber of Commerce/Boston Merchants Association	Boston	MA	14 (1903-1910)	1909-1920
12502	Copeland, Robert Morris	Boston	MA	3 (1867)	
02984	Massachusetts Civic League	Boston	MA	0	1904-1919
02892	Massachusetts Forestry Association	Boston	MA	0	1896-1919
03598	New England Committee on Dutch Elm Disease - F L Olmsted activities on committee	Boston	MA	0	1934-1935
00947	Parkman Fund	Boston	MA	0	1908-1911; 1920-1922
01319	Brookline Education Society	Brookline	MA	0	1903-1908
10734	Financial Records/Olmsted Brothers	Brookline	MA	0	
00020	Olmsted, F. L. Jr.	Brookline	MA		
02919	Olmsted, F.L., - Miscellaneous/Olmsted, Frederick Law, Jr.	Brookline	MA	14 (1911-1928)	1896-1952; 1967-1972
09629	Fort Rodman	New Bedford	MA	14 (1941)	1941
10135	Plimouth Plantation/Plymouth Plantation	Plymouth	MA	14 (1957-1961)	1933; 1956-1961
10054	Navy Training Center	Quincy	MA	0	

Job #	Job Name/Alternative Name	Job Location		Plans	Correspondence
00062	Wye House		MD	0	
03626	Argo Pool/Huron River Improvement/Argo Pool Head Race	Ann Arbor	MI	16 (1905-1916)	1914-1916
07597	Washtenaw Council, Boy Scouts of America/Camp near Dexter	Ann Arbor	MI	0	1925-1926
06465	Whitmore Lake Grade Separation	Lansing	MI	0	1916
10097	State of Mississippi Board of trustees	Jackson	MS	0	1959-1970
02911	Greengate	Nelson	NH	0	
02160	Essex County	Essex County	NJ	0	
02170	Essex County	Essex County	NJ	0	
02180	Essex County	Essex County	NJ	0	
02190	Essex County	Essex County	NJ	0	
02901	A. S. L. A./American Society of Landscape Architects	New York City	NY	106 (1918-1940)	1898-1960; 1975-1979
03440	American Health League/Public Health Defense League	New York City	NY	0	1907-1908
00550	Art Commission of the City of New York	New York City	NY	0	1909; 1913-1914
05673	Hawkes & Prentiss (for a client)/Mrs. Hawkes	New York City	NY	0	1912
06650	Knowles & Bassoe, Architects	New York City	NY	0	1918
03003	National Municipal League	New York City	NY	0	1903-1910
06910	National Municipal League	New York City	NY	0	
03216	Playground Association of America	New York City	NY	0	1906-1910
07396	Blakeman Quintard Meyer, Inc.	Rye	NY	0	1924
07321	McClintock, Gilbert S. M.	Bear Lake	PA	19 (1924-1928)	1924-1938; 1951
06684	Evans and Warner, Architects	Paoli	PA	0	1919
09863	Dawson Job near Philadelphia	Philadelphia	PA	0	1950
03823	Main Line Housing Association	Philadelphia	PA	0	1912
09631	Fort Getty	Jamestown	RI	13 (1940-1941)	1941
09633	Fort Wetherill	Jamestown	RI	31 (1941)	1941
09630	Fort Adams	Narragansett Bay	RI	63 (1937-1941)	1941
01840	Newport	Newport	RI	0	1896-1898
09632	Fort Phillip Kearney/Fort Kearney	Sanderstown	RI	21 (1941)	1941
07611	Wilkinson and Wilkinson	Knoxville	TN	0	1926
07537	Federated Societies on Planning and Parks/Fort Worth Parks	Fort Worth	TX	0	1925-1928
05670	Lawn Beautifying Committee	Norfolk	VA	0	1912
03241	Grade Crossing/Railroad Grade Crossing	Richmond	VA	0	1915
00085	Westover	Westover	VA	0	
	CANADA				
03047	Grand Trunk Pacific Railroad/Morse, Frank W./Grand Trunk Pacific Railway	Montreal	QC	2 (1905-1907)	1905-1908

APPENDIX
Chronology of the Olmsted Firm 1857-1979

DATES	FIRM NAME Partners and Associate Partners
1857 – 1863	FREDERICK LAW OLMSTED AND CALVERT VAUX
1865 – 1872	OLMSTED, VAUX & CO. Frederick Law Olmsted Calvert Vaux † 1895 Frederick Clarke Withers † 1901
1872 – 1884	FREDERICK LAW OLMSTED, LANDSCAPE ARCHITECT Frederick Law Olmsted John Charles Olmsted[1]
1884 – 1889	F. L. & J. C. OLMSTED Frederick Law Olmsted John Charles Olmsted
1889 – 1893	F. L. OLMSTED & CO. Frederick Law Olmsted John Charles Olmsted Henry Sargent Codman † 1893
1893 – 1897	OLMSTED, OLMSTED & ELIOT Frederick Law Olmsted[2] † 1903 John Charles Olmsted Charles Eliot † 1897 Frederick Law Olmsted Jr.[3]
1897 – 1898	F. L. & J. C. OLMSTED Frederick Law Olmsted Jr. John Charles Olmsted
1898 – 1961	OLMSTED BROTHERS, LANDSCAPE ARCHITECTS
1898 – 1903	John Charles Olmsted Frederick Law Olmsted Jr.
1904 – 1906	John Charles Olmsted Frederick Law Olmsted Jr. Associate Partner: James Frederick Dawson

Left: Frederick Law Olmsted, from an Olmsted family photograph.

Right: John Charles Olmsted, February 1907.

1906 – 1920	John Charles Olmsted
	Frederick Law Olmsted Jr.
	Associate Partners:
	James Frederick Dawson
	Percival Gallagher

1906 – 1920   John Charles Olmsted
                Frederick Law Olmsted Jr.
                Associate Partners:
                   James Frederick Dawson
                   Percival Gallagher

1920   John Charles Olmsted † 1920
      Frederick Law Olmsted[4]
      Associate Partners:
         James Frederick Dawson
         Percival Gallagher
         Edward Clark Whiting

1921 – 1927   Frederick Law Olmsted
      Associate Partners:
         James Frederick Dawson
         Percival Gallagher
         Edward Clark Whiting
         Henry Vincent Hubbard

1927 – 1934   Frederick Law Olmsted
      James Frederick Dawson
      Percival Gallagher † 1934
      Edward Clark Whiting
      Henry Vincent Hubbard

1934 – 1938   Frederick Law Olmsted
      James Frederick Dawson
      Edward Clark Whiting
      Henry Vincent Hubbard

1938 – 1941   Frederick Law Olmsted
      James Frederick Dawson † 1941
      Edward Clark Whiting
      Henry Vincent Hubbard
      William Bell Marquis
      Leon Henry Zach[5]

1942 – 1947   Frederick Law Olmsted
      Edward Clark Whiting
      Henry Vincent Hubbard † 1947
      William Bell Marquis

1948 – 1950   Frederick Law Olmsted[6]
      Edward Clark Whiting
      William Bell Marquis

1950 – 1955   Frederick Law Olmsted
      Edward Clark Whiting
      William Bell Marquis
      Carl Rust Parker
      Charles Scott Riley
      Artemas Partridge Richardson

1955 – 1957   Frederick Law Olmsted † 1957
      Edward Clark Whiting
      William Bell Marquis
      Carl Rust Parker
      Charles Scott Riley
      Artemas Partridge Richardson
      Joseph George Hudak

James Frederick Dawson,
Frederick Law Olmsted Jr.
and Percival Gallagher,
date unknown.

1958-1961	Edward Clark Whiting	1962	OLMSTED ASSOCIATES,

1958-1961　Edward Clark Whiting
　　　　　William Bell Marquis
　　　　　Carl Rust Parker[7]
　　　　　Charles Scott Riley
　　　　　Artemas Partridge Richardson
　　　　　Joseph George Hudak

1962　OLMSTED ASSOCIATES,
　　　LANDSCAPE ARCHITECTS
　　　Edward Clark Whiting † 1962
　　　William Bell Marquis[8]
　　　Artemas Partridge Richardson
　　　Joseph George Hudak

1963 – 1979　OLMSTED ASSOCIATES, INC.
　　　　　　Artemas Partridge Richardson[9]
　　　　　　Joseph George Hudak[10]
　　　　　　Associate:
　　　　　　　Erno J. Fonagy

John Charles Olmsted at work in the office at Fairsted, date unknown.

Sources

Olmsted in the Pacific Northwest: Private Estates and Residential Communities, 1873-1959, An Inventory by Catherine Joy Johnson (Seattle: privately printed, 1997): 65-67. She noted that the list was "based on historic Olmsted letterhead, and…verified by entries in *FLO: A Biography of Frederick Law Olmsted* by Laura Wood Roper, and employee records at FLONHS [Frederick Law Olmsted National Historic Site]." Additional information from Arleyn A. Levee, Charles E. Beveridge and Francis R. Kowsky.

Notes

[1] Partial partnership 1878-1884.
[2] Ceased active practice in 1895 and retired in 1897.
[3] Joined firm 1897.
[4] Beginning in 1920, Frederick Law Olmsted Jr. was known as Frederick Law Olmsted.
[5] Left the firm in 1941 to practice elsewhere. Retired in 1965, died in 1966.
[6] Retired from active practice in 1949 but remained a partner and continued to bring in business.
[7] Retired 1960, died 1966.
[8] Retired 1962, died 1978.
[9] Continued to practice in New Hampshire as The Olmsted Office until 2000.
[10] Continued in private practice and teaching.

Credits for Illustrations

The illustrations in this book were provided through the courtesy of the following institutions, organizations and individuals.

Front Cover:
Olmsted Photograph Album Collection. Photograph #930-71 "View Upstream from Longwood Bridge 1920, 28 years after construction." Thos. Ellison, Boston, MA photographer. National Park Service, Frederick Law Olmsted National Historic Site.

Background: Olmsted Lithograph Collection. "General Plan for Improvement of the U. S. Capitol Grounds," n.d. National Park Service, Frederick Law Olmsted National Historic Site.

Inside Cover:
Olmsted Plans and Drawings Collection. Plan #902-z20, "Topographical Map of Bussey Farm Homestead," n.d. National Park Service, Frederick Law Olmsted National Historic Site.

Page ii:
Olmsted Photograph Album Collection, "by Keystone Photo service. No negative. Probably about 1922." Photograph #5950-121. National Park Service, Frederick Law Olmsted National Historic Site.

Page iv:
Job #1 – Frederick Law Olmsted, Sr. Olmsted Family Photographs. Unnumbered photograph. With Marion Olmsted at Rivercliff Cottage, ca. 1895. Photographer unknown. National Park Service, Frederick Law Olmsted National Historic Site.

Background: Olmsted Planting List Collection. National Park Service, Frederick Law Olmsted National Historic Site.

Page vi:
Olmsted Photograph Album Collection. Photograph 918-143 "B.P.D. #662 The Sheep Pasture on Schoolmaster Hill 1 Jun 1904." National Park Service, Frederick Law Olmsted National Historic Site.

Page x:
Photograph by Joel Veak. National Park Service, Frederick Law Olmsted National Historic Site.

Page xii:
Photograph by Joel Veak. National Park Service, Frederick Law Olmsted National Historic Site.

Page xiv:
Architect of the Capitol, negative number 74248.

Page xv:
Photograph by Joel Veak. National Park Service, Frederick Law Olmsted National Historic Site.

Left, top: View of Claremont Park prior to construction, April 14, 1932.
Job #527 – Claremont Park (New York, NY).

Middle: View of Claremont Park during construction, February 21, 1933.
Job #527 – Claremont Park (New York, NY).

Bottom: View of completed Claremont Park, June 16, 1934.
Job #527 – Claremont Park (New York, NY).

Page xvi:
Olmsted Photograph Album Collection. Photograph #673-90 "Vines on side of house, with shrubs and sumac." Photograph by Miss Theodora Kimball. National Park Service, Frederick Law Olmsted National Historic Site.

Page xviii:
Job # 1 – Frederick Law Olmsted, Sr. Olmsted Family Photographs. Unnumbered photograph, photographer unknown, n.d. National Park Service, Frederick Law Olmsted National Historic Site.

Page xx:
Left: Job #20 – Olmsted Brothers Office (Brookline, MA). Olmsted Framed Photograph. Unnumbered photograph. National Park Service, Frederick Law Olmsted National Historic Site.

Right: Job #1 – Frederick Law Olmsted, Sr. Olmsted Family Photographs, unnumbered photograph. Photographer unknown, n.d. from Roper Accession. National Park Service, Frederick Law Olmsted National Historic Site.

Background: Olmsted Lithograph Collection. "Plan of Parkway between Muddy River Gate House and Jamaica Park," 1892. National Park Service, Frederick Law Olmsted National Historic Site.

Page 4:
Olmsted Photograph Album Collection. Photograph #930-71 "View Upstream from Longwood Bridge 1920, 28 years after construction." Thos. Ellison, Boston, MA photographer. National Park Service, Frederick Law Olmsted National Historic Site.

Inset: Olmsted Photograph Collection. Photograph #930-21. National Park Service, Frederick Law Olmsted National Historic Site.

Page 7:
Chicago Park District Special Collections.

Page 8:
Olmsted Photograph Album Collection. Photograph # 8099-2710 [stamped on verso] "Fairchild Aerial Surveys, Inc. Los Angeles CA." Photographer unknown, n.d. National Park Service, Frederick Law Olmsted National Historic Site.

Background: "Topographical Map, Acadia National Park, Hancock County, ME." Edition of 1931. U.S. Geological Survey. Library of Congress, Geography and Map Division.

Page 10:
Job #1 – Frederick Law Olmsted, Sr. Olmsted Family Photographs, signed photograph [formal portrait], Notman Studio, 270 Boylston Street, Boston. National Park Service, Frederick Law Olmsted National Historic Site.

Page 11:
Marsh-Billings-Rockefeller National Historical Park.

Page 12:
Olmsted Plans and Drawings Collection. Plan #9138A-124-sh2. "Otter Cliff Road" September 25, 1935. National Park Service, Frederick Law Olmsted National Historic Site.

Page 13:
Olmsted Photograph #4022-7. Photographer unknown, Jan. 1932. National Park Service, Frederick Law Olmsted National Historic Site.

Page 14:
Olmsted Photograph Album Collection. Loose photo "View from Mount Royal Montreal / JCO 5 Jul 1894." National Park Service, Frederick Law Olmsted National Historic Site.

Background: Olmsted Lithograph Collection. "Design Map," Mount Royal Park, 1877. National Park Service, Frederick Law Olmsted National Historic Site.

Page 17:
Job #2919 – Frederick Law Olmsted, Jr. Olmsted Family Photographs. Unnumbered photograph, "left to right: Percival Gallagher, Frederick Law Olmsted, Jr., James Frederick Dawson," photographer unknown, n.d. National Park Service, Frederick Law Olmsted National Historic Site.

Page 18:
Olmsted Photograph Album Collection. Photograph #529-2059 "Cloister seen through arch" by Harry Perkins, May 1936. National Park Service, Frederick Law Olmsted National Historic Site.

Background: Seattle Parks and Recreation.

Page 20:
Olmsted Planting List Collection. National Park Service, Frederick Law Olmsted National Historic Site.

Page 21:
Friends of Seattle's Olmsted Parks, Arbes/Knight Postcard Collection.

Page 23:
Seattle Municipal Archives Photograph Collection, image #30454.

Page 24:
Seattle Parks and Recreation.

Page 27:
Friends of Seattle's Olmsted Parks, Arbes/Knight Postcard Collection.

Page 28:
Seattle Municipal Archives Photograph Collection, image #4068.

Inset: Olmsted Photograph Album Collection. Photograph #918-61, Album #1 "Photographer D. W. Butterfield taking a view of Refectory Hill, October 8, 1892." National Park Service, Frederick Law Olmsted National Historic Site.

Page 29:
Job #20 – Olmsted Brothers Office (Brookline, MA). Olmsted Office Scrapbook. National Park Service, Frederick Law Olmsted National Historic Site.

Page 30:
Prospect Park Archives.

Page 32:
Olmsted Photo Album Collection. Photo #2405-5, n.d. National Park Service, Frederick Law Olmsted National Historic Site.

Background: Olmsted Lithograph Collection. F.L. and J.C. Olmsted, Landscape Architects. National Park Service, Frederick Law Olmsted National Historic Site.

Page 35:
Job #20 – Olmsted Brothers Office (Brookline, MA). Olmsted Office Scrapbook. National Park Service, Frederick Law Olmsted National Historic Site.

Page 36:
Prospect Park Archives.

Background: Olmsted Lithograph Collection. "Plan of Portion of Park System from Common to Franklin Park, Jan. 1894." National Park Service, Frederick Law Olmsted National Historic Site.

Page 38:
Olmsted Photograph Album Collection. Photograph #7029-234 "the Singing Tower, Mt. Lake Sanctuary," by Van Natta Studio, 1929. National Park Service, Frederick Law Olmsted National Historic Site.

Page 42:
Top: Negative number 61962.2. New York City Department of Parks and Recreation Photo Archives.

Bottom: Central Park Conservancy.

Page 46:
Olmsted Photograph Album Collection. Photograph #2001-43 "by J.F.D. Feb 1918, looking north at St. Charles end of Fountain Plaza, St. Charles entrance showing Tulane U." National Park Service, Frederick Law Olmsted National Historic Site.

Page 50:
Olmsted Plans and Drawings Collection. Plan #1269-35. "General Plan for Shawnee Park," by Olmsted, Olmsted and Eliot, July 1893. National Park Service, Frederick Law Olmsted National Historic Site.

Page 53:
Olmsted Lithograph Collection. "Revised General Plan," 1895. National Park Service, Frederick Law Olmsted National Historic Site.

Page 56:
Top: Olmsted Lithograph Collection. "Plan of Parkway between Muddy River Gate House and Jamaica Park," 1892. National Park Service, Frederick Law Olmsted National Historic Site.

Bottom: Olmsted Lithograph Collection. "General Plan for Branch Brook Park," OBLA, 1901. National Park Service, Frederick Law Olmsted National Historic Site.

Page 60:
Olmsted Plans and Drawings Collection. Plan #700-9-pt1. No title, n.d. National Park Service, Frederick Law Olmsted National Historic Site.

Page 67:
Prospect Park Alliance.

Page 72:
Olmsted Photograph Album Collection. Photograph #917-195 "Bird's Eye View Ontario Power Company." National Park Service, Frederick Law Olmsted National Historic Site.

Page 77:
Olmsted Plans and Drawings Collection. Plan #9138A-91E. Cross Section and Perspective of Culvert Parapets and Auto Guard Rail, Acadia National Park, June 6, 1933. National Park Service, Frederick Law Olmsted National Historic Site.

Page 80:
Rhodeside & Harwell.

Page 82:
Olmsted Plans and Drawings Collection. Plan #3462B-15A "Bird's Eye Study for Pittsburgh Civic Centre," June 1, 1910. National Park Service, Frederick Law Olmsted National Historic Site.

Background: Olmsted Plans and Drawings Collection. Plan #3471-15 "General Plan for Manito Park's Second Addition and Rockwood Addition," January 1910. National Park Service, Frederick Law Olmsted National Historic Site.

Page 84:
Olmsted Plans and Drawings Collection. Plan #3300-8. "Two Suggestions for Cross Section of University Street" November 6, 1908. National Park Service, Frederick Law Olmsted National Historic Site.

Page 89:
Olmsted Plans and Drawings Collection. Plan #3300-63, "Preliminary Plan of Proposed Park Improvement along Boulder Creek," October 1923. National Park Service, Frederick Law Olmsted National Historic Site.

Page 94:
Olmsted Photograph Album Collection. Photograph #3586-354 "Rec'd from Sage Foundation Homes Co. Dec 1914 Front Entrance to house I-F-47 Group XII." National Park Service, Frederick Law Olmsted National Historic Site.

Background: Olmsted Plans and Drawings Collection. Plan #3586-z10, Birds-Eye View, Forest Hills Gardens, 1910. Olmsted Brothers Landscape Architects, Grosvenor Atterbury, Architect. National Park Service, Frederick Law Olmsted National Historic Site.

Page 96:
Olmsted Plans and Drawings Collection. Plan #3276-z1 "View of Victoria, B.C. showing relative position of The Uplands". National Park Service, Frederick Law Olmsted National Historic Site.

Page 97:
Olmsted Lithograph Collection. "General Plan of Riverside. Olmsted, Vaux & Co., Landscape Architects, 1869." Chicago Lithographing Co., Chicago. National Park Service, Frederick Law Olmsted National Historic Site.

Page 103:
Olmsted Lithograph Collection. "First Development of 3200 Acres, Palos Verdes Estates, Feb. 1926." National Park Service, Frederick Law Olmsted National Historic Site.

Page 108:
Olmsted Photograph Album Collection. Photograph #5950-103. Photographer unknown, n.d. National Park Service, Frederick Law Olmsted National Historic Site.

Page 113:
Olmsted Plans and Drawings Collection. Plan #3108-24 "General Plan for Bozanta Tavern and Farm." National Park Service, Frederick Law Olmsted National Historic Site.

Page 115:
Olmsted Lithograph Collection. "General Plan" F.L. and J.C. Olmsted, LA, July 1897. National Park Service, Frederick Law Olmsted National Historic Site.

Page 116:
Olmsted Plans and Drawings Collection. Plan #1032-z46. No title, n.d. National Park Service, Frederick Law Olmsted National Historic Site.

Background: Olmsted Plans and Drawings Collection. Plan #1169-34 "General Plan," 1893, F.L. and J.C. Olmsted. National Park Service, Frederick Law Olmsted National Historic Site.

Page 125:
Top: Olmsted Photograph Album Collection. Photograph #6373-58 "A General Plan of Denison University Situated at Granville Ohio" Frederick Law Olmsted, Landscape Architect, Gehron and Ross, Architects, May 15, 1929. National Park Service, Frederick Law Olmsted National Historic Site.

Bottom: Olmsted Photograph Album Collection. Photograph #6888-18 "Proposed Louisiana State University" OBLA, October 1921. National Park Service, Frederick Law Olmsted National Historic Site.

Page 131:
Olmsted Plans and Drawings Collection, Plan #1169-34, "General Plan," 1893. F.L. Olmsted and Co. National Park Service, Frederick Law Olmsted National Historic Site.

Page 132:
Olmsted Photograph Album Collection. Photograph #98-1, "View of the Old Asylum Grounds formerly the Barwell Estate," n.d., photographer unknown. National Park Service, Frederick Law Olmsted National Historic Site.

Background: Olmsted Plans and Drawings Collection. Plan #3678-12 "Revised Preliminary Plan/Study," OB, 14 June 1911. National Park Service, Frederick Law Olmsted National Historic Site.

Page 134:
Olmsted Plans and Drawings Collection. Plan #190-107 "Preliminary Plan," OBLA, November 16, 1898. National Park Service, Frederick Law Olmsted National Historic Site.

Page 139:
Olmsted Interpositive Collection. Photograph #2825-10. "Looking north from near the water tank. Power house on left. Morgue in centre. Kitchen and dining hall on right. 2d panorama #1. Taken by F. L. Olmsted, Jr., 26th December, 1900." National Park Service, Frederick Law Olmsted National Historic Site.

Page 140:
Olmsted Photograph Album Collection. Photograph #5350-14, photograph by Dawson. National Park Service, Frederick Law Olmsted National Historic Site.

Background: Olmsted Plans and Drawings Collection. Plan #5350-66-pt3 "General Plan," May 1928. National Park Service, Frederick Law Olmsted National Historic Site.

Page 143:
Olmsted Plans and Drawings Collection. Plan #649-7, "Planting Plan for Grounds in Vicinity of Memorial Hall," March 17, 1903. National Park Service, Frederick Law Olmsted National Historic Site.

Page 144:
Olmsted Photograph Album Collection. Photograph #649-1, "Memorial Hall," photograph by Mr. J.C.O., November 11, 1902. National Park Service, Frederick Law Olmsted National Historic Site.

Page 149:
Olmsted Photograph Album Collection. Photograph #1064-243 "Taken by Paul J. Weber, photographer." National Park Service, Frederick Law Olmsted National Historic Site.

Page 150:
Olmsted Historic Negative Collection. Negative #170-204, n.d., photographer unknown. National Park Service, Frederick Law Olmsted National Historic Site.

Background: Olmsted Lithograph Collection. "Guide Map of Biltmore Estate," 1896. National Park Service, Frederick Law Olmsted National Historic Site.

Page 158:
Olmsted Plans and Drawings Collection. Plan #9199-16 (FRLA 45694) "Perspective Sketch of Shelter from Lawn," August 8, 1930. National Park Service, Frederick Law Olmsted National Historic Site.

Page 165:
Olmsted Photograph Album Collection. Photograph #243-4 FLO April, 1928. National Park Service, Frederick Law Olmsted National Historic Site.

Page 170:
Top: Olmsted Photograph Album Collection. Photograph #3494-185 by Alec Macdougall, 1911. National Park Service, Frederick Law Olmsted National Historic Site.

Bottom: Olmsted Photograph Album Collection. Photograph #3494-211 taken by Avery April 20, 1911 rec'd from McDougall. "Mountain has been put in and not in true location – axis of garden centers on mountain." National Park Service, Frederick Law Olmsted National Historic Site.

Page 177:
Olmsted Photograph Album Collection. Photograph #7099-84 Doughty, Oct. 1926. National Park Service, Frederick Law Olmsted National Historic Site.

Page 182:
Olmsted Photograph Album Collection. Photograph #273-164 rec'd from Gleason, 1930. National Park Service, Frederick Law Olmsted National Historic Site.

Inset: Olmsted Photograph Album Collection. Photograph #273-175 rec'd from Miss Johnston, 1930. National Park Service, Frederick Law Olmsted National Historic Site.

Page 189:
Olmsted Photograph Album Collection. Photograph #416-13 "East end and north front of house taken 1905 showing roofed steps leading from carriage drive to front door and three year's growth of shrubbery." Loose photograph, received December 29, 1904. National Park Service, Frederick Law Olmsted National Historic Site.

Page 194:
Top: Olmsted Photograph Album Collection. Photograph #6829-35. "A picture taken two or three years later will show the sky at the left of the pine and palm filled up with cypress pine." Olmsted Brothers, Spring 1932. National Park Service, Frederick Law Olmsted National Historic Site.

Bottom: Olmsted Photograph Album Collection. Photograph #7778-8 "Entrance driveway and forecourt, one year after planting" by Phillips, January 1929. National Park Service, Frederick Law Olmsted National Historic Site.

Page 198:
Photograph by Marshall Webb, Shelburne Farms, Shelburne, VT.

Page 199:
Photograph by Marshall Webb, Shelburne Farms, Shelburne, VT.

Page 204:
Top: Olmsted Photograph Album Collection. Photograph #3491-13, "Tea house on the edge of the cliff," rec'd from C.D. Stimson, March 1915. National Park Service, Frederick Law Olmsted National Historic Site.

Bottom: Olmsted Photograph Album Collection. Photograph #7241-21. Received fall 1927, photographer unknown. National Park Service, Frederick Law Olmsted National Historic Site.

Page 211:
Olmsted Photograph Album Collection. Photograph #133-13, "View of House from Penn Ave. looking ENE," H.J. Heinz Estate, May 15, 1901. Photograph by J.C. Olmsted. National Park Service, Frederick Law Olmsted National Historic Site.

Page 216:
Olmsted Photograph Album Collection. Photograph #3223-130 "The House and Gardens at Krisheim" by H.D. Perkins, n.d. National Park Service, Frederick Law Olmsted National Historic Site.

Page 217:
Olmsted Photograph Album Collection. Photograph #3223-102 "looking south on cross axis of garden" brought by Mr. Dawson, Nov. 1912. National Park Service, Frederick Law Olmsted National Historic Site.

Page 223:
Olmsted Photograph Album Collection. Unnumbered photograph "Lodge at North Easton 'The Arch' Ames Estates, F.L. & J.C. Olmsted Architects," n.d. National Park Service, Frederick Law Olmsted National Historic Site.

Page 228:
Olmsted Photograph Album Collection. Photograph #5883-126 "View of Garden Looking Toward House" August 1927. Photographer unknown. National Park Service, Frederick Law Olmsted National Historic Site.

Page 237:
Olmsted Photograph Album Collection. Photo #673-44 Album #1 "Fairsted," Brookline MA, photographer unknown, n.d. National Park Service, Frederick Law Olmsted National Historic Site.

Page 242:
Olmsted Historic Negative Collection. Negative #170-90, n.d., photographer unknown. National Park Service, Frederick Law Olmsted National Historic Site.

Page 248:
Olmsted Photograph Album Collection. Photograph #6991-20, n.d., photographer unknown. National Park Service, Frederick Law Olmsted National Historic Site.

Background: Olmsted Plans and Drawings Collection. Plan #3277-33-pt1 "General Plan of Hillside Cemetery," Olmsted Brothers Rec'd on Jun 26, 1909. National Park Service, Frederick Law Olmsted National Historic Site.

Page 251:
Olmsted Plans and Drawings Collection. Plan #9685-6 "Plan of a Metropolitan Cemetery for the City of San Francisco Situated in the Suburb of Oakland," n.d. Olmsted, Vaux and Co. National Park Service, Frederick Law Olmsted National Historic Site.

Page 252:
Olmsted Photograph Album Collection. Photograph #9516-42 from Mr. Reinsmith, November 27, 1939. National Park Service, Frederick Law Olmsted National Historic Site.

Page 257:
Olmsted Photograph Album Collection. Photograph #6991-40, n.d., photographer unknown. National Park Service, Frederick Law Olmsted National Historic Site.

Page 260:
Olmsted Photograph Collection. Photograph #5571-22 "walk leading to foot of steps" by H. H. Blossom, October 3 1916. National Park Service, Frederick Law Olmsted National Historic Site.

Page 263:
Olmsted Photograph Album Collection. Photograph #9600-38, August 1941. Photographer unknown. National Park Service, Frederick Law Olmsted National Historic Site.

Page 264:
Olmsted Photograph Album Collection, "factory." Photographer unknown, n.d. National Park Service, Frederick Law Olmsted National Historic Site.

Background: Olmsted Plans and Drawings Collection. Plan #6376-2, "Topographical Map," October 1916. National Park Service, Frederick Law Olmsted National Historic Site.

Page 270:
Olmsted Plans and Drawings Collection. Plan #9218-49 "Planting Plan," August 12, 1940. National Park Service, Frederick Law Olmsted National Historic Site.

Page 274:
Caracas. Olmsted Photograph Album Collection. Photograph #7947-108 "view from pool." Photographer unknown, n.d. National Park Service, Frederick Law Olmsted National Historic Site.

Background: Olmsted Plans and Drawings Collection. Plan #1048-2 "General Plan," July1934. National Park Service, Frederick Law Olmsted National Historic Site.

Page 276:
Olmsted Plans and Drawings collection. Plan #5103-27 "General Plan," January 1912. National Park Service, Frederick Law Olmsted National Historic Site."

Page 279:
Olmsted Photograph Album Collection. Photograph #6451-29, July 1936, photograph by J.F. Dawson. National Park Service, Frederick Law Olmsted National Historic Site.

Page 280:
Olmsted Plans and Drawings Collection. Plan #9275-32 "General Plan," November 1932 National Park Service, Frederick Law Olmsted National Historic Site.

Page 282:
Olmsted Photograph Collection. Photograph #9273-155 "View from British Pacific Properties (Stanley Park in right middle distance)" rec'd from Mr. Anderson, Feb. 8 1937. National Park Service, Frederick Law Olmsted National Historic Site.

Page 284:
Olmsted Photograph Album Collection. Photograph #6950-4, July 26, 1921. Photograph by H.E.M. National Park Service, Frederick Law Olmsted National Historic Site.

Background: Olmsted Plans and Drawings Collection, Plan #3297B-22 "Preliminary General Plan," March 5, 1910. National Park Service, Frederick Law Olmsted National Historic Site.

Page 286:
Top: Olmsted Photograph Album Collection. Photograph #10172-11 "Panorama northwest on San Marco Avenue," June 1964. Photograph by J. Hudak. National Park Service, Frederick Law Olmsted National Historic Site.

Bottom: Olmsted Photograph Album Collection. Photograph #10172-8 "Panorama northeast on San Marco near Pine Street," June 1964. Photograph by J. Hudak. National Park Service, Frederick Law Olmsted National Historic Site.

Page 289:
Olmsted Photograph Album Collection. Photograph #9605-1 "Main Entrance to Church," July 1940. Photographer unknown. National Park Service, Frederick Law Olmsted National Historic Site.

Page 290:
Olmsted Photograph Album Collection. Photograph #3297-126 "South Steps" By Prellwitz, July 1935. National Park Service, Frederick Law Olmsted National Historic Site.

Inset: Olmsted Photograph Album Collection. Photograph #3297-112 "Views of long walk by outer boxwood hedge" Received from Mrs. Bratenahl, Fall 1926. National Park Service, Frederick Law Olmsted National Historic Site.

Page 292:
Photograph, n.d. Jerry Arbes, Seattle, Washington.

Background: Olmsted Plans and Drawings Collection. Plan #902-z20, "Topographical Map of Bussey Farm Homestead," n.d. National Park Service, Frederick Law Olmsted National Historic Site.

Page 294:
Top: Olmsted Photograph Album Collection. Photograph #9800-1 "Temple from East Lawn" by Mr. Byrd, August 15, 1949. National Park Service, Frederick Law Olmsted National Historic Site.

Bottom: Olmsted Plans and Drawings Collection. Plan #813-11 "General Plan," 1936. National Park Service, Frederick Law Olmsted National Historic Site.

Page 296:
Top: Olmsted Photograph Album Collection. Photograph # 902-7 "Syringa Arnold Arboretum," n.d. Photographer unknown. National Park Service, Frederick Law Olmsted National Historic Site.

Bottom: Olmsted Photograph Album Collection. Photograph #902-78, July 1939 "Copied from photographs loaned O.B. July 1939 from Arnold Arboretum files." National Park Service, Frederick Law Olmsted National Historic Site.

Page 298:
Olmsted Photograph Album Collection. Loose photo, n.d. photographer unknown. National Park Service, Frederick Law Olmsted National Historic Site.

Background: Olmsted Lithograph Collection. "Map of Buildings and Grounds of the Jackson Park and Midway Plaisance, World's Columbian Exposition." National Park Service, Frederick Law Olmsted National Historic Site.

Page 300:
Olmsted Photograph Album Collection. Photograph #2739-386. No photographer, n.d. National Park Service, Frederick Law Olmsted National Historic Site.

Page 302:
Olmsted Plans and Drawings Collection. Plan #274-13 "Map of Wooded Island," October 1891. National Park Service, Frederick Law Olmsted National Historic Site.

Page 304:
Olmsted Photograph Album Collection. Photograph #2843-EX-21 "By FLO July 1935 East Garden." National Park Service, Frederick Law Olmsted National Historic Site.

Background: Olmsted Plans and Drawings Collection. Plan #2843-PP692 "Thomas Jefferson Memorial - Plan Showing Location of Structure and Relocation of Roads and Shoreline," Frederick Law Olmsted, Landscape Architects. National Park Service, Frederick Law Olmsted National Historic Site.

Page 307:
Olmsted Photograph Album Collection. Photograph #2843-EX-12 "By F.L. Olmsted July 1935 View from South Lawn Below Fountain." National Park Service, Frederick Law Olmsted National Historic Site.

Page 310:
Job # 1 – Frederick Law Olmsted, Sr. Olmsted Family Photographs. Unnumbered photograph labeled "This photo Mrs. O[lmsted] Sr. thinks about 1890. Taken by Frederick [Law Olmsted Jr.]." National Park Service, Frederick Law Olmsted National Historic Site.

Frederick Law Omsted Jr., date unknown.

Page 311:
Job #2931 – John Charles Olmsted. Olmsted Family Photographs. Unnumbered photograph, labeled "By J. E. Purdy & Co. February 26, 1907." National Park Service, Frederick Law Olmsted National Historic Site.

Page 312:
Job #2919 – Frederick Law Olmsted, Jr. Olmsted Family Photographs. Unnumbered photograph, with James Frederick Dawson and Percival Gallagher, photographer unknown, n.d. National Park Service, Frederick Law Olmsted National Historic Site.

Page 313:
Job #2931 – John Charles Olmsted. Olmsted Family Photographs. Unnumbered photograph, photographer unknown, n.d. National Park Service, Frederick Law Olmsted National Historic Site.

Page 314:
Top: Olmsted Photograph Album Collection. Photograph #527-1062 "View N.W. from 122nd St and Claremont Ave" by Mark Eidlitz, April 14, 1932. National Park Service, Frederick Law Olmsted National Historic Site.

Middle: Olmsted Photograph Album Collection. Photograph #527-1028 "View N.W. from 122nd St and Claremont Ave" by Mark Eidlitz, February 21, 1933. National Park Service, Frederick Law Olmsted National Historic Site.

Bottom: Olmsted Photograph Album Collection. Photograph #527-1028 "View N.W. from 122nd St and Claremont Ave" by Mark Eidlitz, June 16, 1934. National Park Service, Frederick Law Olmsted National Historic Site.

Page 323:
Job #2919 – Frederick Law Olmsted, Jr. Olmsted Family Photographs. Unnumbered photograph, n.d. Photograph mount embossed with the following: "Clinedinst Studio. 733 14th Street NW, Washington, DC." National Park Service, Frederick Law Olmsted National Historic Site.

Page 331:
Photograph by Joel Veak. National Park Service, Frederick Law Olmsted National Historic Site.

Page 332:
Olmsted Photograph Album Collection. Photograph #4022-22 Frederick Law Olmsted, Jr. working in the Everglades, Jan. 1932. National Park Service, Frederick Law Olmsted National Historic Site.

Page 341:
Photo by Joel Veak. National Park Service, Frederick Law Olmsted National Historic Site.

Page 348:
Prospect Park Alliance.

Back Cover:
Used with permission from The Biltmore Company, Asheville, North Carolina.

Background: Olmsted Lithograph Collection. "Plan of Portion of Park System from Common to Franklin Park, Jan. 1894." National Park Service, Frederick Law Olmsted National Historic Site.

Notes

Foreword: Frederick Law Olmsted National Historic Site

[1] Olmsted to Charles Loring Brace, Brookline, March 7, 1882, *The Papers of Frederick Law Olmsted, Volume VII, Parks, Politics, and Patronage 1874-1882*, eds. Charles E. Beveridge, Carolyn F. Hoffman and Kenneth Hawkins (Baltimore, MD: The Johns Hopkins University Press, 2007): 592.

The Olmsteds and the Development of the National Park System

[1] Dwight T. Pitcaithley, "Philosophical Underpinings of the National Park Idea," *Ranger*, Fall 2001.

[2] Richard West Sellars, *Preserving Nature in the National Parks: A History* (New Haven, CT: Yale University Press, 1997): 8.

[3] Olmsted's friend, Unitarian Minister Thomas Star King wrote in an 1863 sermon in San Francisco entitled Lessons from the Sierra Nevada, "Love of nature has its root in wonder and veneration, and it issues in many forms of practical good. There can be no abounding and ardent patriotism where sacred attachment to the scenery of our civil home is wanting." Arliss Ungar, Unitarian Universalist Association, 43rd General Assembly, Long Beach, California, 2004.

[4] Alfred Runte, *National Parks: The American Experience* (Lincoln, NE: University of Nebraska Press, 1997): 9.

[5] Bierstadt's painting of Yosemite Valley's Cathedral Rocks and Carleton Watkin's photograph of the same subject, generously given to the National Park Service by Laurance S. and Mary Rockefeller, are on display at Marsh-Billings-Rockefeller National Historical Park.

[6] Robin W. Winks, *Frederick Billings: A Life* (New York: Oxford University Press, 1991): 281.

[7] Garry Wills, *Lincoln at Gettysburg: The Words that Remade America* (New York: Simon and Schuster, 1992): 144-147.

[8] Rolf Diamant, "Frederick Law Olmsted, Jr." in *National Park Service, The First 75 Years: Preserving our Past for the Future* (Fort Washington, PA: Eastern National Park & Monument Association, 1990): 18.

[9] Ethan Carr, *Wilderness by Design: Landscape Architecture and the National Park Service* (Lincoln, NE: University of Nebraska Press, 1998): 28.

[10] Frederick Law Olmsted, *Yosemite and the Mariposa Grove: A Preliminary Report, 1865* (1865: reprint, Yosemite National Park, CA: Yosemite Association, 1995).

[11] Robin W. Winks, "The National Park Service Act of 1916: 'A Contradictory Mandate'?" in 74 *Denver University Law Review* (1997): 575.

The Olmsted Firm in Canada

[1] Telegram from P. O'Meara, Secretary, City Hall, Montreal, October 5, 1874. Frederick Law Olmsted Papers, Library of Congress.

[2] Frederick Law Olmsted, *Mount Royal: Montreal* (New York: G.P. Putnam's Sons, 1881): 13.

[3] Of the 95 projects 40% were mere inquiries; in 14% of the listings advice was sought and given; reports were written and not acted upon in 9%; reports written and partially built in 5%; and finally in 32% of the Canadian job listings reports were written and fully executed. (Nancy Pollock-Ellwand, "The Olmsted Firm in Canada: A Correction of the Record" in *Planning Perspectives.* 21, no. 3 (July 2006): 289).

[4] In Canada, the Town Planning Institute was formed in 1919, representing a range of practitioners interested in the reform of city design, regulation and governance. In 1934, the Canadian Society of Landscape Architects (which for a time included town planners) was formed. In the United States the situation was reversed, with the American Institute of Planners being created in 1917, almost two decades after the American Society of Landscape Architects was formed in 1899. A major catalyst in the early years of Canadian landscape thought was also the Commission of Conservation (modeled after Theodore Roosevelt's National Commission), which formed in 1909 as an arms length watchdog on natural and human resource management and protection. The first Town Planning Advisor was Thomas Adams. See Alan F. J. Artibise and Gilbert Arthur Stelter, "Conservation Planning and Urban Planning: The Canadian Commission of Conservation in Historical Perspective," in R. J. P. Kain (ed.), *Planning for Conservation* (New York: St. Martin's Press, 1981): 17–36.

5   See Charles E. Beveridge and Carolyn F. Hoffman, eds., *The Master List of Design Projects of the Olmsted Firm 1857-1950* (Boston, MA: Massachusetts Association for Olmsted Parks, 1987) e.g., City of Toronto Waterfront, 1912; City of Montreal Metropolitan Park System Report, 1910; Canadian Pacific Railway's South Mount Royal, Sunalta and Bridgeland, 1909-1910; Hudson Bay Company's Mount Royal Heights, Prince Albert, Saskatchewan, 1913-1914.

6   See *Master List* e.g., The City of Calgary, 1910; Halifax, 1911; London, Ontario, 1919.

7   Nancy Pollock-Ellwand, "Gréber's Plan and the 'Washington of the North': Finding A Canadian Capital in the Face of Republican Dreams". *Landscape Journal*. 20(1), 2001: 48-61.

8   Unpublished Outhet Papers; and *For a Better Montreal. Report of the First Convention of the City Improvement League*. (Montreal: City Improvement League, 1910): 49.

9   Olmsted Employee Records, Frederick Law Olmsted National Historic Site.

10 Olmsted Associates Records, series B, Job #6722, Library of Congress.

11 Floyd S. Chalmers, *A Gentleman of the Press* (Toronto: Doubleday Canada Ltd., 1969): 306.

12 Gordon Culham in a letter to his wife Jessie, May 6, 1919, Unpublished Culham Family Papers: 233.

13 "Landscapers Unite: Form Society Under Presidency of Gordon Culham", *Toronto Star*. March 7, 1934: 10.

City and Regional Planning and Improvement Projects

1   Lewis Mumford, *The Brown Decades: A Study of the Arts of America, 1865-1895* [1931] (New York: Dover Publications, 1955): 91.

2   U.S. Congress. Senate. Committee on the District of Columbia, *The Improvement of the Park System of the District of Columbia*. 57th Congress, 1st Session (Washington, DC: Government Printing Office, 1902).

3   John L. Hancock, "Planners in the Changing American City, 1900-1940," *Journal of the American Institute of Planners* 33, no. 5 (September 1967): 290-303.

4   Susan L. Klaus, *A Modern Arcadia: Frederick Law Olmsted Jr. and the Plan for Forest Hills Gardens*. (Amherst, MA: University of Massachusetts Press in association with the Library of American Landscape History, 2002): 28.

5   Cass Gilbert and Frederick Law Olmsted Jr., *Report of the New Haven Civic Improvement Commission, December 1910* (New Haven, CT: Tuttle, Morehouse & Taylor Company, n.d.); Frederick Law Olmsted Jr., *Pittsburgh: Main Thoroughfares and the Down Town District* (Pittsburgh, PA: Pittsburgh Civic Commission, 1911); Arnold W. Brunner, Frederick Law Olmsted Jr. and Bion J. Arnold, *A City Plan for Rochester* (Rochester, NY: Civic Improvement Committee, 1911).

6   Mel Scott, *American City Planning Since 1890* (Berkeley, CA: University of California Press, 1969): 101, 163.

Subdivisions and Suburban Communities

1   Olmsted, Vaux & Co., "Preliminary Report upon the Proposed Suburban Village at Riverside, Near Chicago, by Olmsted, Vaux & Co. Landscape Architects," in *The Papers of Frederick Law Olmsted, Volume VI, The Years of Olmsted, Vaux, & Co. 1865-1874*, eds. David Schuyler and Jane Turner Censer (Baltimore, MD: Johns Hopkins University Press, 1992).

2   Frederick Law Olmsted Jr., "Notes on the Palos Verdes Project," February 10, 1922, Olmsted Associates Records, Manuscript Division, Library of Congress, Washington, D.C., series B, no. 5920.

Grounds of Residential Institutions

1   *The Papers of Frederick Law Olmsted, Volume VI, The Years of Olmsted, Vaux & Co, 1865-1874*, eds. David Schuyler and Jane Turner Censor (Baltimore, MD: The Johns Hopkins University Press, 1992): 95-98.

Cemeteries, Burial Lots, Memorials and Monuments

1   In *The Papers of Frederick Law Olmsted, Volume V, The California Frontier 1863-1865*, ed. Victoria Post Ranney (Baltimore, MD: The Johns Hopkins University Press, 1990): 473-487.

2   Olmsted to Fischer, March 14, 1875, *The Papers of Frederick Law Olmsted, Volume VII, Parks, Politics, and Patronage 1874-1882*, eds. Charles E. Beveridge, Carolyn F. Hoffman and Kenneth Hawkins (Baltimore, MD: The Johns Hopkins University Press, 2007): 136.

Country Clubs, Resorts, Hotels and Clubs

1   James M. Mayo, *The American Country Club: Its Origins and Development* (New Brunswick, NJ: Rutgers University Press, 1998): 64.

Arboreta and Gardens

1   Ida Hay, *Science in the Pleasure Ground, A History of the Arnold Arboretum* (Boston, MA: Northeastern University Press, 1995): 3.

2   S. B. Sutton, *Charles Sprague Sargent and the Arnold Arboretum* (Cambridge, MA: Harvard University Press, 1970): 80.

3   Cynthia Zaitzevsky, *Frederick Law Olmsted and the Boston Park System* (Cambridge, MA: The Belknap Press of Harvard University Press, 1982): 62.

Resources

Suggestions for Additional Reading

SELECTED WORKS BY FREDERICK LAW OLMSTED

Olmsted, Frederick Law. *Walks and Talks of an American Farmer in England*. (1852; reprint with an introduction by Charles C. McLaughlin, Amherst, MA: Library of American Landscape History, distributed by the University of Massachusetts Press, 2002).

_____. *A Journey in the Seaboard Slave States, With Remarks on Their Economy* (New York: Dix, Edwards & Co., 1856).

_____. *A Journey Through Texas; Or, A Saddle-Trip on the Southwestern Frontier* (New York: Dix, Edwards, & Co., 1857).

_____. *A Journey in the Back Country* (New York: Mason Brothers, 1860).

_____. *The Cotton Kingdom: A Traveller's Observances on Cotton and Slavery in the American Slave States*. (1861; reprint, edited by Arthur Meier Schlesinger, New York: Knopf, 1953; reprint, New York: Da Capo Press, 1996). [This volume consists of extracts from the three listed above it, with an introduction by Olmsted for that edition.]

THE PAPERS OF FREDERICK LAW OLMSTED

Baltimore, MD: The Johns Hopkins University Press (completed volumes, dates and editors listed below).

Volume I, *The Formative Years 1822-1852*. Edited by Charles Capen McLaughlin, 1977.

Volume II, *Slavery and the South 1852-1857*. Edited by Charles E. Beveridge and Charles Capen McLaughlin, 1981.

Volume III, *Creating Central Park 1857-1861*. Edited by Charles E. Beveridge and David Schuyler, 1983.

Volume IV, *Defending the Union, The Civil War and the U.S. Sanitary Commission 1861-1863*. Edited by Jane Turner Censer, 1986.

Volume V, *The California Frontier 1863-1865*. Edited by Victoria Post Ranney, 1990.

Volume VI, *The Years of Olmsted, Vaux & Co. 1865-1874*. Edited by David Schuyler and Jane Turner Censer, 1992.

Volume VII, *Parks, Politics, and Patronage 1874-1882*. Edited by Charles E. Beveridge, Carolyn F. Hoffman and Kenneth Hawkins, 2007.

THE PAPERS OF FREDERICK LAW OLMSTED, SUPPLEMENTARY SERIES

Volume I, *Writings on Public Parks, Parkways, and Park Systems*. Edited by Charles E. Beveridge and Carolyn F. Hoffman, 1997.

SELECTED BIOGRAPHIES AND BOOKS RELATED TO THE WORK OF THE OLMSTED FIRM

The following list consists exclusively of selected published books. There are numerous additional sources of information on Frederick Law Olmsted and the successor firm, including journal articles that are not listed here, as well as more general sources that describe the contributions the Olmsted firm has made to the built environment. The National Association for Olmsted Parks is developing a more complete and comprehensive bibliography of Olmsted publications that will include journal articles and other general sources, to be available at the NAOP website (www.olmsted.org).

Beveridge, Charles E., and Paul Rocheleau. *Frederick Law Olmsted, Designing the American Landscape*. Edited by David Larkin (New York: Rizzoli, 1995).

Birnbaum, Charles, and Robin Karson, editors. *Pioneers of American Landscape Design* (New York: McGraw-Hill, 2000). See biographies of Frederick Law Olmsted, John Charles Olmsted and Frederick Law Olmsted Jr.

Fabos, Julius Gy., Gordon T. Milde and V. Michael Weinmayr. *Frederick Law Olmsted Sr.: Founder of Landscape Architecture in America* (Amherst, MA: The University of Massachusetts Press, 1968).

Fein, Albert. *Landscape into Cityscape: Frederick Law Olmsted's Plan for a Greater New York City* (Ithaca, NY: Cornell University Press, 1968).

_____. *Frederick Law Olmsted and the American Environmental Tradition* (New York: G. Braziller, 1972).

Hise, Greg, and William Deverell. *Eden by Design: The 1930 Olmsted-Bartholomew Plan for the Los Angeles Region* (Berkeley, CA: University of California Press, 2000).

Kelly, Bruce, Gail Travis Guillet and Mary Ellen W. Hern. *The Art of the Olmsted Landscape: His Works in New York City* (New York: Landmarks Preservation Commission and the Arts Publisher, Inc., 1981).

Klaus, Susan L. *A Modern Arcadia: Frederick Law Olmsted Jr. and the Plan for Forest Hills Gardens* (Amherst, MA: University of Massachusetts Press, 2002).

Lambert, Phyllis, editor. *Viewing Olmsted: Photographs of Robert Burley, Lee Friedlander and Geoffrey James* (Montreal: Canadian Center for Architecture; Cambridge, MA: distributed by the MIT Press, 1996).

Lawliss, Lucy Ann. *Residential Work of the Olmsted Firm in Georgia 1893-1937* (Winston-Salem, NC: Southern Garden History Society, 1993).

McPeck, Eleanor M., Keith Morgan and Cynthia Zaitzevsky. *Olmsted in Massachusetts: The Public Legacy* (Brookline, MA: Massachusetts Association for Olmsted Parks, 1983).

Olmsted, Frederick Law Jr., and Theodora Kimball, eds. *Frederick Law Olmsted, Landscape Architect, 1882-1903 (Forty Years of Landscape Architecture)*, 2 vols.: Volume 1, *Early Years and Experiences, Together with Biographical Notes* (New York: G.P. Putnam's Sons, 1922); Volume 2, *Central Park as a Work of Art and as a Great Municipal Enterprise, 1853-1895* (New York: G.P. Putnam's Sons, 1928).

_____. *Frederick Law Olmsted, Landscape Architect 1822-1903* (Cambridge, MA: MIT Press, 1973). [Reprint of the two volumes in one.]

Ranney, Victoria Post. *Olmsted in Chicago* (Chicago, IL: Open Parks Project, 1972).

Rogers, Elizabeth Barlow. *Frederick Law Olmsted's New York* (New York: Praeger, in association with the Whitney Museum of Art, 1972).

_____. *Rebuilding Central Park: A Management and Restoration Plan* (Boston, MA: MIT Press, 1987).

Roper, Laura Wood. *FLO: A Biography of Frederick Law Olmsted* (Baltimore, MD: Johns Hopkins University Press, 1973).

Rybczynski, Witold. *A Clearing in the Distance: Frederick Law Olmsted and America in the Nineteenth Century* (New York: Scribners, 1999).

White, Dana F., and Victor A. Kramer, Editors. *Olmsted South: Old South Critic/New South Planner*, Contributions in American Studies No. 43. (Westport, CT: Greenwood Press, 1979).

Zaitzevsky, Cynthia. *Frederick Law Olmsted and the Boston Park System* (Cambridge, MA: The Belknap Press of Harvard University Press, 1982).

NATIONAL ASSOCIATION FOR OLMSTED PARKS, WORKBOOK SERIES

Volume 1, *Charles Eliot 1857-1897: Held in Trust: Charles Eliot's Vision for the New England Landscape.* By Keith Morgan. 1991.

Volume 2, *An Ecosystem Approach to Woodland Management: The Case of Prospect Park.* By Edward Toth. 1991.

Volume 3, *Landscape Composition Preservation Treatment: Defining an Ethic for Designed Landscapes.* By Charles A. Birnbaum. 1992.

Volume 4, *Frederick Law Olmsted's First and Last Suburbs: Riverside and Druid Hills.* By Darlene R. Roth. 1993.

Volume 5, *The Olmsteds at Biltmore.* By Charles E. Beveridge and Susan L. Klaus. 1995.

ADDITIONAL SOURCES OF INFORMATION

Technical Assistance

Several programs of the National Park Service, such as the Historic Landscape Initiative, may be able to provide technical assistance related to the inventory, evaluation and treatment of historic Olmsted landscapes (www.cr.nps.gov/hps/hli). The National Association for Olmsted Parks occasionally publishes workbooks designed to address specific preservation issues for Olmsted landscapes (see above). For example, NAOP Workbook Volume 3, *Landscape Composition Preservation Treatment: Defining an Ethic for Designed Landscapes* by Charles A. Birnbaum, gives more details on the use of some of these materials. The property may also be eligible or listed on the National Register of Historic Places (www/cr.nps.gov/nr or through State Historic Preservation Office). Anyone considering making any physical changes to the landscape should first consult *The Secretary of the Interior's Standards for the Treatment of Historic Properties with Guidelines for the Treatment of Cultural Landscapes*, which provides general principles for preservation, rehabilitation, restoration and reconstruction (www.cr.nps.gov/hps/hli).

National Association for Olmsted Parks (NAOP)

1111 16th Street, NW, Suite 310
Washington, D.C. 20036
www.olmsted.org

Frederick Law Olmsted National Historic Site (Olmsted NHS)

99 Warren Street
Brookline, MA 02445
www.nps.gov/frla

Highlights of Collections in the Olmsted Archives:

Plans and Drawings, c.1847-1979 (bulk 1882-1970)
Records and Reports, 1857-1954
Job Photographs, 1867-1978
Nitrate Negatives, c.1867-c.1978
Glass Plate Negatives, c.1900
Lithographs, 1877-1979
Planting Lists, 1884-1962

Library of Congress

Manuscript Division

James Madison Memorial Building
101 Independence Avenue, Room LM 101
Washington, D.C. 20540-4680
www.loc.gov/rr/mss

FREDERICK LAW OLMSTED PAPERS (1777 TO 1952; BULK 1838-1903)
Journals, 1777-1888
Correspondence, 1838-1928
Subject File, 1857-1952
Speeches and Writings File, 1839-1903
Miscellany, 1837-1952
1975 Addition, 1821-1924
1996 Addition, 1880-1881
Oversize, 1886

OLMSTED ASSOCIATES PAPERS (1863-1971; BULK 1884-1950)
Series A: Letterbooks, 1884-1899
Series B: Job Files, 1863-1971
Series C: General Correspondence, 1884-1895
Series D: Special Correspondence, 1874-1899
Series E: Business Records, 1868-1950
Series F: Scrapbooks and Albums, 1893-1917
Series G: Miscellany, 1883-1964
Series H: Family Papers, 1868-1903
Oversize Records

Frances Loeb Library

Harvard Design School
48 Quincy Street
Cambridge, MA 02138
www.gsd.harvard.edu/library

John Charles Olmsted Collection

Smithsonian Institution

P.O. Box 37012
Arts and Industry Building, Room 2282
MRC 420
Washington, D.C. 20013-7012
www.nmnh.si.edu/naa/siasc/american_gardens.htm

Archives of American Gardens

New York Botanical Garden

Bronx River Parkway at Fordham Road
Bronx, NY 10458
www.nybg.org

Catalog of Landscape Records in the United States

The Catalog of Landscape Records in the United States, formerly at Wave Hill and now located at the New York Botanical Garden, lists landscape records including plans, drawings and photographs that are contained in other repositories across the country. Information is still being collected and the Catalog focuses on landscape records generally, not just the work of the Olmsted firm.

National Park Service Education Specialist Celena Illuzzi describes drawing from observation at Franklin Park, part of The Art of Landscape – a four-season art exploration of Olmsted's Franklin Park for Boston third graders and parents. Job #918 – Franklin Park (Boston, MA).

Contributors

JULIA S. BACHRACH is historian and preservationist for the Chicago Park District. She holds a master's degree in landscape architecture from the University of Wisconsin-Madison. Ms. Bachrach has produced extensive research and writing on the subject of landscape and architectural history. She has curated numerous exhibitions including "A Force of Nature: The Life and Work of Jens Jensen" at the Chicago Cultural Center in 2002 and "A Century of Progress: Architecture and the 1933-34 Chicago World's Fair" at the Chicago Architecture Foundation in 2004. Ms. Bachrach is the author of the award-winning book *The City in a Garden: A Photographic History of Chicago's Parks* and *Inspired by Nature: The Garfield Park Conservatory and Chicago's West Side* (with Jo Ann Nathan).

CHARLES E. BEVERIDGE, Honorary ASLA, is the world's foremost authority on the work of Frederick Law Olmsted. In his work as an author and scholar, Dr. Beveridge has devoted his 40-year career to the study of Olmsted's philosophies and achievements in landscape architecture. As series editor of the 12-volume *The Papers of Frederick Law Olmsted*, Dr. Beveridge has ensured that Olmsted's ideas and body of work have achieved the acclaim and protection they deserve. Dr. Beveridge was the author, with photographer Paul Rocheleau, of *Frederick Law Olmsted: Designing the American Landscape*. He has served as historical advisor for the PBS film "Frederick Law Olmsted and the Public Park in America," produced by WGBH in 1990, as historical advisor to *National Geographic*'s March 2005 feature article on Olmsted and as consultant on HGTV's Olmsted program in 2001. He has worked closely with landscape architects and communities throughout the United States and Canada to ensure the preservation and ongoing stewardship of Olmsted's work. During his career, Dr. Beveridge has served as historical consultant for forty preservation and/or restoration projects of Olmsted parks and landscapes. He is a Leadership Council member and former board member of the National Association for Olmsted Parks.

Left: Frederick Law Olmsted Jr. working in the Everglades, January 1932.
Job #4022 – Everglades National Park Project (Miami, FL).

ETHAN CARR is an associate professor of landscape architecture at the University of Virginia. He has been active in historical research and landscape preservation practice for more than twenty years. He has a master's degree in art history from Columbia University and a master's in landscape architecture from Harvard University. He received a doctorate in landscape architecture from the Edinburgh College of Art. His book *Wilderness by Design: Landscape Architecture and the National Park Service* received an American Society of Landscape Architects honor award in 1998. His new book, *Mission 66: Modernism and the National Park Dilemma*, was published in 2007 by the Library of American Landscape History and the University of Massachusetts Press. He is a board member of the National Association for Olmsted Parks and chairs the research committee.

LEE FARROW COOK is site manager of Frederick Law Olmsted National Historic Site and John F. Kennedy National Historic Site, where she oversees a range of cultural resource management and visitor programs. For the past twenty-five years, she has held various management and museum positions with the National Park Service, primarily at Olmsted, Longfellow and Kennedy National Historic Sites, located in Brookline and Cambridge, Massachusetts. Ms. Cook holds a master's degree in historic preservation from Boston University and a bachelor's degree in history from Bowdoin College.

ROLF DIAMANT is superintendent of Marsh-Billings-Rockefeller National Historical Park, a national park telling the story of conservation history, the evolution of land stewardship and the emergence of a conservation ethic. From 1987 to 1998 Mr. Diamant was superintendent of Frederick Law Olmsted National Historic Site. He is a contributing author to a number of books including *The Conservation Of Cultural Landscapes, Reconstructing Conservation: Finding Common Ground, Wilderness Comes Home: Re-wilding the Northeast* and *A Citizen's Guide to River Conservation*.

NANCY POLLOCK-ELLWAND is a specialist in cultural landscape history and conservation now heading the School of Architecture, Landscape Architecture, and Urban Design at the University of Adelaide, in South Australia. She has been working on the Olmsted legacy in her native Canada for many years traveling to sites and archives across the country piecing together the story of the Olmsted firm's activity, coupled with and adding to the work that has already been done on another pioneering landscape architect in Canada, Frederick G. Todd. She is now preparing a book on the Olmsted firm called, *Out of America*. She has a doctorate in planning, a master's degree in architecture and a bachelor of landscape architecture degree.

SUSAN L. KLAUS is an independent historian with particular interest in suburban planning and landscape history. Chair of the Leadership Council of the National Association for Olmsted Parks and a former board member, she is the author of *A Modern Arcadia; Frederick Law Olmsted Jr. and the Plan for Forest Hills Gardens*, as well as a number of articles on Olmsted Jr. and the Olmsted firm.

FRANCIS R. KOWSKY is an accomplished author and scholar, who for many years taught the history of art and architecture at Buffalo State College before retiring in 2007. He has written articles and books on 19th-century American architects. The *New York Times* called his book *Country Park and City: The Life and Architecture of Calvert Vaux* "a handsome effort to rescue from comparative oblivion the architect who shared— sometimes more than equally—with Frederick Law Olmsted in the design of Central Park and other New York amenities." He has been a board member of the National Association for Olmsted Parks and currently serves on the board of the Calvert Vaux Preservation Alliance.

LUCY LAWLISS, ASLA, is a cultural resources manager for the National Park Service and has written several award-winning historical landscape publications including *Residential Work of the Olmsted Firm in Georgia 1893-1937*. A board member of the National Association for Olmsted Parks, Ms. Lawliss served as the organization's co-chair from 2002-2005. Ms. Lawliss holds undergraduate and master's degrees in landscape architecture with a certificate in historic preservation from the University of Georgia and is a registered landscape architect.

ARLEYN A. LEVEE is a landscape historian and preservation consultant, specializing in the work of the Olmsted firm. She has concentrated on the work of the later firm of Olmsted Brothers, John Charles and Frederick Law Olmsted Jr., their partners and associates. She has lectured across the country and consulted with professional and community preservation groups concerning the recognition and stewardship of the extensive Olmsted design legacy. She is the author of articles and reports on aspects of Olmsted firm work and its practitioners, and the impact of this design and planning aesthetic upon neighborhoods and cities, both historically and for the future. Ms. Levee has worked extensively with non-profit preservation groups, particularly those concerning historic landscapes, such as the National Association for Olmsted Parks, The Cultural Landscape Foundation and Historic New England. She also is a member of the Belmont Historic District Commission and sits on the Emerald Necklace Restoration Project Advisory Committee.

CAROLINE LOUGHLIN is the co-author of *Forest Park*, a history of a major park in Saint Louis. She is a board member of the National Association for Olmsted Parks, which she has served as secretary, treasurer and co-chair and continues to serve on the steering committee for the Olmsted Research Guide Online. She was a founding board member of Forest Park Forever, which she served as president, and of the Friends of Fairsted, of which she is the treasurer. She volunteers at Mount Auburn Cemetery, where she co-chaired the 175th anniversary committee and is a member of the Steering Committee for the Preservation Initiative.

LAUREN MEIER, ASLA, is a historic preservationist with Pressley Associates in Cambridge, Massachusetts, where she oversees a wide variety of historic landscape preservation projects. She holds a bachelor's degree in botany from Pomona College and a master's in landscape architecture from Harvard University. Ms. Meier was the founding coordinator of the National Park Service's Historic Landscape Initiative in Washington, D.C., and historical landscape architect for the NPS Olmsted Center for Landscape Preservation. Her extensive landscape preservation work nationwide includes the restoration of the landscape at Fairsted, Frederick Law Olmsted's home and office in Brookline, Massachusetts, and many publications devoted to the preservation of historic plant material. She is a board member of the National Association for Olmsted Parks and a former chair of the research committee.

CATHERINE NAGEL is the Executive Director of the National Association for Olmsted Parks. She also oversees the partnership NAOP shares with the City Parks Alliance. Prior to leading NAOP she was the founding executive director of the Japan America Society of Greater Philadelphia, where she initiated and oversaw numerous large-scale projects to establish or enhance regional economic and cultural ties with Japan. Her background also includes work in urban planning and design, economic development and television broadcasting. Ms. Nagel holds a master of landscape architecture degree from the School of Design at the University of Pennsylvania and a bachelor of arts in Japanese Studies from Bucknell University.

ANTHONY REED is an archivist at Frederick Law Olmsted National Historic Site. He received a bachelor's in sociology and women's studies from the University of California, Santa Barbara, and attended Simmons College's Graduate School of Library and Information Sciences, with a concentration in Archives Management. He is active with local and national museum and archival organizations, in addition to providing technical assistance and archival management guidance to National Park Service sites throughout the northeast. Prior to joining the NPS, Mr. Reed worked on archival collections including the Pilgrim Monument in Provincetown, Massachusetts; the Chancery of the Catholic Archdiocese of Seattle; Microsoft Corporate Archives; the Town of Burlington, Massachusetts; the Rare Books & Manuscripts Division of the Boston Public Library and the Peabody Museum of Archaeology and Ethnography at Harvard University.

JILL TREBBE is the supervisory archivist at Frederick Law Olmsted National Historic Site in Brookline, Massachusetts. She received a bachelor's degree in anthropology and sociology with a minor in art history from Mount Holyoke College. She previously worked in various positions at Olmsted NHS, including museum technician and supervisory museum specialist, overseeing work at the offsite archives processing and conservation lab in Springfield, Massachusetts. She received her MLS with a concentration in Archives Management from the Simmons Graduate School of Library and Information Science. She is a member of the Simmons College chapter of Beta Phi Mu, the international honor society for library and information sciences studies.

Index to Job Locations in Lists

Index lists only the first page number for locations with more than one consecutive page.

Children at play at Fairsted. Job #673 – F.L. Olmsted Estate/Fairsted (Brookline, MA).

Index to Names in Essays and Illustrations

A page number in italics indicates an illustration on that page. Index lists only the first page number for subjects with more than one consecutive page. The names and locations used for jobs in the index are those used by the Olmsted firm as shown in the lists.

Children approaching the Long Meadow in Prospect Park, Brooklyn. Job #509 – Prospect Park (New York City, NY).